BIOLOGICAL DEGRADATION
OF CELLULOSE

ORGANIC CHEMISTRY MONOGRAPHS

Consultant Editors

Dr. J. W. Cook, f.r.s.
Vice-Chancellor, University of Exeter

and

Professor M. Stacey, f.r.s.
Mason Professor and Head of Department of Chemistry
University of Birmingham

Biological Degradation of Cellulose

J. A. GASCOIGNE
M.Sc., Ph.D., A.R.I.C., A.C.T.(Birm.)

and

MARGARET M. GASCOIGNE
M.Sc.

BUTTERWORTHS

LONDON · TORONTO · SYDNEY · WELLINGTON · DURBAN

1960

BUTTERWORTH & CO. (PUBLISHERS) LTD.
88 KINGSWAY, LONDON, W.C.2

AFRICA: BUTTERWORTH & CO. (AFRICA) LTD.
               DURBAN: 33/35 Beach Grove

AUSTRALIA: BUTTERWORTH & CO. (AUSTRALIA) LTD.
               SYDNEY: 8 O'Connell Street
               MELBOURNE: 430 Bourke Street
               BRISBANE: 240 Queen Street

CANADA: BUTTERWORTH (CANADA) LTD.
               TORONTO: 1367 Danforth Avenue

NEW ZEALAND: BUTTERWORTH & CO. (NEW ZEALAND) LTD.
               WELLINGTON: 49/51 Ballance Street
               AUCKLAND: 35 High Street

Made and Printed in Great Britain
by C. Tinling & Co. Ltd., Liverpool, London and Prescot

PREFACE

In 1951 one of the authors was confronted with the task of searching the chemical and textile literature for rot-proofing processes for cellulosic textiles, and this led to studies of the biological agents which bring about cellulose decomposition. About that time there appeared the excellent book by Dr R. G. H. Siu on the *Microbial Decomposition of Cellulose*, with its masses of information on every aspect of the subject and with particular reference to cotton textiles. Now, some nine years later, Siu's book still remains an inspiration and guide to all who work in this field, and the present authors are deeply indebted to Dr Siu. In 1954 the authors started work on the preparation and purification of cellulolytic enzymes in the Department of Chemistry of the University of Birmingham, and realized that there was no comprehensive account of these enzymes. At the suggestion of Professor M. Stacey, F.R.S., we decided to attempt a survey of these enzymes and we must record our deep gratitude to Professor Stacey for his constant advice and encouragement both in the preparation of this book and in our experimental researches.

The biological breakdown of celluloses has importance in other fields beside textile technology, and this account tries to summarize the enzymological background to the very important effects of cellulose decomposition by all living agencies in the textile, wood, paper and fermentation industries, and in animal digestion. Our aim has been to deal with the enzymes concerned and with processes in which the primary action is enzymic, rather than to deal with the numerous technologies in which micro-organisms are used. No claim that this account of cellulases is complete can be made, but it is hoped that papers omitted will be accessible through the numerous reviews cited.

We wish to acknowledge the help and advice of the Director and our colleagues at the British Rayon Research Association, especially the library staff, of Professor E. J. Bourne, Drs S. A. Barker and J. W. Bell. We also wish to thank the publishers for their unfailing patience and constant guidance during the preparation of this book.

John A. Gascoigne
Margaret M. Gascoigne

British Rayon Research Association,
Manchester, 22.
February, 1960.

CONTENTS

THE CHEMISTRY AND PHYSICS
OF CELLULOSE

CELLULOSE occurs abundantly in Nature, notably as the principal constituent of the cell walls of most plants. It may be present in a relatively pure state, as in the cellulose of the cotton plant, or in close association with many other compounds, such as the hemicelluloses and lignin of wood and bast fibres.

Sources of Cellulose

The large amounts of cellulose required for modern industrial processes are obtained from widely differing botanical sources; woody matter, seed hairs, bast fibre, straw, stalks and hulls are all used for various purposes. Such natural sources contain varying amounts of cellulose, as can be seen from *Table 1*.

Table 1. Cellulose Content of Natural Sources

Raw Material	Cellulose Content %
Wood	40–50
Cotton	91
Flax	82
Ramie	85
Jute	65–75
Kapok	55–65

Wood, in addition to cellulose, contains lignin (20–30%), hemicelluloses and other polysaccharides (10–30%), and of all cellulosic materials it is the most widely used. It is freed from non-cellulosic components by various methods to produce cellulose pulp[1], which forms the raw material for most of the viscose rayon, paper, nitrocellulose and other derivatives now being produced. Cotton, the purest natural source of cellulose[2], is the unicellular fibre obtained from the seed of the cotton plant, from which it is removed mechanically before further purification. The seed hair consists of three parts, a lumen or central canal, the secondary

1

thickening which is cellulose, and the primary wall or cuticle which apparently forms a protective layer. Fibre lengths vary in different types of cotton ranging from 0·9 inch (Indian) to 2·5 inches (Sea Island); a model of a cell wall is shown in *Figure 1*.

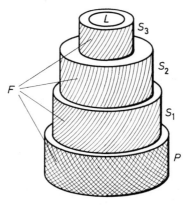

Figure 1—Model of cell wall (Nakao, Usuda and Migita[172])
(by courtesy, *Journal of the Society of Textile and Cellulose Industries, Japan*).
P, Primary wall; S_1, Secondary wall, outer layer;
S_2, Secondary wall, middle layer; S_3, Secondary wall,
inner layer; L, Lumen; F, Fibril.

The bast fibres (phloem or inner bark) are multicellular, and form part of the vascular bundle of various plants; those used for textile purposes include flax, ramie, hemp and jute. The flax plant is the source of the textile fibre linen, which is obtained from the stalk by a process known as retting; this involves the decomposition of the woody matter surrounding the cellulose fibres, followed by drying of the retted flax and mechanical removal of the woody material. Ramie fibre has been widely used for studying the structure of cellulose, as very clear X-ray diffraction diagrams can be obtained from it. A summary of other sources of cellulose which have been investigated widely and are used for many purposes has been given by Ward[3].

CHEMICAL STRUCTURE

From whatever source it is derived cellulose has basically the same chemical structure. It was shown by hydrolysis, acetolysis and methylation studies that cellulose consists essentially of anhydro-glucose residues [4-6]. Subsequent work established that the glucose molecules are present in the β–glucopyranose form and are linked together through an ether bridge connecting the carbon atom at position 1 in one molecule to the carbon atom at position 4 in the adjacent molecule[7–10]. The formula of the repeating unit resembles that of the disaccharide cellobiose and the chemical structure of cellulose is usually represented by the formula given in *Figure 2*.

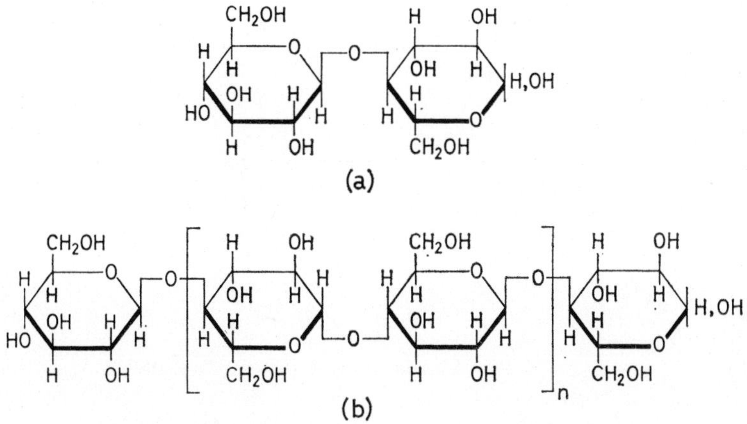

Figure 2—Chemical structure of (a) cellobiose and (b) cellulose.

Molecular Size

Physical and chemical methods have both been applied with varying degrees of success to the problem of the molecular size of the high polymer cellulose. Chemical methods are based on determinations of the ratio of end groups to the rest of the molecule, the proportion of either non-reducing or reducing end groups (or both) being measured[9, 11–14]. Physical methods, which include osmometry[15–19], viscometry[20], light scattering[21] and ultracentrifugal sedimentation[22, 23], have given higher values than the purely chemical methods. The values obtained may be expressed as molecular weight or degree of polymerization (DP), that is the number of anhydroglucose units in the molecule. Methods of molecular weight determination, such as osmometry and cryoscopy rely upon the laws of dilute solutions, and the quantity measured is proportional to the number of solute molecules present and the values obtained by such methods will be 'number average' degrees of polymerization $(\overline{P_n})$. On the other hand, methods like viscometry measure quantities proportional to the mass of the units present and so will yield 'weight average' degrees of polymerization $(\overline{P_w})$.

Similarly other average values of DP will result from light scattering or ultracentrifuge methods[24]. Since the molecular chains of cellulose differ in length, the application of any method to a cellulose sample (without prior fractionation) can only give rise to the value for 'average DP'. Typical results for different types of cellulose have been given by Kraemer[25] from intrinsic viscosity measurements (see *Table 2*); however, other work[26-28] suggests that the DP may be

Table 2. Molecular Weight of Cellulose

Substance	$\overline{P_w}$	Molecular Weight $\times 10^{-3}$
Native cotton cellulose	>3500	>570
Purified cotton linters	1000–3000	150–500
Commercial regenerated cellulose	200–600	30–90
β–cellulose	15–90	3–15
γ–cellulose	<15	<3

considerably higher. The limitations and advantages of the various methods have been reviewed by Purves[29].

Anomalies in the Structure of Cellulose

In addition to $(1\to4)\beta-$ linked glucopyranose units the presence of a smaller number of non-glucosidic linkages in the cellulose chain has been proposed; the chemical nature, number and location of these linkages, amounting to about one per cent of the total, are still debatable[30]. However carefully it is purified cellulose always contains a small quantity of carboxyl groups; Schmidt *et al.* found 0·28 per cent of such groups which originated from an occasional glucuronide unit[31]. Several hypotheses concerning the presence of acid-sensitive linkages have been put forward. Pacsu and Hiller[29, 32] consider that these are present as acetal or hemi-acetal bonds, which may cross-link adjacent cellulose chains. Other types of cross-linkages have also been proposed[33-35]. According to Schulz and Husemann[36], the native cellulose molecule contains 3100 ± 100 anhydroglucose units which are linked by $(1\to4)\ \beta$–glucosidic linkages except for five equally spaced glucuronic acid residues, which may be decarboxylated under certain conditions to xylopyranoside units; these latter units hydrolyse about 1500 times faster than the glucopyranoside units of the chain.

The important question of whether or not native cellulose, with a degree of polymerization of several thousands, contains a very

4

small number of 'weak' bonds or of readily hydrolysable cross-links has not received a decisive answer, but no purely chemical evidence has been put forward for the presence of such modified linkages[37]. In a hydrolytic study of the kinetics of chain degradation of Egyptian cotton, Sharples[38] came to the conclusion that weak bonds of the type proposed by Schulz[39] and Pacsu[30] were definitely absent; regeneration from benzyl trimethylammonium hydroxide in the absence of oxygen produced a cellulose whose properties accorded with less than one acid-labile linkage per 2900 glucose residues being present in the original chain molecules. Regeneration from copper-containing reagents produced celluloses containing randomly distributed linkages which were approximately 10,000 times more sensitive to acids than the usual glucosidic type; such linkages appear to be produced from a limited number of special sites in the chain and amount to one such linkage per 660 glucopyranose units. In spite of this convincing picture, Husemann and Springler[40] still do not believe in random attack and again conclude that periodic weak links of a chemical nature exist. It may well be that anomalous linkages, if they do exist, may be revealed during the enzymic hydrolysis of cellulose.

Crystalline Structure

It is evident from a study of X-ray diffraction diagrams that the major part of native cellulose has a crystalline arrangement. These diffraction patterns, which consist principally of clearly defined rings or arcs, also show a diffuse halo from which it is concluded that the crystallinity is discontinuous, and amorphous areas are interspersed among the imperfectly arranged crystalline regions. Different cellulosic materials have varying degrees of crystallinity; even in the crystalline regions the arrangement of the molecules varies with the previous history of the sample. Four such crystalline modifications of cellulose have been recognized, of which Cellulose I is found in the native cellulosic fibres while Cellulose II occurs in regenerated and mercerized fibres[41]. The size of the crystalline micelles has been estimated to be about 60 to 100Å in diameter and from 600 to 1500Å in length, the dimensions varying with the source of the cellulose[42-44]. In certain fibres, including cotton, ramie and wood, these micelles are arranged so that they are oriented in the direction of the fibre axis. Further details of the structure of the unit cell of cellulose have been given in the book on *Cellulose and Cellulose Derivatives* edited by Ott, Spurlin and Grafflin[45]. There is no abrupt change from the well-ordered crystalline regions to the amorphous regions, but rather a gradual change from crystalline areas to areas of considerably reduced crystalline order. It has been shown that the length of the cellulose molecule is such that individual chains pass through several crystalline micelles and through the intervening amorphous areas.

Various values have been obtained for the relative amounts of crystalline and amorphous regions[46]. Chemical methods rely on the relative activities of the two regions, the amorphous area being more reactive and accessible to reagents. Physical methods include X-ray diffraction techniques, and density determinations in which the rate of penetration of liquids into the fibre is measured; again, more rapid penetration occurs in the amorphous regions. Frequently such data are presented as the amount of amorphous material or as the 'accessibility' of the sample; the two terms are not necessarily synonymous. Values obtained by different methods range from 50 to 99 per cent crystallinity for native cellulose and from 25 to 79

Table 3. Amorphous Contents of Celluloses

Material	Method	Amorphous Content %	Ref.
Cotton	X-ray diffraction	30	50
	Density	40	51
	Formylation	28	52
Ramie	Infra-red Spectra	very small	57
	Thallous ethylate	0·25	53
Bacterial Cellulose	D_2O exchange, I.R.	30	54
Viscose Rayon	X-ray diffraction	30	55
(Oriented)	D_2O exchange, I.R.	74	54
Acetate Rayon			
(saponified)	D_2O exchange, I.R.	75	55

per cent for regenerated celluloses; *Table 3* shows the results obtained by various methods. The method of Mann and Marrinan[54] involving heavy water exchange and infra-red spectroscopy, and that involving reaction with thallous ethylate[56] deserve particular consideration. Both physical and chemical properties of cellulosic fibres depend to a large extent on the relative amounts and arrangements of the crystallites. For example, all cellulosic fibres are strong, but ramie fibres have the crystallites oriented almost parallel to the fibre axis producing brittleness in this particularly strong fibre. While a high degree of crystallinity and perfect orientation result in great strength and rigidity, there is also a decrease in elasticity;

these properties are illustrated in *Table 4*. The effect of molecular organization on the mechanical properties of viscose fibres has been reviewed by Ingersoll[47], and a much more detailed treatment of the chemistry and physics of cellulose will be found in the recent book edited by Honeyman[173].

Table 4. Strength and Elasticity of Celluloses[48]

Material	Tenacity (g/denier)	Dry Elongation (% increase in length at the break)
Cotton	3–6·3	3–7
Acetate rayon (saponified)	4·8–6·5	6–6·5
Acetate rayon	1·2–1·8	23–30
Acetate rayon (high impact)	1·5	50
Viscose rayon	1·8–3·1	14–20
Bemberg rayon	1·7–2·3	15–20
Wool (*non-cellulosic*)	1·0–1·7	20–35

REACTIVITY OF CELLULOSE

Even when it feels 'dry' cellulose contains a certain amount of moisture which varies with the relative humidity and temperature of the surroundings. Cotton which has been dried by heating, quickly absorbs, on exposure to cold air, most of the moisture it had lost. Since this moisture content depends on atmospheric conditions to such a large extent the accepted moisture regain from the bone-dry condition for commercial purposes is taken as 8·5 per cent[49]. Cellulose shows a distinct hysteresis effect, the water content at any particular humidity and temperature depending on the prior treatment of the sample (e.g. whether it was brought to equilibrium from a lower humidity by absorption of moisture or from a higher humidity by desorption)[58]. In general, regenerated celluloses (viscose) at all humidities show a greater water uptake than cotton cellulose. As the physical properties of cellulose depend on its previous history, especially with regard to atmospheric conditions, it is essential to 'condition' the sample carefully under the exact conditions of humidity and temperature to be used in any determinations of its properties[59]. Most chemical reactions involving cellulose are carried out on the partly crystalline fibrous material, and in most technical processes the fibre structure is swollen in order to render all portions of the fibre available for reaction. The amorphous areas swell and

7

react first, followed by a swelling of the outer layers of the crystallites, thereby exposing the molecules for penetration by the reagent causing alteration or disruption of the strong associative forces. These forces (hydrogen bonds) are strongest in the crystalline regions; unless these hydrogen bonds can be broken by the penetrating reagent and the bonds prevented from reforming by chemical reaction of the swollen structure with the reagent, the cellulose will remain insoluble in liquids. Three steps may be distinguished in the action of such swelling agents[60]: (a) at low concentrations of the reagent, reactions occur within the amorphous region producing no change in X-ray diffraction patterns, (b) with further reagent the micelles become swollen, the diffraction pattern becomes more diffuse with the disappearance of the crystalline regions, and a complex may be formed between the reagent and the swollen cellulose, and finally (c) the complete dissolution of the cellulose. A review of the reactivity of cellulose has been given by Cumberbirch[61].

Effect of Alkalies

The treatment of cellulosic fibres with alkaline solutions is one of the oldest and most important processes in the textile industry. Treatment of cotton fibres, under tension to prevent shrinkage, with sodium hydroxide solution (25–30%) is known as 'mercerizing'; the process causes swelling of the fibre, which then takes dyes more easily than untreated cotton fibres, in addition the mercerized fibre has a smooth, lustrous appearance. 'Soda cellulose', an important intermediate in the production of regenerated cellulose, is produced by the treatment of suitable wood pulp or cotton linters with a weaker sodium hydroxide solution (20%). Such alkaline treatments produce chemical as well as physical reactions within the fibre; the reactions and their extent depend on the original condition and nature of the fibre, the concentration of the alkali, its nature, on the temperature of the reaction and the presence or absence of oxygen. In the cold, sodium hydroxide solutions up to 2M concentration react with the amorphous regions, while higher concentrations enter the crystallites. The alkali cellulose formed at sodium hydroxide concentrations of 3 to 4·5M (12–18%) has been assigned the formula $(C_6H_{10}O_5)_2.NaOH$; whilst at still higher concentrations (5–10M) of alkali the complex approximates to $C_6H_{10}O_5.NaOH$ [62]. All the alkali metal hydroxides exert this swelling action on cellulose[63].

The chain length and chemical nature of different celluloses are indicated to some extent by their solubility in alkali. For example, native cellulose which is insoluble in sodium hydroxide solution of

17·5 per cent concentration is known as 'α–cellulose' and consists of molecules of average DP above 200. Neutralization of the soluble portion at this concentration precipitates the 'β–cellulose' which contains material with shorter chains (DP ca 15 to 200) of anhydroglucose units (β–glucans) together with associated mannans and pentosans. Finally, the material remaining in the neutralized solution is termed 'γ–cellulose', and has a DP of under 15; in addition to low molecular weight glucans it contains xylans, arabans and polyuronides. The chemical degradation of celluloses in alkaline solutions has been studied in detail by many workers[64-66]; oxygen has a profound effect in such reactions.

Effect of Electrolytes

Numerous salt solutions (e.g. zinc chloride, calcium thiocyanate, potassium iodide) induce swelling of cellulose and in some cases complete dissolution may result. Acids also cause swelling and finally solution of cellulose. At low acid strengths, swelling of the amorphous regions occurs without change in the X-ray diffraction pattern, while higher concentrations disrupt the crystalline regions, and under certain conditions microfibrils have even been revealed in regenerated celluloses[67]. Sulphuric acid at 50 per cent concentration causes swelling of cellulose, while above a concentration of 78 per cent carbonization and solution occur; nitric acid solutions (67·5 to 74·5%) have a mercerizing action, while at higher concentrations (77–80%) dissolution occurs with some nitration. Concentrated hydrochloric acid (36–37% HCl) has a mercerizing effect, whilst the fuming acid (38·9% HCl) causes gelatinization and solution. Similar effects are brought about by phosphoric acid; studies of cellulose hydrolysis in this acid have been presented by Bauer and Pacsu[69], and by Marchessault and Rånby[171].

The chemical action of acids on cellulose is the catalysis of the cleavage of glucosidic bonds leading to a reduction in molecular weight, the production of reducing sugars and a rapid fall in the tensile strength of the fibre. The course of acid hydrolysis of various celluloses has been followed by Sharples[38,68]; the similarity between acid and enzymic hydrolyses of cellulose is discussed later (Chapter VI). Partially hydrolysed cellulose is known as 'hydrocellulose', while more extensive degradation leads to the production of cello-dextrins. On further hydrolysis (or acetolysis) a series of oligo-saccharides, comprised of (1→4)–linked β–glucose units, are produced; in the complete hydrolysis of cellulose the only product is glucose. Other reactions in which acids play some part are oxidation, esterification and etherification.

9

Oxidation of Cellulose

Oxidative attack on cellulose occurs at the ends of the molecular chain or at points along its length with the formation of aldehydic and carboxylic groups. The properties of the 'oxycellulose' produced depend on the conditions of oxidation and the nature of the oxidizing agent; these factors control the relative numbers of acid and aldehyde groups produced[70], and if the latter groups predominate, the product is known as 'reducing oxycellulose'. Oxidized celluloses can also be classified according to the specificity with which certain hydroxyl groups are oxidized. Thus, such reagents as nitrogen dioxide, lead tetra-acetate and periodic acid oxidize specific hydroxyls, whilst other oxidants, such as permanganate, chromates, chlorite and hypohalites, bring about less specific changes in structure. It has been shown that periodic acid cleaves the bond linking the carbon atoms attached to secondary hydroxyl groups, the product being typical of the reducing oxycelluloses[71,72,80]. The primary hydroxyl is most easily oxidized by nitrogen dioxide, giving rise to an acidic oxycellulose[79]; these reactions may be expressed by the following equations:

The physical changes occurring on oxidation follow a similar pattern of specificity; non-specific oxidants (chromic acid) produce little change in the X-ray diffraction diagram of the fibre, whereas periodate and nitrogen dioxide enter the ordered regions of the cellulose and react there as well as in the amorphous regions[73,74]. In general, oxidation brings about a rapid decrease in the strength of the fibre and renders it more sensitive to further degradation by alkali. The oxidation of cellulose by chlorite has been studied by Davidson and Nevell[75], whilst Schürz[76] has recently discussed the nature of the various oxidations.

DERIVATIVES OF CELLULOSE

Cellulose Acetate

The esterification of cellulose was first performed by Shutzen-berger in 1865, but it was left to Miles[77] in 1904 to realize the commercial possibilities of cellulose acetate. The formation of esters from cellulose is analogous to the esterification of simple alcohols, but occurs at a slower rate. The acetylating mixture used comprises (a) an acetylating reagent (in practice, generally acetic anhydride), (b) a catalyst or starter, and (c) the liquid solvent (diluent). The catalyst must be capable of swelling the cellulose while the diluent may be a liquid in which the product of the reaction dissolves (e.g. acetic acid) or from which it is precipitated (e.g. benzene); sulphuric acid and zinc chloride have been used as dehydrating agents. The reaction may be pictured as:

The product is the triacetate, usually prepared as an amorphous powder precipitated from acetic acid solution by the addition of water. The powder is soluble in only a few solvents, such as glacial acetic acid. Solubility is increased by removal of some of the acetyl groups or by partial depolymerization of the cellulose chain. The partially de-acetylated product is soluble in acetone and contains $2 \cdot 1$ to $2 \cdot 6$ acetyl groups per anhydroglucose unit (i.e. a degree of substitution (DS) of $2 \cdot 1$ to $2 \cdot 6$). In the original patent, the triacetate was prepared first in acetic acid and dilute acetic acid containing sulphuric acid was added; after standing for 14 hours at $50 °C$, the solution was diluted with water to precipitate the 'secondary' acetate. There is some evidence[78] that the acetyl group attached to carbon atom 6 of the anhydroglucose unit is removed, leaving a primary alcohol group in the cellulose acetate. The secondary acetate contains 36 to $41 \cdot 6$ per cent acetyl groups, while the triacetate contains up to $44 \cdot 8$ per cent acetyl groups. Acetate rayon is produced by dissolving the secondary acetate in acetone and forcing the dope downwards through spinning nozzles into an ascending stream of air.

B
11

The esterification of cellulose with nitric acid is spoken of, incorrectly, as 'nitration'. Cellulose reacts with nitric acid, in the presence of a dehydrating agent (e.g. sulphuric acid) to produce mixtures of the mono-, di-, and trinitrates[81]. During this reaction considerable degradation of the cellulose chain itself occurs. The nitrogen contents of commercial nitrates vary from 10·5 to 13·7 per cent. Harland[82] has studied this 'nitration' and has prepared nitrates with little degradation of the cellulose, and with nitrogen contents of up to 14·1 per cent.

Cellulose Xanthate

Esterification of cellulose with dithiocarbonic acid, produces a very useful intermediate in the rayon industry—'cellulose xanthate'; this process was the original one developed by Cross and Bevan for making viscose. Wood pulp is steeped in sodium hydroxide solution until thoroughly swollen. After ageing, it is treated with carbon disulphide to give an orange-coloured crumbly mass. The solution of this material in sodium hydroxide solution is 'ripened' for several days and is then extruded into an acid bath, which liberates the cellulose as a coagulated fibre. It is thought that the solution of xanthate before ripening contains only one xanthate group to every two anhydroglucose units[83]. During ripening some hydrolysis occurs in addition to changes in the colloidal properties of the solution. The whole reaction, much simplified, may be written as[83]:

$$ROH + CS_2 + NaOH \rightarrow R-O-\overset{\displaystyle S}{\overset{\displaystyle \|}{C}}-SNa \xrightarrow{H^+} R-O-\overset{\displaystyle S}{\overset{\displaystyle \|}{C}}-SH \rightarrow$$

Cellulose $\qquad\qquad ROH + CS_2$

The viscose rayon produced has a higher amorphous content than the cellulose from which it was prepared, and is therefore more reactive, as indicated by the increased absorption of dyestuffs, and a higher degree of swelling in water. The crystalline form (Cellulose II) of viscose rayon ('regenerated' cellulose) is also different from that of native celluloses[84,85].

Cellulose Ethers

Cellulose does not react with etherifying agents unless a suitable swelling agent is present; concentrations as high as 76 per cent of sodium hydroxide are necessary in the preparation of ethers with high degrees of substitution. The alkali cellulose is then reacted with compounds like ethylene chlorhydrin, ethylene oxide, alkyl chlorides and chloroacetic acid. An excellent account of such ethers has been given by Savage, Young and Maasberg[86]. Hydroxyethylcelluloses with degrees of substitution from 0·3 to 1·7 have been prepared[87], whilst Morgan reports an apparent DS of 4·1 for one sample[88]. Such products are soluble in water and alkalis, but are insoluble in organic solvents.

Another water soluble ether has been produced by the action of a mixture of ethyl chloride and ethylene oxide under pressure on alkali cellulose [103]; the properties of this ethylhydroxyethylcellulose have been described by Jullander[104]. The basic repeating unit appears to be:—

This ether has been used in studies on the enzymic degradation of cellulose. The usual degree of substitution in sodium carboxymethylcellulose is 0·8 or less, but a DS of 2·7 has been achieved by repeated treatment with monochloroacetate[89]. These ethers are soluble in water giving solutions of high viscosity; they find extensive use as sizing agents for textiles, in food-products as thickening agents and in washing powders. The hydrolysis of the ether, catalysed by enzymes, can be followed by measuring the decrease in viscosity of its solution and this aspect is discussed in detail later (Chapter VI). Most alkyl celluloses have degrees of substitution around 2 to 2·6; the methyl ether is water soluble, while higher ethers are more soluble in organic solvents, but the degree of substitution has a pronounced effect upon solubility. Mahoney and Purves[174] have described a method for the determination of the distribution of alkyl groups in ethers. These ethers find uses in textile, leather and paper sizing, printing inks, lacquers, coatings, plastics and solution thickeners. Other ethers include benzyl, cyanoethyl, carboxyethyl and aminoethyl celluloses.

SUBSTANCES ASSOCIATED WITH CELLULOSE IN NATURE

Cellulose occurs in Nature in close association with many other substances, such as the hemicelluloses, lignin, pectin and other polysaccharides. Similar carbohydrates also occur in many animal, plant and microbial cells. Detailed accounts of these substances have been given by Whistler and Smart[90], Norman[91], and Brauns[92].

Hemicelluloses, Lignin and Pectin

Apart from cellulose, the hemicelluloses form one of the major constituents of the native plant cell; the term is generally used to indicate the less water-soluble cell wall polysaccharides of land plants, excepting cellulose and the pectins. The hemicelluloses include all the cell wall polysaccharides 'which are removable from untreated tissues by extraction with hot or cold dilute alkali, and which can be hydrolysed with dilute acids to give the constituent monosaccharide units'[91]. Two distinct types of polysaccharide are recognized: (i) the polyuronide hemicelluloses, containing uronic acid groups, and (ii) the cellulosans, which do not characteristically contain hexuronic acid units, although some carboxyl groups may be present in that form. These two classes appear to have different situations and, perhaps, different functions in the cell wall. The polyuronide hemicelluloses, which are apparently part of the system which penetrates and covers the cellulose matrix, contain glucuronic and galacturonic acids, the accompanying sugar units being hexoses or pentoses (or both). These polysaccharides are thought to be linked to lignin, at least to some extent, probably by a glycosidic linkage[93].

The cellulosans, which until extracted exist only in association with cellulose and are to some degree oriented in the micellar structure, form the pulp fractions known as β– and γ–celluloses. Their chemical constitution, like that of the polyuronide hemicelluloses, has been elucidated completely in a few cases only. Xylan is one of the most widely-occurring cellulosans, and is the principal constituent of corn-cob hemicellulose; it gives a high yield of D-xylose on acid hydrolysis[94], while crystalline oligosaccharides, containing the $(1\rightarrow4)\beta$–xylosidic linkage, have been prepared from it[95]. Studies on esparto xylan led to the conclusion that it has a branched structure, the linkage at the branch-point being a $(1\rightarrow3)\beta$–bond; no uronic acids are present[96]. On the other hand, the xylan of pear cell walls contains a D–glucuronic acid unit, attached to the penultimate xylose unit of one arm of a Y–shaped molecule[97]. While many hemicelluloses are of the xylan-glucuronide type, other preparations have been found to contain arabinose, galactose, mannose and galacturonic acid; in the hemicelluloses of certain seed-pods, grasses and leaves galactose is the principal constituent[98].

Lignin.—In wood, the amount of lignin and hemicelluloses together approach the cellulose content. A detailed account of the

14

structure and properties of lignin has been given by Brauns[99]. The basic unit of this polymer is a phenylpropane molecule:

$$\text{[benzene ring]}-CH_2-\underset{|}{CH}-CH_3$$

It is thought that lignin has its origin in carbohydrate, and Nord and his associates have proposed the following pathway for its bio-synthesis[100–102]:

carbohydrate → shikimic acid → p–hydroxyphenylpyruvic acid → [intermediate] → lignin.

Pectin.—All young plant tissues, fruits and tubers contain a group of polysaccharides known as pectic substances, but as the plant tissues mature there is a decrease in their pectic content. These substances are present initially in the plant in an insoluble form, probably in combination with other cell wall constituents, but they can be extracted by treatment with dilute acids[91], or with enzymes; they can be recovered from solution by precipitation with alcohol or acetone[90]. Pectins contain galacturonic acid and its methyl ester. For enzymic use, pectin should contain at least 80 per cent anhydro-galacturonic acid and over 7 per cent methoxyl[105]. Dissolution of pectin in dilute sodium hydroxide solution, followed by the addition of hydrochloric acid (0·5N) precipitates pectic acid. Further puri-fication involves de-ionization and precipitation from aqueous solution with acidified ethanol[106].

Other Polysaccharides

Lichenin.—Lichenin was considered for many years to be a type of cellulose, but differences between the two polysaccharides have now been established. Lichenin is an important constituent of Iceland Moss (*Cetraria islandica*), and has also been isolated from *Evernia vulpina, Usnea barbata* and *Parmelia furfuracea*[107]. This poly-saccharide can be hydrolysed quantitatively to glucose, and con-verted to cellobiose by acetolysis[108] or by enzymic action[109]. However, it is soluble in hot water; the optical rotations of its derivatives and its X-ray diffraction pattern[110] all differ from those of cellulose. It was finally confirmed that only about 70 per cent of the β–glucosidic linkages in lichenin are (1→4), the remainder being (1→3)[111,112].

Chitin.—The nitrogen-containing polysaccharide chitin, which is very resistant to hydrolysis, forms the organic skeletal substance of insects, fungi and crustacea. The polysaccharide consists of long chains of N–acetylglucosamine units connected through $(1{\rightarrow}4)\beta$–glucosidic linkages. This structure is analogous to that of cellulose, differing principally in the substitution of the N–acetylamino-group for the hydroxyl group at the carbon atom in position 2:

Tunicin.—This substance, also known as animal cellulose, is obtained from certain organisms, such as *Phallusia mammilata*, *Ascidia mentula* and *Polycarpa varians*[113], all of which belong to the class *Tunicata*. Chemically, tunicin has the same structure as cellulose[114], but X-ray diffraction studies[115] indicate that it appears to have a high degree of lateral order. It differs from other celluloses in some aspects of its solution behaviour[116], and in that it yields different volumes of gas on destructive distillation[117]. Celluloses from certain algae, notably *Valonia*, also have very high degrees of crystallinity.

ENZYMES

The various forms of cellulose and its associated substances have been discussed and now consideration must be given to the ways in which these and other substances are broken down in Nature. Enzymes have been defined[118] as 'definite chemical substances of organic nature, thermolabile, elaborated by plants, animals and micro-organisms, and capable of increasing the velocity of a chemical reaction without being used up in the process, or becoming a part of the product formed'. These highly specific biological catalysts can usually be extracted from the organism in which they are produced, and are nearly always protein in nature. Since it was noticed, in 1783, that meat was liquified by the gastric juice of hawks, and the adoption of the term 'enzyme' in 1878, this branch of biological chemistry has advanced to cover the catalysis of all living processes; the culmination was reached in 1926 when Sumner crystallized the enzyme urease[119]. The specificity of these catalysts is remarkable; often the reactants have to be of a specific structure or the enzyme will only act as a catalyst when a unique molecular species is present. For example, the enzyme arginase acts in the hydrolysis of L–arginine, but has no action with D–arginine. Enzymes

16

which are 'group specific' act as catalysts for changes involving a number of compounds or 'substrates' having some common structural feature; thus an α–glycosidase catalyses the hydrolysis of substrates containing the α–glycosidic linkage (as in maltose, amylose or methyl α–D–glucoside).

Most of the known enzymes may be placed in one of the following four classes[118]:

1. Enzymes which catalyse electron transfers; e.g. oxidation and reduction.

2. Enzymes which catalyse the addition or removal of water; e.g. hydrolysis and hydration.

3. The 'desmolases', enzymes which catalyse the cleavage or formation of a carbon–carbon bond without group transfer.

4. Enzymes which catalyse the transfer of a radical from one molecule to another; included in this class are transglycosylases and transphosphorylases, the radicals involved being a monosaccharide and a phosphoric acid group respectively.

The addition of -ase to the root of the noun designating the substrate with which the enzyme acts is the usual device for naming enzymes (e.g. esterase, glycosidase, ribonuclease). The enzyme may be secreted from the cell in which it is formed into the surrounding medium (*extracellular* enzyme), or it may be retained within the cells of the organism or plant (*intracellular* enzyme). In the breakdown of cellulose by plants, animals and micro-organisms in the presence of air and water, hydrolysis, hydration, oxidation and reduction all play some part. The hydrolysis of cellulose to cellobiose and glucose (catalysed by the enzyme *cellulase*) is followed by the other processes, which are catalysed by enzymes occurring in the same plant or organism, or in one living in symbiosis with it. Even the initial stage of hydrolysis is not so simple as described here and much more detailed consideration of this stage and of the hydration stage is given later. The discussion of these types of reactions will be limited here to those processes likely to be encountered in biological systems which metabolize cellulose and other polysaccharides.

OXIDATION AND REDUCTION

The transfer of electrons is catalysed by *oxidases* and *dehydrogenases*; the former are able to catalyse the use of molecular oxygen directly as a hydrogen acceptor to form water, while most dehydrogenases act specifically upon certain substrates to remove hydrogen, transferring it to an acceptor (such as methylene blue or a flavoprotein). However, some aerobic dehydrogenases are known which generally catalyse the reduction of molecular oxygen to hydrogen peroxide.

Such enzymes are often conjugated proteins in which the protein part (*apoenzyme*) of the molecule is combined with a prosthetic group such as iron, copper, or adenineflavin dinucleotide (AFD).

The glucose dehydrogenase[120,121], found in mammalian livers, cannot utilize gaseous oxygen, and before the dehydrogenation of D–glucose can be catalysed an alternative hydrogen acceptor must be present. The catalysis also requires the presence of a *co-enzyme*; such co-enzymes are usually nucleotides, and in this case it is probable that diphosphopyridine nucleotide (DPN or *co-enzyme I*) is required[122]. On the other hand, the glucose oxidase (*notatin*) of fungi (in particular of *Penicillium notatum*) cannot utilize methylene blue as a hydrogen acceptor, and gaseous oxygen must be present. The product of dehydrogenation with both enzymes is D–gluconic acid, which is formed via the δ–lactone, as shown below:

Notatin contains two molecules of AFD per enzyme molecule, and has a molecular weight of 152,000[123,124]. Although this enzyme has not a very high specificity (the dehydrogenations of D–xylose, D–mannose, L–arabinose and D–galactose are also catalysed to a small extent), it finds use in the removal of free glucose from solution in the study of oligosaccharide formation by fungi[125]. It has been shown[118], on the other hand, that animal liver glucose dehydrogenase is absolutely specific for the oxidation of D–glucose.

The ease with which enzymes enable reactions to take place is remarkable; for example, succinic acid is resistant to hot nitric acid, yet it is oxidized readily in the presence of enzymes from many organisms. The reduction of biological substances can be regarded as the reverse of their oxidation, and as enzymes are able to catalyse both forward and reverse reactions, some dehydrogenases are able to act as reductases under suitable conditions. Indeed, biological reactions come to a state of dynamic equilibrium in which the enzyme is catalysing both reactions; this situation may be represented:

$$AH_2 + X \rightleftharpoons A + XH_2$$

where AH_2 and A are the reduced and oxidized substrate respectively, while X and XH_2 are the oxidized and reduced forms of the electron acceptor (often, a hydrogen acceptor). In many such enzymic reactions, the equilibrium lies to one side, thus a single direction for the reaction is favoured; a typical example is the oxidation of ethanol to acetaldehyde in the presence of DPN and the enzyme *alcohol dehydrogenase* found in yeasts and bacteria[126,127]. This reaction follows the pattern given above and may be represented:

$$\text{Enzyme}$$
$$C_2H_5OH + DPN \rightleftharpoons CH_3CHO + DPN.H_2$$

In the absence of a hydrogen acceptor (e.g. methylene blue), the reduced co-enzyme ($DPN.H_2$) cannot be re-oxidized, so that the equilibrium position lies far over to the right; in other words, oxidation of ethanol predominates, rather than the reduction of acetaldehyde.

HYDRATION

The hydrases catalyse the addition of water to a compound without causing any cleavage of the molecule. The addition of water to fumaric acid to give L–malic acid is catalysed by the enzyme *fumarase*; this enzyme is absolutely specific for both the substrate and the product. The formation of phosphopyruvic acid by extraction of a water molecule from 2–phosphoglyceric acid is brought about by the enzyme *enolase*:

$$
\begin{array}{ccc}
CH_2OH & & CH_2 \\
| & & \| \\
H-C-O-PO_3H_2 & \rightleftharpoons & C-O-PO_3H_2 + H_2O \\
| & & | \\
COOH & & COOH
\end{array}
$$

This enzyme is a conjugated protein, the metal present being probably magnesium; the protein part of the molecule is not enzymically active and requires the addition of manganese, zinc or magnesium ions to activate it. Enolase has a molecular weight of approximately 65,000[128].

From a study of the water absorption and desorption characteristics of cellulose, it appears that a small amount of water combines with dry cellulose in an exothermic reaction. The absorbed water contracts and does not then give the X-ray diffraction pattern of liquid water; the mode of binding of such water is not known with certainty, but it is unlikely that covalent bonds are formed as they are in the case of fumarase action. Further water can be taken up, which is then bound by capillary forces only. The fact that cellulose

19

never occurs in a living system in a dry state raises the problem whether *hydrases* could exist which would facilitate hydration and liquid transport between cellulose fibrils. Further attention is given in Chapter VI to the existence of enzyme systems which 'open up' the structure of native celluloses, enabling hydrolytic enzymes to catalyse further breakdown.

HYDROLYSIS

The use of enzymes for hydrolytic processes has been known for many years in the textile industry, particularly for the removal of starch (*desizing*) from cellulosic fibres. While *rot-steeping* and *acid-steeping* have been used[129], desizing is generally accomplished with the aid of crude carbohydrases (known under such trade names as *Diastafor, Enzymase,* and *Nervanase*), while proteolytic enzymes (*Gelatase*) can be used for removing gelatin size from rayon. Crude carbohydrases, containing starch hydrolysing enzymes (*amylases*), have been prepared from barley malt, other plants, and from micro-organisms. The use and methods of testing such enzyme extracts have been described by numerous workers[130-132], and also in the trade literature.

No further consideration need be given here to the proteolytic enzymes, but other hydrolytic enzymes include esterases (such as sulphatases, phosphatases and lipases), nucleases and amidases. Throughout the remainder of this book the main emphasis will be placed on the carbohydrases catalysing the hydrolysis of cellulose and related substances, but many such enzymes are known which catalyse the hydrolysis of linkages other than the $(1 \rightarrow 4)\beta$–glycosidic linkages found in cellulose and xylan. These include α–glycosidases of differing specificities and action patterns, β–glycuronidases, sucrases, pentosanases, inulase, hyaluronidase, lysozyme, thio-glycosidases and pectinases; the discovery of bacterial and fungal polysaccharides in recent years adds greatly to this list, since micro-organisms can frequently metabolize the products they produce[133]. In the hydrolysis of starch a complex picture of enzymic reactions has been built up, and in order to demonstrate some of the problems which arise in any study of cellulose hydrolysis, the action of amylases on starch, which may be regarded in some ways as the α–analogue of cellulose, will be considered in some detail. Starch contains two principal components in varying amounts, but usually the linear molecule amylose comprises 20 to 28 per cent, and the branched molecule amylopectin 72 to 80 per cent of starch. Amylose consists of two to three hundred D–glucose units uniformly linked by $(1 \rightarrow 4)\alpha$–glucosidic bonds; this arrangement produces a helix-like molecule. In amylopectin, the amylose structure is also present together with side-chains of (1→4)–linked α–glucose units which are linked to the amylose chain through (1→6)α–branch points; these structures are represented in *Figure 3*. The hydrolysis of these

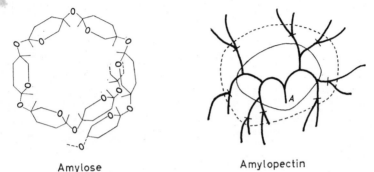

Amylose   Amylopectin

Figure 3—Schematic diagrams of the structure of starch components
(From *Structural Carbohydrate Chemistry*, by courtesy, J. Garnet Miller Ltd.)

A, Reducing group
- - -, Limit of action of β–amylase
+, Limit of action of α–amylase
——, Limit of action of β–amylase in second treatment

compounds is catalysed by two principal enzymes, known as α– and β–amylases (the prefixes do not refer to the configuration of the glucosidic linkage attacked, but to the change in optical rotation produced on hydrolysis). General reviews of these enzymes have been given by Hopkins[134] and by Whelan[135,173].

Action of β–Amylase

This enzyme occurs in resting seeds, which are better sources than the growing plants; in particular, ungerminated barley, wheat, potatoes and soya-beans are richer in β–amylase than in α–amylase, while crystalline β–amylase has been prepared from the sweet potato[136] and from malt[137]. The sweet potato enzyme exhibits optimum activity between pH values of 4 to 5 in both acetate and citrate buffer solutions, and the enzyme is inactivated by ascorbic acid or when its sulphydryl groups are oxidized[138]. Malt β–amylase has not the high thermal stability of α–amylase; heating at 70° inactivates the former but not the latter enzyme[139]. The hydrolysis of a starch gel, catalysed by β–amylase, results in a rapid production of reducing sugars, but only a slow decrease in the viscosity of the gel. Both amylose and amylodextrins containing 4 to 8 glucose units are cleaved readily to maltose, but maltotriose[140] is not hydrolysed. The enzyme cannot bring about the hydrolysis of the $(1\rightarrow6)a$–glucosidic link at the branch points in amylopectin, nor can such linkages be bridged over, so that attack on the inner $(1\rightarrow4)a$–glucosidic bonds cannot be effected in the presence of β–amylase alone. Even with amylose, the hydrolysis produces only 70 per cent of the expected amount of maltose, and from a crude soya-bean amylase another enzyme (termed Z–enzyme) has been isolated which can effect the cleavage of the β–amylase-resistant linkages; it has been suggested that Z–enzyme is a β–glucosidase, but this seems unlikely and the exact nature of the resistant link is still in doubt[141,142]. The rapid rate of cleavage of the outer chains of the multi-branched amylopectin in the presence of β–amylase and the mechanism of hydrolysis of an oxidized amylose (in which a carboxyl group was produced at the reducing end of the chain by hypoiodite oxidation) leads to the conclusion that the maltose units split off in β–amylase-catalysed hydrolysis are stripped from the non-reducing end of the polymer[143].

Whole starch solutions are rapidly hydrolysed in the presence of β–amylase with the production of approximately 52 per cent of the theoretical amount of maltose; a much slower hydrolysis then takes place until about 65 per cent of this theoretical quantity is reached[144]. At this stage the solution still remains viscous and a β–amylase limit dextrin has been separated from it; the outer chains of the amylopectin branches have been removed leaving this intact dextrin. Whereas amylopectin contains only one end group for every thirty glucose units, the limit dextrin has one end group for every ten to twelve units[145]. Acid hydrolysis of this limit dextrin or hydrolysis in the presence of a–amylase breaks down the $(1\rightarrow6)-a$ glucosidic linkages at the branch points and further attack by β–amylase can then occur.

Action of a–Amylase

Many germinated seeds contain a–amylase, and a crystalline enzyme has been prepared from a commercial malt extract[146]. Other crystalline amylases have been prepared from saliva[147], the pancreas[148], the fungus *Aspergillus oryzae*[149], and from *Pseudomonas saccharophilia*[170]. This enzyme also catalyses the hydrolysis of starch gel, but in this case the viscosity falls rapidly and the production of dextrins of low molecular weight is evidenced by a small increase in the reducing power of the solution; a gradual appearance of fermentable sugars then follows. These two distinct modes of enzymic hydrolysis have led to the terms *liquefying* and *saccharifying* enzymes for α– and β–amylases respectively. The dextrins produced initially in an α–amylase-catalysed attack contain about six D–glucose units. While the enzyme is unable to bring about the hydrolysis of (1→6)α–glucosidic linkages, it can by-pass these and can also bridge across phosphate groups to hydrolyse (1→4)α–glucosidic linkages; thus, dextrins containing such (1→6)α–linkages and phosphate groups tend to accumulate in the early stages of the hydrolysis. In the case of amylopectin, the branch-points remain resistant, but the inner long chains become accessible to enzymic attack[150]. The α–amylases from different sources have differing hydrogen ion concentrations for their optimum activities; crystalline pancreatic α–amylase has an optimum activity at pH 6·9, the crystalline enzyme from malt between pH 4·7 and 5·4, while the optimum pH value for the *Aspergillus oryzae* enzyme lies between 5·5 and 5·9. Other differences between α–amylases are shown by their requirements for chloride ions, and their degree of inactivation by the proteolytic enzyme trypsin.

Another interesting enzyme has been obtained from the cell-free culture filtrates of *Bacillus macerans*; in its presence starch and glycogen (another branched polysaccharide) are hydrolysed to cyclic *Schardinger dextrins*, which contain six to eight D–glucose units linked by (1→4)α–bonds into a ring. These rings are similar in size to the repeating unit of the helical structure suggested for amylose[151,152]. From starch some 60 per cent of Schardinger dextrins can be produced, while the yield from amylose is about 70 per cent.

TRANSFERASES

Phosphorylases

The transfer of a phosphoric acid group in a glycoside to another molecule is catalysed by the phosphorylases. These enzymes have been found in animals, plants and micro-organisms; crystalline forms (*P–enzyme*) have been prepared from potatoes[153], and from rabbit muscle[154]. The catalysed reaction is reversible and may be written:

$$\text{R—O—R}' + \text{O}^-\text{—P(=O)—OH}(\text{OH}) \rightleftharpoons \text{R—O—P(=O)—OH}(\text{O}^-) + \text{R}'\text{OH}$$

In the case of amylose (R—O—R′) in the presence of inorganic phosphate and a phosphorylase, α–D–glucose 1–phosphate is formed in good yield by repetitions of the process[155]. However, for the reverse

23

reaction to occur, it is essential to have present a *primer* molecule, such as a trace of an amylodextrin; it is then possible to synthesize long chains of $(1\rightarrow4)a$–linked glucose units. Phosphorylase appears to function by lengthening the chains of all primer molecules simultaneously, rather than by converting one primer molecule into amylose before adding to another[156]. In the presence of arsenate, potato phosphorylase catalyses the hydrolysis of amylose to glucose, probably through the formation of an unstable glucose 1–arsenate[157]. The branched-chain molecules amylopectin and glycogen undergo only partial breakdown in the presence of *P*–enzyme, with the formation of a limit dextrin. This enzyme cannot act at or near the $(1\rightarrow6)a$–linked branch points, and a *debranching* factor (*R–enzyme*) has been found in potato and yeast, which catalyses the cleavage of such bonds, thus setting free the single glucose unit stub left attached at the branch point to the long inner chains[158,159]. Another type of debranching factor (*amylo–1:6–glucosidase*) has been isolated from rabbit muscle; this enzyme is only able to catalyse the hydrolysis of a terminal $(1\rightarrow6)$–linkage, and so has no action in the breakdown of either glycogen or amylopectin prior to the action of muscle phosphorylase[160]. Manners has discussed the action of phosphorylases upon the different linkages present in these branched polysaccharides[133].

The synthesis of amylopectin from amylose is brought about by a transglucosylation in the presence of *Q–enzyme*; this enzyme has no action on glucose 1–phosphate unless a phosphorylase is also present[161,162]. This synthesis of $(1\rightarrow6)a$–glucosidic linkages by means of Q–enzyme is either irreversible or else the equilibrium lies far over to the side of the synthetic reaction. Q–enzyme from potatoes has been crystallized by Gilbert and Patrick[163]. Another transglucosylase has been found in potatoes, which catalyses reversibly disproportionating reactions between maltodextrins (amylodextrins) by the simultaneous scission and synthesis of $(1\rightarrow4)a$–linkages. For example, this enzyme (*D–enzyme*) can catalyse the transfer of a maltosyl radical from one maltotriose molecule to another, giving a mixture of glucose and maltopentaose. Higher dextrins are disproportionated to give chain molecules sufficiently long to form red iodine complexes[164,165]. D–enzyme differs from Q–enzyme in its capacity for catalysing the reverse reaction, and also its action with short-chain dextrins; Q–enzyme requires a minimum chain length of about forty glucose units in order to effect branching[166]; another difference is, of course, the type of linkage produced by each enzyme. The role of D–enzyme in starch metabolism has been discussed recently by Whelan[173].

Thus, it is now possible to break down or build up amylose, amylopectin and glycogen, and the rôle of phosphate in such processes must be borne in mind when considering the biological synthesis or degradation of cellulose. The differences between cellulose and amylose are principally the configuration of the glucosidic bonds (α in amylose, β in cellulose), and the solubility of the molecules in water, together with the physical natures of the two substances. However, the brief review of *starch enzymes* presented here serves to show the complexity, but completeness, of the enzymic story of a polysaccharide, and to act as a spur to greater endeavours to place cellulose degradation and synthesis in the same happy position. Even so, the mechanism of starch synthesis and degradation remains a subject of discussion (e.g. see ref. 173).

PRODUCTION OF ENZYMES

Many living organisms produce certain enzymes regardless of the materials on which they are growing. A typical example is the enzyme *invertase* which catalyses the hydrolysis of sucrose to glucose and fructose; it is produced by yeasts growing on practically any medium, and therefore, the enzyme is regarded as *constitutive*, although a larger quantity of invertase is produced if the medium contains sucrose[167]. However, some enzymes can only be produced by the organism in response to a particular compound being present in the growth medium, and are, therefore, termed *adaptive* or *inducible*. The distinction between the two classes of enzyme is often a quantitative one only; many inducible enzymes are produced in small quantities without their particular substrates being present. The enzymes catalysing the hydrolysis of cellulose generally belong to the inducible class; they are not produced in many cases if the micro-organism is grown on a sucrose-containing medium. However, this aspect of cellulase production is discussed later, although the whole subject of induction of enzyme formation is still a matter for controversy; the subject has been reviewed by Spiegelman[168] and King[169].

REFERENCES

1. HOLZER, *Cellulose and Cellulose Derivatives*, ed. Ott, Spurling and Grafflin, 1954, p. 511, Interscience, New York.
2. GUTHRIE, HOFFPAUIR, STANSBURY AND REEVES, *U.S. Dept. Agric., Bur. Agric. Ind. Chem.*, Publn. AIC–61 (1949)
3. WARD, *Cellulose and Cellulose Derivatives*, ed. Ott, Spurling and Grafflin, 1954, p. 9 *et sqq.*, Interscience, New York.

4. IRVINE AND SOUTAR, *J. chem. Soc.* 1920, **117**, p. 1489.
5. MONIER WILLIAMS, *J. chem. Soc.* 1921, **119**, p. 803.
6. IRVINE AND HIRST, *J. chem. Soc.* 1922, **121**, p. 1585.
7. CHARLTON, HAWORTH AND PEAT, *J. chem. Soc.* 1926, p. 89.
8. HAWORTH, *Helv. chim. Acta*, 1928, **11**, p. 547.
9. HAWORTH AND MACHEMER, *J. chem. Soc.* 1932, p. 2270.
10. HAWORTH, HIRST AND THOMAS, *J. chem. Soc.* 1931, p. 824.
11. HAWORTH, MONTGOMERY AND PEAT, *J. chem. Soc.* 1939, p. 1899.
12. BERGMANN AND MACHEMER, *Ber. dtsch. chem. Ges.* 1930, **63B**, pp. 316, 2304.
13. MARTIN, SMITH, WHISTLER AND HARRIS, *Amer. Dyest. Rep.* 1941, **30**, p. 628.
14. MARTIN *et al.*, *J. Res. Nat. Bur. Stand.* 1941, **27**, p. 449.
15. JULLANDER AND SVEDBERG, *Nature, Lond.* 1944, **153**, p. 523.
16. MEYER AND WOLFF, *Kolloidzschr.* 1939, **89**, p. 194.
17. MONTONNA AND JILK, *J. phys. Chem.* 1941, **45**, p. 1374.
18. SCHULZ, *Z. phys. Chem.* 1932, **A158**, p. 237.
19. SCHULZ, *J. prakt. Chem.* 1942, **161**, p. 147.
20. STAUDINGER, *Die hochmolecularen organischen Verbindungen*, 1932, Springer, Berlin.
21. DEBYE, *J. appl. Phys.* 1944, **15**, p. 338.
22. KRAEMER AND LANSING, *J. phys. Chem.* 1935, **39**, p. 153.
23. SVEDBERG AND PEDERSEN, *The Ultracentrifuge*, 1940. Clarendon Press, Oxford.
24. KRAEMER, *J. Franklin Inst.* 1941, **231**, p. 1.
25. KRAEMER, *Industr. Engng Chem.* 1938, **30**, p. 1200.
26. GRALEN AND SVEDBERG, *Nature, Lond.*, 1943, **152**, p. 625.
27. HESS AND WELTZIEN, *Annalen*, 1925, **442**, p. 46.
28. GOLOVA, *Akad. Nauk. S.S.S.R.* 1943, **1**, p. 29. [*Chem. Abstr.* 1946, **40**, p. 457.]
29. PURVES, *Cellulose and Cellulose Derivatives*, ed. Ott, Spurling and Grafflin, 1954, pp. 54 *et sqq.*, Interscience, New York.
30. PACSU, *J. polym. Sci.* 1947, **2**, p. 565.
31. SCHMIDT, HECKER *et al.*, *Ber. dtsch. chem. Ges.* 1934, **67B**, p. 2037.
32. HILLER AND PACSU, *Text. Res. J.* 1946, **16**, pp. 243, 564.
33. HAWORTH, *Chem. and Ind.* 1939, p. 917.
34. EKENSTAM, *Ber. dtsch. chem. Ges.* 1936, **69**, p. 549.
35. HESS AND STEURER, *Ber. dtsch. chem. Ges.* 1940, **73B**, p. 669.
36. SCHULZ AND HUSEMANN, *Z. phys. Chem.* 1942, **B52**, p. 23.
37. ASPINALL, Biochem. Soc. Symposium No. 11 (1953), p. 42.
38. SHARPLES, *J. polym. Sci.* 1954, **14**, p. 95.
39. SCHULZ, *J. polym. Sci.* 1948, **3**, p. 365.
40. HUSEMANN AND SPRINGLER, *Makromol. Chem.* 1957, **24**, p. 79.
41. WARD, *Text. Res. J.* 1950, **20**, p. 363.
42. MARK AND MEYER, *Z. phys. Chem.* 1929, **B2**, p. 115.
43. HESS, TROGUS, AKIN AND SAKURADA, *Ber. dtsch. chem. Ges.* 1931, **64**, p. 408.

44. KRATKY AND SAKARA, *Kolloidzschr.* 1944, **108**, p. 169.
45. MARK et al., *Cellulose and Cellulose Derivatives*, ed. Ott, Spurling and Grafflin, 1954, p. 217 *et seq.* Interscience, New York.
46. NICKERSON, *Advances in Carbohydrate Chemistry*, Vol. 5 (1950), p. 103, Academic Press, New York.
47. INGERSOLL, *J. appl. Phys.* 1946, **17**, p. 924.
48. HARTSUCH, *Introduction to Textile Chemistry* (1950), p. 112, Wiley, New York.
49. MARSH, *Introduction to Textile Bleaching* (1951), p. 38, Chapman and Hall, London.
50. HERMANS AND WEIDINGER, *J. polym. Sci.* 1949, **4**, p. 135.
51. HERMANS, *Physics and Chemistry of Cellulosic Fibres* (1949), Elsevier, New York.
52. TARKOW, *Tech. Pap. Pulp Pap. Ind.*, *N.Y.* 1950, **33**, p. 595.
53. HARRIS AND PURVES, *Paper Trade J.* 1940, **110**, p. 29.
54. MANN AND MARRINAN, *Trans. Faraday Soc.* 1956, **52**, p. 492.
55. MARK, *J. phys. Chem.* 1940, **44**, p. 764.
56. ASSAF, HAAS AND PURVES, *J. Amer. chem. Soc.* 1944, **66**, p. 59.
57. ELLIS AND BATH, *J. Amer. chem. Soc.* 1940, **62**, p. 2859.
58. URQUHART AND WILLIAMS, *J. Text. Inst.* 1925, **16**, p. 155.
59. WILSDEN in *The Times Trade and Engineering Supplement*, October, 1939.
60. SISSON AND SANER, *J. phys. Chem.* 1939, **43**, p. 687.
61. CUMBERBIRCH, *Reports on the Progress of Applied Chemistry*, Vol. 40, 1955, p. 451, Soc. of Chem. Industry, London.
62. NICOLL, COX AND CONAWAY, *Cellulose and Cellulose Derivatives*, ed. Ott, Spurling and Grafflin, 1954, p. 827, Interscience, New York.
63. HEUSER AND BARTUNEK, *Cellulosechemie* 1925, **6**, p. 19.
64. KENNER, *Chem. and Ind.* 1955, p. 727.
65. CORBETT AND KENNER, *J. chem. Soc.* 1955, p. 1431.
66. RICHARDS, SEPHTON AND MACHELL, *J. chem. Soc.* 1957, pp. 4492, 4500.
67. DLUGOSZ AND MICHIE, *Polymer*, 1960, **1**, p. 41.
68. SHARPLES, *J. polym. Sci.* 1954, **13**, p. 393.
69. BAUER AND PACSU, *Text. Res. J.*, 1952, **22**, p. 385.
70. BIRTWELL, CLIBBENS AND RIDGE, *J. Text. Inst.* 1925, **16**, p. T13.
71. GOLDFINGER, MARK AND SIGGIA, *Industr. Engng Chem.* 1943, **35**, p. 1083.
72. HUFFMANN, *Dissertation Abstracts*, 1957, **17**, p. 980.
73. DAVIDSON, *J. Text. Inst.* 1941, **32**, p. T109.
74. NEVELL, *J. Text. Inst.* 1951, **42**, p. T130.
75. DAVIDSON AND NEVELL, *J. Text. Inst.* 1957, **48**, p. T356.
76. SCHÜRZ, *Oesterr. Papier-Ztg.* 1957, **63**, pp. 7, 9.
77. MILES, U.S. Pat. 838,350 (1904).
78. CRAMER AND PURVES, *J. Amer. chem. Soc.* 1939, **61**, p. 3458.
79. UNRUH AND KENYON, *J. Amer. chem. Soc.* 1942, **64**, p. 127.
80. JACKSON AND HUDSON, *J. Amer. chem. Soc.* 1937, **59**, p. 2049.
81. BARSHA, *Cellulose and Cellulose Derivatives*, ed. Ott, Spurling and Grafflin, 1954, p. 713, Interscience, New York.
82. HARLAND, *J. Text Inst.* 1954, **45**, p. 678P.

83. KLINE, *Cellulose and Cellulose Derivatives*, ed. Ott, Spurling and Grafflin, 1954, p. 959, Interscience, New York.

84. MEYER AND MISCH, *Helv. chim. Acta*, 1937, **20**, p. 232.

85. ANDRESS, *Hoppe-Seyl. Z.* 1929, **34**, p. 190.

86. SAVAGE, YOUNG AND MAASBERG, *Cellulose and Cellulose Derivatives*, ed. Ott, Spurling and Grafflin, 1954, p. 882 *et seq.*, Interscience, New York.

87. COHEN AND HAAS, *J. Amer. chem. Soc.* 1950, **72**, p. 3954.

88. MORGAN, *Industr. Engng Chem. (Anal.)* 1946, **18**, p. 500.

89. McLAUGHLIN AND HERBST, *Canad. J. Res.* 1950, **28B**, p. 731.

90. WHISTLER AND SMART, *Polysaccharide Chemistry*, 1953, Academic Press, New York.

91. NORMAN, *Cellulose and Cellulose Derivatives*, ed. Ott, Spurling and Grafflin, 1954, p. 459, Interscience, New York.

92. BRAUNS, *Cellulose and Cellulose Derivatives*, ed. Ott, Spurling and Grafflin, 1954, p. 480, Interscience, New York.

93. BRAUNS AND YIRAK, *Paper Trade J.* 1947, **125**, p. 55.

94. WHISTLER, BOWMAN AND BACHRACH, *Arch. Biochem.* 1948, **19**, p. 25.

95. WHISTLER AND TU, *J. Amer. chem. Soc.* 1952, **74**, p. 3609.

96. CHANDA, HIRST, JONES AND PERCIVAL, *J. chem. Soc.* 1950, p. 1289.

97. CHANDA, HIRST AND PERCIVAL, *J. chem. Soc.* 1951, p. 1240.

98. BUSTON, *Biochem. J.* 1935, **29**, p. 196.

99. BRAUNS, *The Chemistry of Lignin*, 1952, Academic Press, New York.

100. SCHUBERT, ACERBO AND NORD, *J. Amer. chem. Soc.* 1957, **79**, p. 251.

101. NORD, SCHUBERT AND ACERBO, *Naturwiss.* 1957, **44**, p. 35.

102. ACERBO, SCHUBERT AND NORD, *J. Amer. chem. Soc.* 1958, **80**, p. 1990.

103. SÖNNERSKOG, *Svensk. Papperstidn.* 1945, **48**, p. 413.

104. JULLANDER, *Svensk. Papperstidn.* 1952, **55**, p. 197.

105. KERTESZ, *The Pectic Substances*. 1951, Interscience, New York.

106. WILLIAMS AND JOHNSON, *Industr. Engng Chem. (Anal.)* 1944, **16**, p. 23.

107. KARRER, STAUB AND STAUB, *Helv. chim. Acta*, 1924, **7**, p. 159.

108. KARRER, JOOS AND STAUB, *Helv. chim. Acta*, 1923, **6**, p. 800.

109. PRINGSHEIM AND KUSENACK, *Hoppe-Seyl. Z.* 1924, **137**, p. 265.

110. HERZOG, *Hoppe-Seyl. Z.* 1926, **152**, p. 119.

111. MEYER AND GÜRTLER, *Helv. chim. Acta*, 1947, **30**, p. 751.

112. BOISSONNAS, *Helv. chim. Acta*, 1947, **30**, p. 1703.

113. SUTRA, *C.R. Acad. Sci.*, Paris, 1932, **195**, p. 181

114. ZECHMEISTER AND TÓTH, *Hoppe-Seyl. Z.* 1933, **215**, p. 267.

115. RÅNBY, *Arkiv Kemi*, 1952, **4**, p. 241.

116. VAN DER WYK AND SCHMORAK, *Helv. chim. Acta* 1953, **36**, p. 385.

117. VIEL, *C.R. Acad. Sci.*, Paris, 1939, **208**, p. 1689.

118. SUMNER AND SOMERS, *Chemistry and Methods of Enzymes*, 1953, Academic Press, New York.

119. SUMNER, *J. biol. Chem.* 1926, **69**, p. 435.

120. HARRISON, *Biochem. J.* 1932, **26**, p. 1295.

121. BRUNELLI AND WAINO, *J. biol. Chem.* 1949, **177**, p. 75.

122. ANDERSSON, *Hoppe-Seyl. Z.* 1934, **225**, p. 57.

123. COULTHARD, MICHAELIS, *et al.*, *Biochem. J.* 1945, **39**, p. 24.

124. KEILIN AND HARTREE, *Nature, Lond.*, 1946, **157**, p. 801.
125. BUSTON AND JABBAR, *Biochim. Biophys. Acta*, 1954, **15**, p. 543.
126. LEHMANN, *Biochem. Z.* 1934, **274**, p. 321.
127. EULER, ADLER AND HELLSTROM, *Hoppe-Seyl Z.* 1936, **241**, p. 239.
128. BÜCHER, *Biochim. Biophys. Acta*, 1947, **1**, p. 467.
129. FARGHER AND PROBERT, *J. Text. Inst.* 1927, **18**, p. T559.
130. EVANS, *J. Soc. Dyers and Col.* 1935, **51**, p. 318.
131. SCOTT, *Industr. Engng Chem.* 1940, **32**, p. 784.
132. LENK, *J. Soc. Dyers and Col.* 1942, **58**, p. 138.
133. MANNERS, *Quart. Rev. Chem. Soc., Lond.* 1955, **9**, p. 73.
134. HOPKINS, *Advances in Enzymology*, Vol. 6, 1946, p. 389, Interscience, New York.
135. WHELAN, *Biological Transformations of Starch and Cellulose*, 1953, p. 17, Biochemical Soc. Symposia No. 11.
136. BALLS, WALDEN AND THOMPSON, *J. biol. Chem.* 1948, **173**, p. 9.
137. MEYER, FISCHER AND PIGUET, *Helv. chim. Acta*, 1951, **34**, p. 316.
138. ENGLAND, SOROF AND SINGER, *J. biol. Chem.* 1951, **189**, p. 217.
139. KNEEN, SANSTEDT AND HALLENBECK, *Cereal Chem.* 1943, **20**, p. 399.
140. MYRBÄCK AND AHLBORG, *Biochem. Z.* 1942, **311**, p. 213.
141. NEUFELD AND HASSID, *Arch. Biochem. Biophys.* 1955, **59**, p. 405.
142. PEAT, THOMAS AND WHELAN, *J. chem. Soc.* 1952, p. 722.
143. BÖTENBLAD AND MYRBÄCK, *Biochem. Z.* 1941, **307**, p. 129.
144. PIGMAN, *J. Res. Nat. Bur. Stand.* 1944, **33**, p. 105.
145. MEYER, WERTHEIM AND BERNFELD, *Helv. chim. Acta*, 1941, **24**, p. 212.
146. SCHWIMMER AND BALLS, *J. biol. Chem.* 1949, **179**, p. 1063.
147. MEYER, FISCHER, STAUB AND BERNFELD, *Helv. chim. Acta*, 1950, **33**, p. 1060.
148. FISCHER AND BERNFELD, *Helv. chim. Acta.* 1948, **31**, p. 1839.
149. FISCHER AND MONTMOLLIN, *Helv. chim. Acta*, 1951, **34**, p. 1987.
150. LOHMAR, *J. Amer. chem. Soc.* 1954, **76**, p. 4608.
151. FRENCH, KNAPP AND PAZUR, *J. Amer. chem. Soc.* 1950, **72**, p. 5150.
152. FRENCH, LEVINE, NORBERG *et al.*, *J. Amer. chem. Soc.* 1954, **76**, p. 2387.
153. BAUM AND GILBERT, *Nature, Lond.*, 1953, **171**, p. 983.
154. GREEN, CORI AND ONCLEY, *J. biol. Chem.* 1943, **151**, p. 21.
155. SUMNER AND SOMERS, *Arch. Biochem.* 1944, **4**, p. 11.
156. BAILEY AND WHELAN, *Biochem. J.* 1952, **51**, p. xxxiii.
157. KATZ AND HASSID, *Arch. Biochem.* 1951, **30**, p. 272.
158. HOBSON, WHELAN AND PEAT, *J. chem. Soc.* 1951, p. 1451.
159. MARUO AND KOBAYASHI, *Nature, Lond.*, 1951, **167**, p. 606.
160. CORI AND LARNER, *J. biol. Chem.* 1951, **188**, p. 17.
161. BARKER, BOURNE, PEAT AND WILKINSON, *J. chem. Soc.* 1950, p. 3022.
162. BEBBINGTON, BOURNE, STACEY AND WILKINSON, *J. chem. Soc.* 1952, pp. 240, 246.
163. GILBERT AND PATRICK, *Biochem. J.* 1952, **51**, p. 181.
164. PEAT, WHELAN AND REES, *Nature, Lond.*, 1953, **172**, p. 158.
165. PEAT, WHELAN AND JONES, *J. chem. Soc.* 1957, p. 2490.
166. PEAT, WHELAN AND BAILEY, *J. chem. Soc.* 1953, p. 1422.

167. VON EULER AND NILSSON, *Hoppe-Seyl. Z.* 1925, **143**, p. 89.
168. SPIEGELMAN, *The Enzymes*, ed. Sumner and Myrbäck, 1950. Vol. I, p. 267. Academic Press, New York.
169. KING, *Science Progress*, 1959, **47**, p. 293.
170. MARKOVITZ, KLEIN AND FISCHER, *Biochim. Biophys. Acta*, 1956, **19**, p. 267.
171. MARCHESSAULT AND RÅNBY, *Svensk. Papperstidn.* 1959, **62**, p. 230.
172. NAKAO, USUDA AND MIGITA, *J. Soc. Text. and Cellulose Industries, Japan*, 1959, **15**, p. 274.
173. HONEYMAN (ed.), *Recent Advances in the Chemistry of Cellulose and Starch*, 1959, Heywood, London.
174. MAHONEY AND PURVES, *J. Amer. chem. Soc.* 1942, **64**, pp. 9, 15.

II

ENZYMES INVOLVED IN REACTIONS
OF β-LINKED GLYCOSIDES

THE term *cellulase* has often been applied to impure enzymes catalysing not only the hydrolysis of cellulose (to cellodextrins, cellobiose and glucose), but also the hydrolysis of other β–glycosides and active also in transglycosylation reactions. However, much work has been done on these carbohydrates, and some account of these enzymes must be given before proceeding to a detailed account of the breakdown of cellulose in biological systems. In any perusal of the literature of this subject, care must be taken to ascertain the exact definition and the specific nature of the enzymic reactions involved. While it is acknowledged that this review is by no means comprehensive, it will serve to draw attention to the more important carbohydrases concerned in the reactions of β–linked glycosides.

β–Glucosidase

This enzyme occurs notably in almonds, although it is present in many other seeds, in plants, yeasts and other micro-organisms; probable mammalian sources are the kidney, liver and intestines. β–Glucosidase has also been detected in potatoes[1] and marine algae[2]. The term *emulsin* is applied to almond extracts containing this enzyme, but such preparations often contain many other enzymes. Ground, defatted almonds are extracted with 25 per cent saturated ammonium sulphate solution, and the enzyme is then precipitated by adding further ammonium sulphate until 50 per cent saturation is reached[3]; another method extracts the enzyme from almonds with zinc sulphate solution, followed by removal of some impurities with tannin and finally, precipitation of the crude enzyme *Rohferment* with further tannin[4]. This crude enzyme can be purified by precipitation with silver acetate under alkaline conditions, at 0°, followed by removal of silver ions from a suspension of this precipitate with hydrogen sulphide; the purified enzyme is then removed from solution by the addition of acetone and ether[5]. Other methods of preparing β–glucosidase have been given by Jermyn[6] (from *Stachybotrys atra*), by Nisizawa and co-workers[7] (from *Irpex lacteus*), and by Koyata[8] (from *Aspergillus niger*). Other methods

31

of purification, such as adsorption on kaolin or alumina, have been discussed by Veibel[9].

The Action of β–Glucosidases

By definition, such enzymes should catalyse only the hydrolysis of carbohydrates containing one or more glucose units linked to each other or to an aglycone in the β–configuration; the aglycone may be an alcohol (as in methyl–β–D–glucoside), a phenol (as in p–nitrophenyl–β–glucoside) or another sugar molecule (as in lactose). However, even purified samples of β–glucosidases catalyse the hydrolysis of β–xylosides[10]. The position is complicated further by claims that, for example, a so-called crystalline cellulase catalyses the hydrolysis of the aglycone linkage in p–nitrophenyl–β–D–cellobioside, but not that in salicin[11]. The effect of substitution in the glucose moiety has been described by Baumann and Pigman[12], whilst Helferich[13] has investigated extensively the influence of the aglycone group; Table 1 shows the relative glucoside values obtained

Table 1. Relative Specificity of a β–Glucosidase[13]

Aglycone	β–Glucoside Values
Methanol	0·034
n–butanol	0·3
phenol	0·33
o–cresol	4·3
m–cresol	0·55
p–cresol	0·12
salicylaldehyde	8·6
saligenin	1·7
vanillin	13
iso–vanillin	2·5

for such hydrolyses, the higher values indicating the greater rate of hydrolysis. The specificity of these enzymes has been shown by Japanese workers[14] to depend on their origin; for example, apricot β–glucosidase has high activity in the hydrolysis of o–cresyl–β–D–glucoside and little activity with the p–cresyl isomer, whereas the opposite order holds for the enzyme prepared from the fungus *Aspergillus niger*. However, the value of such observations must be examined carefully, until it has been shown that the extracts used have only β–glucosidase activity, and that other related, relatively unspecific enzymes (e.g. β–galactosidases, invertases) probably present have no action on the substrates hydrolyzed. A large volume of careful work on the β–glucosidase of the fungus *Stachybotrys atra* has been published by Jermyn[6,20]. The use of such carbohydrases for the structural analysis of polysaccharides has been discussed recently by Manners[35].

PROPERTIES OF β–GLUCOSIDASES

Effect of Enzyme Concentration

In order to establish desirable standard conditions in the determination of β–glucosidase activity, Weidenhagen[15] proposed that the substrate concentration [S] should be fixed at 0·1338M at the optimum pH value and a temperature of 30°; the enzyme concentration [E] was to be expressed as the weight of the enzyme preparation (or pure β–glucosidase) present in 50 ml. of the reaction mixture. Under such conditions the enzyme value (E.V.) would be given by the equation:

$$E.V. = \frac{k}{[E] \log^2}$$

where k is the reaction constant calculated from the first order equation over the range 30 to 50 per cent hydrolysis. At a first approximation the velocity (v) of hydrolysis is then given by

$$v = k'[S],$$

but as k' often varies with the extent of hydrolysis, an average value for the interval stated above is preferred. The choice of a standard substrate is wide; most workers use salicin, but attention

Table 2. Effect of Enzyme Concentration on the Enzyme Value

Enzyme Concentration (g/50 ml)	$k \times 10^4$ from 1st order kinetics	$k/g \times 10^4$
0·438	131	300
0·0438	13·1	300
0·00876	2·66	300
0·00438	1·09	250

must be drawn to the neat fluorimetric method of Robinson[16], using 4–methylumbelliferone–β–D–glucoside as a substrate in the determination of β–glucosidase activity.

Although it is essential to impose standard conditions in the measurement of enzyme activities, the insolubility of many β–glucosides leads to the choice of a low substrate concentration (e.g. [S] $= 0.052$M); applying the conditions and equations given above, the activity (from the E.V. equation) is described as the *Wertigkeit* or *enzyme efficiency*[15]. The effect of [E] on the reaction rate constant for the hydrolysis of sucrose in the presence of a crude β–glucosidase from *Aspergillus niger* is shown in *Table 2*[71].

Hydrogen Ion Concentration and Temperature Effects

As with most enzyme-catalysed reactions, the hydrolysis of β–glucosides shows optimum rates at certain pH values; for example, the enzymic hydrolyses of *n*–butyl– and *o*–cresyl–β–D–glucosides have optima at pH values between 4.0 and 5.0[17]. The nature of the buffer solution used and its ionic strength both have effects on this optimum pH value. The influence of hydrogen ion concentration on the activity of almond β–glucosidase in the hydrolysis of certain natural β–glucosides is illustrated in *Table 3*[18,33]. In the presence of

Table 3. Dependence of Optimum pH value on nature of Substrate

Substrate	Optimum pH Value
Amygdalin	6·0
Helicin	5·3
Salicin	4·4
Arbutin	4·1

McIlvaine buffer (citric acid–sodium phosphate) the pH value–activity curves for *S. atra* β–glucosidase reactions show an optimum and also a second peak. Jermyn found that the Michaelis constant (*Km*) varied with both pH value and buffer solution composition for these hydrolyses and by extrapolation of the curve of V_{max} against buffer concentration, arrived at a value for V_{max} at zero buffer concentration. Using these data, it was possible to reduce the secondary peak in the pH–activity curve, and the *S. atra* β–glucosidase then had a single flat maximum at around pH 4.5 and a slight shoulder at pH 6.0. However, the non-equivalence of this curve (for acetate buffer) and the citrate–phosphate curve showed that the effects of specific ions had not been eliminated[20]. If a β–glucosidase solution is maintained at low pH values (e.g. 2.5–3.0) in buffer solutions, and then brought to a pH value around 5.0, the residual activity is found to fall with time. Thus *S. atra* β-glucosidase is stable to above 30° at pH 4, but is inactivated immediately after holding at pH 3·6, even at 0°. Thus, the ionic environment affects the stability as well as the activity of the enzyme[20].

Unlike many acid–catalysed hydrolyses, the rate of enzymic hydrolysis increases with temperature until a maximum value is reached, and then the rate decreases as the temperature continues to rise. As may be expected with proteins, higher temperatures are often responsible for bringing about some denaturation of the enzyme. The effect of temperature on enzyme activity is further discussed in Chapter V. Jermyn[20] pointed out that in spite of the profound effects of pH value, ionic strength, temperature, substrate nature and concentration on the activity of β-glucosidase, the apparent energy of activation in the hydrolysis of several aryl–β–glucosides was little changed by differences in pH value and substrate nature. In general, the activation energies associated with enzymic hydrolysis of β-glucosides are much lower than the energies in the acid-catalysed reactions[19]. For example, the acid hydrolyses of cellobiose and of cellulose had energies *c.* 30,000 cals. per mole[21] while Jermyn's values for *S. atra* β-glucosidase in the hydrolyses of aryl–β-glucosides are around 8,000 cal. per mole[20]. Some of the properties of the extracellular β-glucosidases of a number of fungi grown in shake culture were sufficiently alike to lead Jermyn to suggest that these β-glucosidases conform to some common pattern[34].

β-Glucosidase Composition

Thomas[22] found that partially purified cellulase from *S. atra* was closely associated with a polysaccharide, while Fischer[23] showed that the stability of his yeast invertase depended on the presence of an associated polysaccharide. The purification of β-glucosidases often reaches the point where it is impossible to remove further carbohydrate from the enzyme. It has been suggested[24,25] that the residue, 3 to 6 per cent of carbohydrate material, constitutes the 'holding group', responsible for anchoring the glucoside in the formation of the enzyme-substrate complex. Until a relationship between enzyme activity and carbohydrate material has been firmly established, and it has been shown that similar hydrolases need the presence of a non-protein moiety before they are active, this hypothesis must be regarded critically. Jermyn[20] found that the carbohydrate, associated with the *p*–nitrophenyl–β–D–glucosidase of *S. atra*, was essential to the stability of the enzyme, but not to its activity. Dialysis of β-glucosidase solutions over a wide range of hydrogen ion concentrations does not affect enzymic activity, so that the hydrolysis is catalysed without the necessity for dialysable co-enzymes. It has been predicted[26] that the point of specific attachment of β–glucosides to all β–glucosidases would be the hydroxyl group at C_3 of the glucose molecule. Jermyn[20] showed that no competitive inhibition occurred in β–glucoside hydrolysis when a compound having the opposite configuration at C_3 to that of glucose was present; another condition for specific attachment between enzyme molecule and substrate was probably the configuration about C_1, but the β–linkage does not need to be through an oxygen atom, as phenyl–β–D–thioglucoside acts both as a substrate and an inhibitor for *S. atra* β–glucosidase. However, other β–glucosidases appear unable to hydrolyse this thioglucoside[9].

The mechanism of carbohydrase action has been discussed by Jermyn[27], who attempts to correlate his findings on the β–glucosidase of *S. atra* with current theories of enzyme action and to fit these observations into a broad conception covering the present position of our knowledge of carbohydrate hydrolysing and transferring enzymes. Koshland[28] suggests that more than one type of reaction mechanism and intermediate complex are involved in such reactions. His findings involve competing hydrolase and transferase actions, the retention of configuration, the breaking of the glycosyl–oxygen bond rather than the oxygen–aglycone bond, and these results can be fitted into a two stage reaction scheme[29]:

$$EO - H + RO\text{–glycosyl} \rightarrow EO\text{–glycosyl} + RO - H \quad \text{(i)}$$
$$EO - \text{glycosyl} + R'O\text{–H} \rightarrow EO\text{–H} + R'O - \text{glycosyl} \quad \text{(ii)}$$

where E represents the enzyme, R represents the aglycone in a transferase reaction, and in a hydrolase reaction $R' = H$. Thus, the activity of carbohydrases that act as transferases with retention of configuration depends on the simultaneous binding at contiguous sites on the enzyme of two suitable substrate molecules. Jermyn[27] pictures the overall reaction as:

$$\text{Gly–OR} + \text{POQ} \rightleftharpoons \text{Gly–OP} + Q^+ + RO^-,$$

where Gly represents the glycosyl radical, and P, Q and R represent hydrogen atoms, or suitable organic radicals; this reaction, in principle, is reversible, but the free energy change drives the reaction sufficiently far to the right in most β–glucosidase–catalyzed reactions for Gly–OR to be termed the *substrate* and POQ the *acceptor*. The blocking of one or both active centres of the enzyme molecule inhibits the enzyme; the centres occupied normally by the substrate may be occupied by competitive inhibitors while the 'acceptor centres' can be bound by anticompetitive inhibitors. This conception of the union of substrates with two active centres had its origin in the work of von Euler[30] and has been discussed further by Pigman[31,32]. The thought-provoking paper of Jermyn[27] and the review by Veibel[9] are worthy of further study for their detailed treatment of the *double displacement* mechanism of β–glucosidase action.

ENZYMIC SYNTHESIS OF GLYCOSIDES

It has been seen above that enzymic hydrolysis and transfer may be two competing reactions. Often the concentration of water is so high that, unless the enzyme has no tendency to use water as an acceptor, transfer to other acceptors present in comparatively low concentration would not be detected; thus, hydrolysis has been most frequently observed. The equations (i) and (ii) given above do not reveal the complete story; Koshland[28] has shown that the direct single-step transfer from the asymmetric carbon atom leads to inversion of the glycosidic bond. A second transfer, accompanied by a second inversion, would lead to the same bond configuration in the final product as in the original glycoside:

$$\alpha\text{–glycosyl} - OR + EO - H \rightarrow \beta\text{–glycosyl} - OE + HO - R$$
$$\beta\text{–glycosyl} - OE + HO - R' \rightarrow \alpha\text{–glycosyl} - O\text{–}R' + EO - H$$

Evidence for this Walden inversion in one-step processes exists in the phosphorylation involving maltose (an α–linked glucoside) and an enzyme from *Neisseria meningitidis* which gives rise to β–glucose–1 phosphate[36] and also in the formation of β–maltose by the β–amylase catalysed hydrolysis of amylose[37].

It has been shown, in reactions carried out in the presence of H_2 ^{18}O and catalysed by transferases, that the transferred radical is a glycosyl radical and not in the glycoside form[28,38]. In reactions catalysed by many β–glucosidases, simple hydrolysis results when no acceptor is present or if the enzyme has an absolute specificity requirement for water molecules. If efficient acceptor molecules are present in high concentration, as is the case where the original glycoside (*donor*) is also an efficient acceptor compared with other acceptors which may be present, the transfer reaction leads principally to oligosaccharides. However, if the acceptor molecules are present in only trace amounts (perhaps as impurities in the donor) and if the acceptor activity of these molecules does not decline after successive transfers, the major products of the reaction are polysaccharides. Another possibility is that while the donor molecule is a poor acceptor, a single transfer of a suitable radical may convert it to an efficient acceptor and polysaccharides would again result. Thus, the initial acceptors in such transfers act as primers for polysaccharide synthesis[39].

In the breakdown of cellulose by enzymic hydrolysis, it will be seen later that β-glucosidases of varying specificities play important rôles and the transferase activity of such enzymes must be considered when interpreting hydrolyses where oligosaccharides and cellodextrins are produced. Thus, Crook and Stone[40] were able to show that a partially purified enzyme system from *Aspergillus niger* catalysed the transfer of a glucosyl radical from cellobiose and other oligosaccharides of the cellulose series leading to higher saccharides, although prolonged incubation led to glucose; similar transferase activities were detected in extracts from *Myrothecium verrucaria*, *Aspergillus aureus* and snail gut. From another fungus (*Chaetomium globosum*), an enzyme extract has been prepared which catalyses the production of cellotriose and probably cellotetraose from cellobiose, especially if the glucose formed is removed by enzymic oxidation with notatin (see Chapter I) to prevent reversal of the reaction[41]. It will be noted that this transglycosylase is similar to the trans-α-glycosylases of many bacteria (e.g. amylomaltase or the amylase of *Bacillus macerans*) in that, not only is the configuration of the donor molecule retained in the product, but also the $(1\rightarrow4)$ linkages. In many other trans-β-glycosylations involving fungal enzymes the $(1\rightarrow4)$ linkage is not necessarily conserved; thus with the growth of *A. niger* on cellobiose the β-analogue of panose [O-β-D-glucopyranosyl - $(1\rightarrow6)$ -O-β-D-glucopyranosyl - $(1\rightarrow4)$-D-glucopyranose] was formed together with only a small amount of cellotriose, while the glucose produced was metabolized further by the growing mycelium[42]. Later work[43] with growing cultures of *A. niger*, resting cells and cell free extracts acting on cellobiose led to the transfer of a glucosyl radical to another cellobiose molecule, to other β-linked disaccharides or to glucose giving rise to mixtures of trisaccharides; the principal linkage formed was $(1\rightarrow6)$ β, but synthesis of $(1\rightarrow2)$ β, $(1\rightarrow3)$ β and $(1\rightarrow4)$ β linkages was also obtained. Other acceptors in this transglycosylation were D- and L-xylose, L-sorbose and N-acetylglucosamine. Transfer of a glucosyl radical from cellobiose to D-xylose in the presence of cell free extracts of *A. niger* has resulted in the isolation of the disaccharide 3-O-β-D-glucopyranosyl-D-xylose[44]. These observations show that these transferases have a lower order of acceptor (or receptor) specificity than the fungal trans-α-glycosylases, although even in the latter it has been observed that from maltose, both *iso*maltose and panose can be obtained[45]. *A. niger* has also been used to synthesize nigeran, a polysaccharide with alternate $(1\rightarrow3)$ α and $(1\rightarrow4)$ α linkages[46], and Stacey[47] has remarked that the substrate is probably the nigerose unit (3–O–α–D–glucopyranosyl–D–glucose) whose molecules are joined together by $(1\rightarrow4)$ α linkages in the manner of block polymer formation. This review has been limited principally to a discussion of the types of transglycosylation which may be expected to occur with cellulose hydrolysis products, but accounts of transfers involving these and other donors and acceptors have been given by Edelman[39], Stacey[48] and by Barker and Bourne[49]. No certain answer can yet be given to refute Weidenhagen's contention[50] that hydrolysis and transglycosylation cannot be ascribed to the same enzyme.

OTHER CARBOHYDRASES

Cellobiase.—The preparation of a β–glucosidase of such specificity that only cellobiose can act as a substrate has not yet been achieved. In most preparations from cellulose-degrading organisms β–glucosidases have been found; the activity of such enzymes has been determined using a number of substrates containing the β–link, such as cellobiose, salicin, p–nitrophenyl–β–cellobioside and p–nitrophenyl–β–D–glucoside. As has already been mentioned the extracellular β–glucosidase of *S. atra* is specific for many β–glucosides, but any configurational change or substitution in the D–glucopyranose ring leads to compounds which do not act as substrates[20]; from this work it must be stressed that many of the cellobiases reported in the literature must be regarded as relatively unspecific β–glucosidases until it has been proved that only the hydrolysis of the $(1\rightarrow4)$ β glucosidic linkage, as in cellobiose or even the cello-oligosaccharides, is catalysed. A cellobiase without action on other β–glucosides has been found in malt extract[51]; in this case the holosidic bond of p–nitrophenyl–β–cellobioside is cleaved but not the aglycone bond. However until this degree of definition is reached in all cases, enzymes (which catalyse the hydrolysis of other β–glucosides) will continue to be termed 'cellobiases'; such enzymes have been found in animal rumens, molluscs, plant seeds and fungi; the early work of Pringsheim[52] showed some evidence for the hydrolysis of cellobiose to glucose by a bacterium, *Cellulobacillus*, and he recorded the thermal instability of the enzyme responsible. Later Pringsheim[53,54] was able to show that barley malt solutions lost their cellobiase activity on ageing. On germination, the cellobiase activity of barley malt increased, reaching a maximum at the seventh to eighth day, and then declined sharply; the enzyme had an optimum pH value of 4·0 to 4·5 and an optimum temperature of $37°$[55]. The cellobiase activity of barley and other cereals has been recorded by Preece and Hoggan[56].

Considerable efforts have been made to separate cellobiase and lichenase (see later). In Pringsheim's work the aged malt solutions retained lichenase activity, showing that the two enzymes were different. The gut juice of the snail *Helix pomatia* contains a cellobiase[57] and this enzyme has been separated from an accompanying lichenase by fractional adsorption on aluminium hydroxide[58]. This technique has been applied with success to the enzymes from the fungus *Aspergillus niger*; however sharp separations were not generally achieved[60]. The pH value optimum for these enzymes lies between $4·5$ and $5·0$[59,61]. Cellobiase has been found in the rumen and caecum of the cow, but not in its intestine or stomach[62]; it seems likely that the origin of this cellobiase can be attributed to the alimentary microflora. Festenstein[63] has shown that the transferase activity of a cellobiase from sheep rumen micro-organisms, with an optimum pH value of 5 to 6, only becomes appreciable in solutions containing at least 5 per cent of cellobiose. The activity of this enzyme was completely inhibited by glucono–1:4–lactone, whereas an enzyme catalyzing the hydrolysis of carboxymethylcellulose was only inhibited to a maximum of 60 per cent.

The fungal cellobiases have received most attention, although it is impossible to draw up any scheme for the correlation of enzyme properties from different fungi. The cellobiase from *Poria vaillantii*[64] has optimum activity at pH $4·2$, and remains active over the pH range $3·5$ to $5·0$; storage of the enzyme outside these limits for 24 hours affects the activity when it is again brought to pH $4·2$, 50 per cent or more of the activity being lost. The thermal stability followed the pattern of most cellobiases, complete inactivation being achieved by holding the enzyme solution at $70°$ for 10 minutes; the optimum activity was recorded at $50°$. The enzyme was activated by the presence of cobalt and manganese ions, although mercuric ions, reducing and oxidizing agents had little effect on the activity; compounds which react with thiol groups in the proximity of the active centre of the enzyme, such as p–chloromercuribenzoic acid and phenylmercuric nitrate, did not influence cellobiase activity. Although transglycosylase activity has not been demonstrated with this enzyme, it cannot be regarded solely as a cellobiase, the activity on p–nitrophenyl–β–D–glucoside being greater than that on cellobiose; salicin was also hydrolysed. Kooiman *et al.*[65,66] and Aitken *et al.*[67] have also shown the presence of a β–glucosidase, catalysing the hydrolysis of cellobiose, in extracts from *Myrothecium verrucaria*; these enzymes are all inactivated on heating above $60°$.

Whitaker[68] has shown that a purified cellulase from the same species catalysed the hydrolysis of cellobiose and higher $(1{\rightarrow}4)$ β oligoglucosides. However, he noted that, on thermal denaturation, greater loss in activity of the enzyme was shown towards substrates of lower molecular weight; thus the apparent cellobiase activity was completely lost after storage for 5 minutes at 75·6°, whereas there was still 19 per cent residual activity towards cellopentaose after this treatment. In fact, Whitaker suggests that one enzyme only is responsible for all such hydrolyses, the differential effects being interpreted that the enzyme, like the substrate, can undergo structural changes whose effects on enzyme activity vary with the degree of polymerization of the substrate. Toyama[69] has shown the presence of a cellobiase in extracts from *Trichoderma koningi* (*T. viride*). The intracellular β–glucosidase of *S. atra*[70] catalysed the hydrolysis of cellobiose, $(1{\rightarrow}4)$ β linked glucosaccharides up to a chain length of eleven glucose units, and some aryl–β–glucosides, but it was not active in the hydrolysis of swollen cellulose or carboxymethylcellulose. These results may be compared with those of Grassmann *et al.*[60] who found that a cellobiase from *A. niger* (separated from cellulase by adsorption on aluminium hydroxide) hydrolysed cellobiose, cellotetraose and cellohexaose, but had no action on dextrins of higher molecular weight. The separated cellulase action on tri- and tetrasaccharides was very small, and it had no action on substances with a molecular weight below 1000. Small amounts of the intracellular β–glucosidase from *S. atra* were produced by growth of the fungus on glucose or maltose as sole carbon sources, whereas large quantities were produced from cellobiose. The enzyme had an optimum pH value between 5 and 5·5. The rate of hydrolysis was linear with time and was proportional to the enzyme concentration. The relation between rate of hydrolysis and substrate concentration, using cellobiose and p–nitrophenyl–β–D–glucoside as substrates, gave rectilinear plots in the Lineweaver-Burk method, and the Michaelis constants were $3 \cdot 9 \times 10^{-4}$M and $2 \cdot 0 \times 10^{-4}$M respectively[70]; the Michaelis constant for Jermyn's extracellular β–glucosidase[20] from the same fungus acting on p–nitrophenyl–β–D–glucoside, was 3×10^{-5}M, and that for a cellobiase from a sheep rumen β–glucosidase[72] was found to be 9×10^{-4}M. The transferring activity of cellobiases has been described in the previous section.

Cellulase.—There has been no satisfying proof that only a single enzyme is involved in the catalysis of the hydrolysis of cellulose. The nature of the substrate itself must be taken into account, and factors such as crystallinity, accessibility, degree of polymerization, degree

41

of substitution and solubility must all be considered. It would appear unlikely that a single enzyme could act in the hydrolyses of native cellulose (e.g. cotton), of a regenerated cellulose (e.g. viscose rayon) and of a soluble derivative (e.g. carboxymethyl-cellulose). Thus, no single definition can be provided for the term 'cellulase' and other terms such as C_x, C_1, S factor and *dehydrogen-bondase* have arisen to account for the various changes observed in cellulose during enzymic action. However, the remainder of this book is devoted to this enzymic action and, particularly in Chapter VI, it will be seen that there is much conflicting evidence for uni-enzymatic and multi-enzymatic hypotheses for cellulose breakdown.

Lichenase.—It will be recalled that lichenin is a water-soluble polysaccharide containing 80 to 160 D–glucose units[73], 30 per cent of which are linked in $(1\rightarrow3)$ β configuration, whilst the remainder are linked $(1\rightarrow4)$ β[74]. A wide variety of sources[75] for enzymes catalysing the hydrolysis of this polysaccharide are known, many of which also contain cellulase. Partially purified lichenases have been obtained from the snail *Helix pomatia*[57], from malt[76,77] and from fungi such as *Aspergillus oryzae* and *Merulius lacrymans*[78,79].

In general lichenin is hydrolysed to glucose; the early stages of the reaction follow first order kinetics[57,76], but later stages follow the Schütz rule[57,80]. Karrer[57,80] has defined a lichenase unit as the amount of the enzyme which brings about the hydrolysis of one gram of lichenin (in 1·5 per cent solution) to the extent of 20 per cent in 3 hours at 37° and pH 5·28. The optimum pH value varies with the source, but often lies between 4·5 and 5·9, although the lichenase from *Cytophaga* sp. shows an optimum at pH 7·0[79]. The fact that it has been possible to hydrolyse 84 per cent of lichenin with the aid of snail lichenase[81] is in favour of the thesis that cellulase and lichenase are different enzymes.

The separation of these enzymes from one another and from cellobiase has been achieved at least partially, by fractional pre-cipitation of *A. oryzae* aqueous extracts with mixtures of ethanol and ether[78]. However it has yet to be proved conclusively that cellulase and lichenase are different enzymes.

Chitinase.—Chitin may be considered as an analogue of cellulose in which each glucose unit is replaced by N–acetylglucosamine (2–acetamido–2–deoxy–D–glucose). This analogy must not be carried too far as the physical nature of the two polymers show many differences. However, many enzyme extracts, which contain cellu-lases, are able also to bring about the hydrolysis of chitin. Karrer and Hofmann[82] have described the preparation of a chitinase from snails; this enzyme has maximum activity at pH 5·2 and the principal product of hydrolysis is N–acetylglucosamine[83]. A similar enzyme has been prepared by chromatography on a bauxite column of glycerol extracts from snail digestive juices; also present were a chitodextrinase and a chitobiase[84,85]. Hackman[86] has isolated a chitinase from the gut of the snail, *Helix aspersa*, and here enzymic hydrolysis produced traces of D–glucosamine in addition to the N–acetyl compound.

Many fungi and bacteria attack chitin and a review of these micro-organisms has been given by Daste[87]; and, indeed, snail chitinase has been shown to arise from the microflora of the digestive tract[88]. The enzymes from *Streptomyces griseus* have been studied in some detail[89,90]; they can be separated into two chitinases and a chitobiase by zone electrophoresis on starch. The chitobiase could be separated from the chitinases by ammonium sulphate fractionation; this chitobiase was irreversibly adsorbed on bauxite and was heat-labile. It catalysed the hydrolysis of the β–phenyl-glucoside of N–acetylglucosamine as well as chitobiose and chito-triose. The chitinases were active in the hydrolysis of chitin to N–acetylglucosamine and N,N¹–diacetyl-chitobiose without the formation of detectable amounts of higher saccharides. Chito-dextrin was cleaved randomly producing a number of intermediate saccharides; but in no case were the homologous oligosaccharides of D–glucosamine hydrolysed. The chitinases of this fungus have also been studied by Charles[91]. The results of the fungal and bacterial breakdown of chitin are complicated frequently by the existence of oxidative and transferring enzymes which bring about hydrolysis accompanied by the formation of acetic acid and ammonia[92]. A wide range of soil and water bacteria have been examined for the production of extracellular chitinases; the enzyme appeared to be constitutive in many species of bacteria[93]. An extracellular enzyme, which has been found in *Escherichia coli* cultures, was able to catalyse the de-acetylation of N–acetylglucosamine[94]. Tracey[95] has reviewed the chemistry and biochemistry of chitin and a useful account has also been given by Kent and Whitehouse[96].

THEORIES OF CELLULOSE DECOMPOSITION

Cellulose, accompanying hemicelluloses and other polysaccharides are degraded in Nature by fungi, bacteria, protozoa, plants and animals. However, the higher forms of life rely on symbiotic micro-organisms for the digestion of the more insoluble polysaccharides. As cellulose is probably the most abundant organic compound existing in Nature, it has been adopted by man for the manufacture of paper, textiles, plastics, explosives, foodstuffs, surface coatings, cordage, marine and constructional timbers, and furniture, to give only a brief list. It is obviously a matter of great concern that cellulosic materials are so readily decomposed by micro-organisms. As far back as 1924 the annual loss in the United States of America due to decay (both biological and physical) in wood products amounted to 400 million dollars[97], while similar bills have been recorded for losses in cotton duck, tentage, fishing nets, and tropical kit. Here, then, is a major field of enzymic activity, and until recently the mode of cellulose decomposition had not been the subject of detailed study. Even now, purely empirical methods of protection against decay are employed on a lavish scale; for example, in 1929, some 25 million gallons of preservative were used to protect timber alone[98]. Before considering, in detail, the enzymes which catalyse cellulose degradation, the *cellulases*, some general hypotheses of the way in which cellulose is broken down biologically must be mentioned. Hoppe-Seyler[99] in 1883 was probably the first to record the decay of cellulose by animals and plants, while de Bary[100] noted, three years later, that the fungus *Peziza sclerotium* secreted enzymes which 'dissolved' cellulose. Later it was noticed that the macerated tissue of *Botrytis* had strong cellulose-decomposing activity[101]. From these early observations two principal theories for the initial stages of this enzymic decomposition have grown, although it must be pointed out that all classes of enzymes are found in organisms which break down cellulose, so that it is sometimes difficult to distinguish between initial, secondary and higher orders of decomposition.

Oxidative Degradation

When fungi grow on wood and other forms of cellulose an increase in the acidity of the region or culture medium has been noticed; this increase was considered to be due to the oxidation of reducing, or potential reducing, groups and carbinol groups to carboxyl groups[102,103]. Winogradsky[104] drew attention to the similarities between chemically produced oxy-celluloses and filter paper which had been attacked by bacteria. The degraded cellulose had acidic properties, did not reduce Fehling's solution to cuprous oxide, had a strong affinity for dyes like methylene blue, and was partially soluble in alkalis giving a yellow-coloured solution. Loicjanskaja[105] grew *Cytophaga* (a cellulose-decomposing bacterium) on filter paper and determined the uronic acid content, as well as the furfural yield from the alkali-soluble fraction, both before and after attack. The increase in these values during breakdown was taken as proof of oxidative attack. Later work[106] confirmed these findings, but could not agree with the inference advanced. From cellulose suspensions which had been attacked by *Cytophaga*, Walker and Warren[107] removed fibrous material and were able to precipitate an acidic gum by the addition of ethanol to the culture. The action of hydrochloric acid on this gum led to the products (furfural and carbon dioxide) expected from a polyuronide. Thus, the gum was thought to represent an intermediate stage in cellulose attack, and further, all primary carbinol groups along the cellulose chain had been oxidized to carboxyl groups. At this stage, the molecule became unstable and partially oxidized fragments were then broken down further, but not completely, by the bacteria. Having shown that two-thirds of the cellulose was converted to carbon dioxide and that the acidic gum, which on acid hydrolysis gave, *inter alia*, xylose, accounted for a large part of the remaining one-third, Walker and Warren stated 'to account in this manner for the occurrence of this mucilage implies that any given molecule is only partially consumed, which we find easier to believe than that a certain proportion (two-thirds) of the oxidized cellulose is completely consumed and the remainder not further attacked'. It does not appear justified to suggest that the oxidation to a polyuronide would necessarily produce instability, and certainly not to such an extent as to bring about breakdown into water soluble fragments. Similarly, oxidation of carbinol end-groups would not lead to this fragmentation, and it is to be expected that some uronic acid groups would be found in the residual fibrous material. In fact, it has been shown[106] that the residual cellulose was not oxidized to a greater extent than it was prior to attack. Indeed, uronic acid groups introduced chemically into cellulose were preferentially removed during bacterial attack. The so-called bacterial 'oxycellulose' has been shown to be a polyuronide containing some pentose groups. The oxidative theory also requires the bacteria to produce an extracellular oxidase system; however, the product of such oxidase activity (i.e. oxycellulose) is still water insoluble and not available for intracellular metabolism. On the other hand, scission of chains to water soluble fragments would provide energy for the cell, but then it is difficult to see why the insoluble product should accumulate. Under conditions in which oxygen was excluded from well-established cultures of *Sporotrichum carnis* on cellulose, a reducing substance, probably glucose, was shown to accumulate[108]. In the metabolism of soil fungi using cellulose as a sole carbon source no significant changes in the pH values of the media occurred. It has been shown[109] that the major metabolic products from the breakdown of glucose by fungi are carbon dioxide and fungal mycelium. A similar pattern is followed in the fungal degradation of cellulose[110], as much as 50 per cent of the cellulose carbon being used to build up mycelium. Cellulose-decomposing, anaerobic bacteria produce large quantities of acids, but these result from secondary breakdown, as will be seen later. With the current ideas about the crystallinity of cellulose and the comparative resistance of crystalline regions to chemical and biological attack, many of the older ideas on an oxidative mechanism for cellulose breakdown must be discarded, and the considerable evidence for a hydrolytic mode of attack must be presented.

Hydrolytic Attack

It will be recalled the amylases catalyse the hydrolysis of amylose to the disaccharide maltose. A similar mode of attack may be looked for in the breakdown of cellulose, although certain facts must be born in mind:

(a) cellulose is insoluble in water, whereas amylose is soluble,

(b) amylose has a helical structure, whereas the cellulose molecule probably has a straight chain,

(c) the linkages in cellulose and amylose are of uniform types, although the configurations of the respective disaccharides exhibit differences. In cellobiose, each glucopyranose ring is rotated through $180°$ with respect to its neighbour.

The uniformity of linkages in cellulose (i.e. all are $(1\rightarrow4)\ \beta$) makes it difficult to see why different enzyme systems, as in the $\alpha-$ and $\beta-$amylases, should exist, although suggestions have been made that plant celluloses have 'amylose-type' structures, while bacterial and animal celluloses are akin to amylopectin and glycogen, respectively[111]. The evidence against branching and anomalous linkages has been presented in Chapter I; however, the present view of cellulose as a partly crystalline polymer leads to a necessity for the existence of several enzymes, or at least, one enzyme with multiple functions, capable of catalysing the following changes:

(i) the hydrolysis of amorphous regions,

(ii) the swelling of crystalline regions, or the rupture of hydrogen bonds in the crystalline regions to give linear molecules which then react as (i),

(iii) reaction (i) may lead to the production of cellobiose units, in which case a further reaction would be the hydrolysis of cellobiose to glucose,

(iv) the transglycosylation of di- and oligo-saccharides,

(v) the breakdown of anomalous linkages (if any) in both cellulose and its primary products of hydrolysis.

The degradation of native celluloses and the accessibility of crystalline regions to enzymic attack are discussed in detail in Chapter VI, but many early workers were able to demonstrate that the primary attack on cellulose by micro-organisms, seed extracts, molluscs and enzymes derived therefrom was by hydrolysis. However, no evidence has yet been found for the hydrolysis of cellulose by the action of phosphorylases, which play such an important rôle in starch breakdown, although Fåhraeus[112] has mentioned this possibility. Pringsheim[52] in 1912 suggested that two hydrolases (carbohydrases) were active in the hydrolysis of cellulose, these being a cellulase catalysing the production of cellobiose and a cellobiase enabling the disaccharide to be hydrolysed to glucose. Although Pringsheim claimed to have demonstrated the production of cellobiose and glucose by the growth of micro-organisms in a cellulose-containing medium to which an antiseptic had been added to suppress thermophilic 'oxidative' fermentation, the identification of the disaccharide left much to be desired. However, Pringsheim showed that the temperature at which the cellobiase was inactivated was lower than the corresponding temperature for the cellulase; thus, by growing the micro-organisms at 67° to 70° cellobiose accumulated without being further hydrolysed to glucose. Nearly twenty years were to elapse before Pringsheim's results could be substantiated. Inhibition of oxidation by the addition of toluene to a thermophilic culture and growth at 65° enabled Woodman and Stewart[113] to prove the hydrolysis of cellulose to glucose, although no cellobiose could be detected. It was left to Simola[114] in 1931 to give support to Pringsheim's hypothesis. From work with two species of *Cellulobacillus* growing on cellulose, the production of cellobiose and glucose was confirmed, both sugars being identified by reducing values, specific optical rotations, and the melting-points of their osazones. In addition, the disaccharide was hydrolysed to glucose with the aid of the β–glucosidase emulsin. This striking demonstration of the hydrolytic theory was further supported by Simola's preparation of cell-free enzyme extracts obtained by ultra-filtration from toluene-treated cultures. The optimum activity of the enzymes lay between pH 5·0 and 6·0 using a phosphate buffer solution, while the optimum pH value for the cellobiase action was between 4·5 and 5·5. Karrer[57,115] had earlier shown similar properties for cellulase-containing extracts from the snail. Although several later workers were unable to obtain evidence for the production of cellobiose in their cultures, it is interesting to note that

Vartiovaara[108], as already mentioned, showed the accumulation of a reducing substance when growing *Sporotrichum carnis* in a limited air supply, whereas in aerated cultures, other non-reducing water soluble compounds were obtained. These latter compounds could be hydrolysed by acids to reducing sugars, and it seems probable that the presence of transglycosylases and other enzymes in the fungal culture brought about the synthesis of these probable polysaccharides.

The accumulation of glucose in a culture will tend to prevent the hydrolysis of further cellulose, and this effect must be remembered when considering any substantial breakdown of cellulose. However, if the glucose produced extracellularly can be further broken down, probably intra- as well as extra-cellularly, by the action of oxidative enzymes the way lies open for further hydrolysis of cellulose. From this, and a great deal of other evidence which will be presented throughout the remainder of this book, it must be concluded that the primary act of cellulose breakdown is one of hydrolysis, and the purely oxidative theory can no longer be maintained.

REFERENCES

1. BARUAH AND SWAIN, *Biochem. J.* 1957, **66**, p. 321.
2. DUNCAN, MANNERS AND ROSS, *Biochem. J.* 1956, **63**, p. 44.
3. SUMNER AND SOMERS, *Chemistry and Methods of Enzymes*, 1953, p. 109, Academic Press, New York.
4. HELFERICH, WINKLER, *et al.*, *Hoppe-Seyl. Z.* 1932, **208**, p. 91.
5. HELFERICH AND WINKLER, *Hoppe-Seyl. Z.* 1932, **209**, p. 269.
6. JERMYN, *Austr. J. Biol. Sci.* 1955, **8**, p. 541.
7. KOBAYASHI, WAKABAYASHI AND NISIZAWA, *Rep. Faculty Textiles and Sericult.*, Shinshu Univ., Japan, 1952, **2**, p. 102.
8. KOYATA, *J. Biochem. Japan*, 1950, **37**, p. 301; 1951, **38**, p. 109.
9. VEIBEL, *The Enzymes*, 1950, Vol. I, Pt. I, ed. Sumner and Myrbäck, Academic Press Inc., New York.
10. HELFERICH, *Ergeb. Enzymforsch.* 1933, **2**, p. 74.
11. NISIZAWA, *J. Biochem. Japan*, 1955, **42**, p. 825.
12. BAUMANN AND PIGMAN, *The Carbohydrates*, 1957, p. 579, ed. W. Pigman, Academic Press, New York.
13. HELFERICH, *Ergeb. Enzymforsch.* 1938, **7**, p. 83.
14. MIWA, CHENG, FUJISAKI, AND TOISHI, *Acta Phytochim. Japan*, 1937, **10**, p. 155.
15. WEIDENHAGEN, *Handbuch der Enzymologie*, 1940, p. 538, ed. Nord and Weidenhagen, Akademisches Verlagsges, Leipzig.
16. ROBINSON, *Biochem. J.* 1956, **63**, p. 39.
17. VEIBEL AND LILLELUND, *Enzymologia*, 1940, **9**, p. 161.
18. WILLSTÄTTER AND OPPENHEIMER, *Z. phys. Chem.* 1922, **121**, p. 183.

19. VEIBEL AND FREDERIKSEN, *Kgl. Danske Videnskab. Selskab., Mat-fys. Medd.* 1941, **19**, No. 1.
20. JERMYN, *Austr. J. Biol. Sci.*, 1955, **8**, pp. 541, 563, 577.
21. FREUDENBERG, KUHN *et al.*, *Ber. dtsch. chem. Ges.* 1930, **63B**, p. 1510.
22. THOMAS, *Austr. J. Biol. Sci.* 1956, **9**, p. 156.
23. FISCHER, E. H., *Arch. Sci. Genève* 1954, **7**, p. 131.
24. HELFERICH AND PIGMAN, *Hoppe-Seyl. Z.* 1939, **259**, p. 253.
25. HELFERICH, RICHTER AND GRÜNTER, *Ber. Verhandl. sächs. Akad. Wiss. Leipzig, Math.-phys. Klasse* 1938, **89**, 385.
26. GOTTSCHALK, *Advances in Carbohydrate Chemistry*, 1950, Vol 5, p. 49.
27. JERMYN, *Science*, 1957, **125**, p. 12.
28. KOSHLAND, *Symposium on the Mechanism of Enzyme Action*, ed. McElroy and Glass, 1954, John Hopkins Press, Baltimore, U.S.A.
29. MYRBÄCK, *Ann. Acad. Sci. Fennicae*, Ser. A, 1955, No. 60, p. 226.
30. VON EULER, *Hoppe-Seyl. Z.* 1925, **143**, p. 79.
31. PIGMAN, *J. Res. Nat. Bur. Stand.* 1941, **27**, p. 1.
32. PIGMAN, *Advances in Enzymology*, 1944, Vol. 4, p. 41.
33. VULQUIN, *C.R. Soc. Biol., Paris* 1911, **63**, pp. 270, 763.
34. JERMYN, *Austr. J. Biol. Sci.* 1959, **12**, p. 213.
35. MANNERS, *Structural Analysis of Polysaccharides*, Lect., Monographs & Reports, Royal Inst. of Chemistry, No. 2, 1959.
36. FITTING AND DOUDOROFF, *J. biol. Chem.* 1954, **199**, p. 153.
37. FREEMAN AND HOPKINS, *Biochem. J.* 1936, **30**, p. 451.
38. KOSHLAND AND STEIN, *Federation Proc.* 1953, **12**, p. 233.
39. EDELMAN, *Advances in Enzymology*, 1956, Vol. 17, p. 189.
40. CROOK AND STONE, *Biochem. J.* 1953, **55**, p. xxv.
41. BUSTON AND JABBAR, *Biochim. Biophys. Acta*, 1954, **15**, p. 543.
42. BARKER, BOURNE AND STACEY, *Chem. and Ind.* 1953, p. 1287.
43. BARKER, BOURNE, HEWITT AND STACEY, *J. chem. Soc.* 1955, p. 3734.
44. BARKER, BOURNE, HEWITT AND STACEY, *J. chem. Soc.* 1957, p. 3541.
45. BARKER AND CARRINGTON, *J. chem. Soc.* 1953, p. 3588.
46. BARKER, BOURNE AND STACEY, *J. chem. Soc.* 1953, p. 3084.
47. STACEY, *Istituto Lombardodi Scienze e Lettre, Rendi. Sci.*, 1955, **89**, p. 84.
48. STACEY, *Advances in Enzymology*, 1954, Vol. 15, p. 301.
49. BARKER AND BOURNE, *Quart. Rev. Chem. Soc.* 1953, **7**, p. 56.
50. WEIDENHAGEN, *Z. Zuckerind.* 1956, **81**, p. 469.
51. NISIZAWA AND WAKABAYASHI, *Symp. on Enz. Chem. (Japan)*, 1951, **6**, p. 26; 1952, **7**, p. 97.
52. PRINGSHEIM, *Hoppe-Seyl. Z.* 1912, **78**, p. 266.
53. PRINGSHEIM AND MEIBOWITZ, *Hoppe-Seyl. Z.* 1923, **131**, p. 267.
54. PRINGSHEIM AND KUSENACK, *Hoppe-Seyl. Z.* 1924, **137**, p. 265.
55. ENDERS AND SAJI, *Biochem. Z.* 1940, **306**, p. 430.
56. PREECE AND HOGGAN, *J. Inst. Brewing* 1956, **62**, p. 486.
57. KARRER, STAUB, WEINHAGEN AND JOOS, *Helv. chim. Acta*, 1924, **7**, p. 144.
58. KARRER AND LIER, *Helv. chim. Acta*, 1925, **8**, p. 248.
59. GRASSMANN, STADLER AND BENDER, *Annalen*, 1933, **502**, p. 20.

60. GRASSMANN, ZECHMEISTER, TOTH AND STADLER, *Annalen*, 1933, **503**, p. 167.
61. ZECHMEISTER, TOTH, FÜRTH AND BARSONY, *Enzymologia*, 1941, **9**, p. 155.
62. IWATA, WATANABE AND MIYAKE, *J. Agric. Chem. Soc. Japan*, 1953, **27**, p. 733.
63. FESTENSTEIN, *Biochem. J.* 1958, **69**, p. 562.
64. SISON AND SCHUBERT, *Arch. Biochem. Biophys.* 1958, **78**, p. 563.
65. KOOIMAN, ROELOFSEN AND SWEERIS, *Enzymologia*, 1953, **16**, p. 237.
66. KOOIMAN, *Enzymologia*, 1957, **18**, p. 371.
67. AITKEN, EDDY, INGRAM AND WEURMAN, *Biochem. J.* 1956, **64**, p. 63.
68. WHITAKER, *Canad. J. Biochem. Phys.* 1956, **34**, p. 102.
69. TOYAMA, *J. Ferment. Technol.* 1955, **33**, p. 266.
70. YOUATT, *Austr. J. Biol. Sci.* 1958, **11**, p. 209.
71. PIGMAN, *J. Res. Nat. Bur. Stand.* 1943, **30**, p. 159.
72. FESTENSTEIN, *Biochem. J.* 1958, **70**, p. 49.
73. CARTER AND RECORD, *J. chem. Soc.* 1939, p. 664.
74. MEYER AND GÜRTLER, *Helv. chim. Acta*, 1947, **30**, p. 751.
75. PIGMAN, *The Enzymes*, 1951, p. 737, ed. Pigman and Myrbäck, Academic Press Inc., New York.
76. PRINGSHEIM AND BAUR, *Hoppe-Seyl. Z.* 1928, **173**, p. 188.
77. GOERDELER, *Z. Naturforsch.* 1948, **36**, p. 403.
78. FREUDENBERG AND PLOETZ, *Hoppe-Seyl. Z.* 1939, **259**, p. 19.
79. FÅHRAEUS, *Experientia*, 1946, **2**, p. 413.
80. KARRER AND STAUB, *Helv. chim. Acta*, 1924, **7**, p. 916.
81. KARRER, JOOS AND STAUB, *Helv. chim. Acta*, 1923, **6**, p. 800.
82. KARRER AND HOFMAN, *Helv. chim. Acta*, 1929, **12**, p. 616.
83. KARRER AND FRANCOISE, *Helv. chim. Acta*, 1929, **12**, p. 986.
84. ZECHMEISTER AND TOTH, *Enzymologia*, 1939, **7**, p. 168.
85. ZECHMEISTER, TOTH AND VAJDA, *Enzymologia*, 1939, **7**, p. 170.
86. HACKMAN, *Austr. J. Biol. Sci.* 1954, **7**, p. 169.
87. DASTE, *L'Année Biologique*, 1956, **32**, p. 473.
88. JEUNIAUX, *Arch. Int. Physiol.* 1950, **58**, p. 350; 1951, **59**, p. 242.
89. BERGER AND REYNOLDS, *Biochim. Biophys. Acta*, 1958, **29**, p. 522.
90. REYNOLDS, *J. gen. Microbiol.* 1954, **11**, p. 150.
91. CHARLES, *C.R. Soc. Biol., Paris* 1955, **149**, p. 1307.
92. VELDKAMP, *Thèse Wageningen et Mededelingen van de Landbouwhoge-school te Wageningen Nederland*, 1955, **55**, p. 127.
93. CLARKE AND TRACEY, *J. gen. Microbiol.* 1956, **14**, p. 188.
94. ROSEMAN, *Federation Proc.* 1954, **13**, p. 283.
95. TRACEY, *Rev. Pure and Appl. Chem. (Australia)*, 1957, **7**, p. 1.
96. KENT AND WHITEHOUSE, *Biochemistry of Aminosugars*, 1955, Butterworths, London.
97. CARTWRIGHT AND FINDLAY, *Decay of Timber and its Prevention*, 1946, H.M.S.O., London.
98. HUNT AND GARRATT, *Wood Preservation*, 1938, MacGraw Hill, New York.

 99. HOPPE-SEYLER, *Ber. dtsch. chem. Ges.* 1883, **16**, p. 122.
100. DE BARY, *Botan. Ztg.* 1886, **44**, p. 377.
101. MARSHALL WARD, *Ann. Bot. Lond.* 1888, **2**, p. 319.
102. FALCK AND HAAG, *Ber. dtsch. chem. Ges.* 1927, **60**, p. 225.
103. LÜDTKE, *Biochem. Z.* 1936, **285**, p. 89.
104. WINOGRADSKY, *Ann. inst. Pasteur*, 1929, **43**, p. 549.
105. LOICJANSKAJA, *C. R. Acad. Sci., U.R.S.S.* 1937, **14**, p. 381.
106. NORMAN AND BARTHOLOMEW, *Soil Sci. Proc. Soc.* 1940, **5**, p. 243.
107. WALKER AND WARREN, *Biochem. J.* 1938, **32**, p. 31.
108. VARTIOVAARA, *Acta Agral. Fennicae*, 1935, **32**, p. 1.
109. WHITAKER, *Canad. J. Bot.* 1951, **29**, p. 159.
110. NORMAN AND FULLER, *Advances in Enzymology*, 1942, Vol. 2, p. 239.
111. VAN DER WYK AND SCHMORAK, *Helv. chim. Acta*, 1953, **36**, p. 385.
112. FÅHRAEUS, *Symbolae botan. Upsalienses*, 1947, **9**, p. 1.
113. WOODMAN AND STEWART, *J. agric. Sci.* 1928, **18**, p. 713.
114. SIMOLA, *Ann. Acad. Sci. Fennicae*, 1931, **A34**, p. 1.
115. KARRER AND SCHUBERT, *Helv. chim. Acta*, 1928, **11**, p. 229.

III

SOURCES OF CELLULASES

DURING recent years, extracts from many animals, plants and micro-organisms have been shown to contain enzymes which catalyse the hydrolysis of cellulose. The following list shows such cellulase sources, together with the properties of their enzymes and substrates used to reveal cellulase activity. It should be noted that the term 'cellulase', used here, implies enzymes active in the degradation of either cellulose or cellulose derivatives or both. This list is by no means exhaustive, but only those extracts which are claimed to be cell-free have been included. Later chapters describe the purification and properties of cellulases which have been studied in greater detail and attention is drawn to these in the list.

ABBREVIATIONS USED IN THE LIST

C.M.C.—carboxymethyl cellulose, usually used as the sodium salt.

Repptd.—reprecipitated.

F.P.—filter paper.

All temperatures are given on the Centigrade scale.

ANIMAL CELLULASES

Source		Properties	Substrates	Observations	Ref.
MOLLUSCS *Helix pomatia* (snail)	1.	Opt. pH 4·0; heating at 100° for 5–10 min does not completely inactivate. Mixture of CuSO₄ (1%) and HCN (3%) inhibitory, also glutathione and cysteine in phosphate buffer.	Hydroxyethyl cellulose		1
	2.	Opt. pH 5·2–5·4.		Cellulase and lichenase separated by fractional pptn. with EtOH–Et₂O mixtures.	2
	3.	Opt. pH 5·0–6·0, inactivation rapid above pH 9·0 and below pH 4·0. Inactivated by heating 86° for 10 min, using cellophane substrate; using C.M.C. substrate some activity retained after 10 min at 100°. High concns. of NaCl and CaCl₂ inhibitory.	Cellophane, C.M.C., ethylmethyl cellulose.	Also used extracts from *H. aspersa*. Preparations freed from bacteria by centrifugation.	3
	4.	Opt. pH 5·5	Cellophane		4
	5.	pH value–activity curves given Inactivation begins at 45–50°, complete at 60°; opt. temp. 36°.	Cellophane	Degradation of tobacco leaf with this and other enzymes.	5
	6.	Opt. pH 5·28			6, 7
	7.				7, 8
	8.	Opt. pH 5·6; inactivated by heating at 70° for 5 min, inhibited by (NH₄)₂SO₄, stimulated by added protein.	C.M.C. H₃PO₄-swollen cotton linters.	Partially purified (Ch. IV).	9
	9.		Fibrous cuprammonium rayon.	Partially purified (Ch. IV).	10
	10.		Repptd. cellulose.	Glucose only produced on hydrolysis.	11

53

Source	Properties	Substrates	Observations	Ref.
Dolabella scapula	Opt. pH 5·1		Found in digestive juice in stomach and intestine.	12
Mytilus and *Ostrea*		Finely-divided F.P. suspension.	From crystalline style material dissolved in buffer solution. Relationship between spirochaetes in style and cellulolytic activity not established. Detected reducing sugars.	13
Xylophaga dorsalis		Fine sawdust.	Extracted with sea water. No conclusive evidence for freedom from bacteria.	14
Cryptochiton stelleri	Opt. pH < 4·0		In sugar-gland juice. Enzymes may be produced by symbiotic bacteria.	15
Pterocera crocata	Opt. pH 5·85	F.P., algae.	Found in stomach fluid, origin not determined.	16
Caelatura hautecoeuri ruellani and *Melanoides tuberculata*	More active at pH 5·5 than at pH 7·0. Activity destroyed by boiling.	Cellulose suspension, algal cell walls.	Style material dissolved in buffer. Possibility of microbial origin should not be ignored.	17
Mya arenaria and *Mactra solidissima*		Regenerated cellulose (dialysis tubing).	Extracts of clam styles, F.P. not attacked.	18
Modiola modiolus		Hydroxyethyl cellulose.	Extracts from sperms and seminal fluid contained cellulolytic activity.	19
Bankia setacea (ship worm)		Ground sawdust, F.P.	Extracted from anterior end of digestive tract, present in livers and digestive diverticula; said to be elaborated by organism itself.	20
Bankia indica (ship worm)		Sawdust, regenerated F.P.	Present in digestive diverticula and crystalline style.	21
Teredo (ship worm) 1.	Opt. pH 5·6 to 6·7; activity destroyed by heating at 100° for 5 min.	Regenerated cellulose	Found in gut homogenate. No cellulose degrading bacteria or protozoa detected in digestive system.	22

54

No.	Organism	Substrate	Conditions	Remarks	Ref.
2.				Concentration of enzyme described in Ch. IV.	23
3.				Present in liver.	12
	ECHINODERMS *Psammechinus miliaris* (sea urchin)	Hydroxyethyl cellulose	Opt. pH 6·0	Seminal fluid and sperm extracts contained cellulase.	19
	PROTOZOA *Endoplodinium neglectum* (cattle ciliate)	Cotton suspension treated with HCl acid.	Opt. pH *c*. 5·0, active pH range 4·0 to 6·0. Inhibited by boiling.	Extracted whole organisms previously freed from bacteria and cellulose débris used in culture.	24
	Trichomonas termopsidus (intestinal flagellate of termites and roaches).	Cellulose resuspended from LiCl solution, F.P.	Inactivated on heating at 100° for 10 min. Opt. temp. 26°.	Extracted whole organisms.	25
	Soil amoebae	C.M.C. and finely-divided cellulose.		Chitinase also present.	26
	NEMATODES *Ditylenchus destructor* and *Ditylenchus dipsaci*.			Chitinase also present in *D. destructor* extracts.	27
	ARTHROPODS *Termes obesus* (termite)	C.M.C. and methylethyl cellulose.	Inhibited by 0·1M Zn⁺⁺ and chromate ions.	Present in hind gut of workers, probably elaborated by bacteria.	28
	Ctenolepisma lineata (silver fish)	Regenerated cellulose.	Opt. pH 4·0 and 6·0	Cultivated bacteria-free insects. Enzyme contained in cell-free extracts of mid-gut.	29
	Cerambyx cerdo and *Xestobium rufovillosum* (beetles)	Plant tissues		Used filtered undiluted gut juices, and checked for absence of bacteria. Enzyme claimed to be produced by insects.	30
	Nasutitermes exitiosus } *Coptotermes lacteus*	Cellulose, chitin.	Opt. pH 5·5.	Differences observed between different forms of insect with substrates of different degrees of degradation.	31

55

Source	Properties	Substrates	Observations	Ref.
Stromatium fulcum (beetle)	Opt. pH 5·6	F.P., lichenin and ligno-cellulose.	Centrifuged gastric juice of larvae. May be due to bacteria.	32
Dixippus morosus			Used digestive fluid containing products of salivary glands.	33
Limnoria lignorum		Finely-divided cellulose suspension.	Enzyme present in homogenate of enteric diverticula. Attempts to detect micro-organisms failed.	34
ANNELIDS *Lumbricus terrestris* and other earthworms	Opt. pH 5·5	C.M.C. and finely-divided cellulose.	Probably produced by worms; enzyme in fore-half of intestinal wall.	35

PLANT CELLULASES

Source	Properties	Substrates	Observations	Ref.
1. Tobacco plants.	Opt. pH 5·4. Partially inactivated on heating at 55° for 3 min.	C.M.C. and repptd. cellulose.		36
2. Bean leaves, beetroot, spinach beet, woody night-shade roots, vegetable marrow and asparagus butts.		C.M.C.	pH of sap in all cases > 5·0.	37 36

Source		Substrate	Properties	Remarks	Ref.
BARLEY Embryos				Enzyme in water in which embryos steeped.	38
Sprouted and unsprouted				Slight activity in aqueous extracts, also found in malt and tannin preparations.	39
Green malt		Ethylhydroxyethyl cellulose.	Opt. pH 5·0; heating at 60° and pH 5·0 inactivates in 30 min. Inhibited by chromium, lactose and cellobiose.	Purified enzyme stimulated by glucose, mannose, xylose, and low concn. of cellobiose (Ch. IV and V).	40
Malt	1.	Hydroxyethyl cellulose.	Opt. pH 3·0		1
	2.	Cellulose dispersed by LiCl, Ca(SCN)$_2$ and H$_2$SO$_4$ solutions.			41
	3.	Hydroxyethyl cellulose.	Opt. pH 4·0; heating at 60° and pH 5·0 for 5 min reduces activity by >50%. Isoelectric point, pH 5·0.		42
Other barley sources.	1.	C.M.C.		Cellulase separated from hemicellulase (Ch. IV).	43
	2.	Barley β-glucosan.		Correlated cellulase activity with autolysis.	44
ALGAE Cladophora rupestris		Cellodextrin and C.M.C.	Opt. pH 5·1; relatively heat stable, only slight inactivation on heating at 60° for 15 min.		45
Ulva lactuca, Laminaria digitata and Rhodymenia palmata		Cellodextrin and C.M.C.			45
LICHENS belonging to the families Usneaceae, Cladoniaceae, Parmeliaceae and Umbilicariaceae.		Cellophane and viscose filaments.		Aqueous extract of sterilised air-dried lichens prepared.	46

FUNGAL CELLULASES

Source	Properties	Substrates	Observations	Ref.
BASIDIOMYCETES				
Collybia velutipes 1.			Cellulase production from variants studied.	47
2.		Cellulose sol.	Structural studies on cellulose.	48
Coprinus sclerotigenus		C.M.C.	Effect of growth medium on cellulase production studied.	49
Hydnum henningsii	Opt. pH 3·0, opt. temp. 37°, inactivated over 50°.	Repptd. cellulose.	Enzyme concentrate prepared (Ch. IV).	50
Irpex lacteus 1.		C.M.C. and p-nitrophenyl-β-cellobioside.	Enzyme crystallised and properties studied (Ch. IV, V).	51, 76, 118
2.	Stimulated by $MnSO_4$ or $MnCl_2$.		Some purification (Ch. IV).	52
Merulius lacrymans			Press juice from cultures. Lichenase and β-glucosidase also present (Ch. IV).	53
Polyporus annosus		Cellulose sol.	Structural studies on cellulose.	48
P. palustris		C.M.C. and F.P.	Enzyme partially purified (Ch. IV).	54
Polystictus sanguineus	Opt. pH 5·3		Mechanism of action of wood protective agents studied.	55
Poria vaillantii	Opt. pH 3·2, stable over range pH4–6. Opt. temp. 60°. Activated by Mn and Co ions, inhibited by Hg^{++} and certain thiol reagents.	C.M.C., cotton linters, Solka floc, repptd. cellulose, alkali-swollen cellulose, H_3PO_4-swollen cellulose.	Enzyme partially purified and properties studied (Ch. IV, V).	56
Puccinia graminis	Opt. pH 5·5, opt. temp. 50°. Inhibited by $AgNO_3$, $CuSO_4$, $ZnSO_4$, $Hg(OAc)_2$ + cysteine, iodoacetate.	C.M.C., barley β-glucosan, mannogalactan.	Extract ground uredospores with 0·6% NaCl solution. Hemicellulase also present.	57
Tricholoma fumosum	Opt. pH 5·0.	Cellulose sol.		58

Organism	Conditions	Substrate	Remarks	Ref.
T. nudum	Opt. pH 5·0, stable pH 4·0–7·0. Opt. temp. 30°, activity reduced 60% by heating at 60° for 20 min. Inhibited by NaF and cellobiose, stimulated by Ca^{++} in phosphate buffer.	Cellulose sol, repptd. cellulose, native cellulose.		58
ASCOMYCETES Ceratocystis ulmi	Opt. pH 5·0, active pH range 2·0–8·0. Inhibited by Ag and Hg ions, sodium pentachlorophenate, 4-chloro-2-phenylphenol.	C.M.C.	Causative organism of Dutch elm disease.	59
Ceratostomella ulmi		C.M.C., cotton.		60
Chaetomium globosum 1.		C.M.C., cellulose sulphate, viscose rayon, linters, alkali cellulose, cellulose dextrin.	Studied products of hydrolysis (Ch. VI).	61
2.		C.M.C.	Also from C. causiaeformis, C. turgidopilosum and C. indicum.	49
3.		Native cotton, ball milled cotton, ground cellophane.		62
4.		Cotton linters.	'S' factor present in filtrate.	63
C. indicum		C.M.C., H_3PO_4–swollen cellulose.	Studied effect of shaking on cellulase action.	64
Neurospora crassa			Enzyme produced at 35°, but not at 25°.	65
Sclerotium rolfsii		C.M.C.	Causative agent of southern stem rot. C_x enzyme present in juice of infected tomatoes.	66
PHYCOMYCETES Karlingia rosea		C.M.C.	Intra- and extra-cellular cellulases detected.	49
Phytophthora cactorum, P. citricola, P. parasitica.			Intra- and extra-cellular cellulases detected.	68
Pythium spp.			Intra- and extra-cellular cellulases detected.	67
Saprolegniaceae			Intra- and extra-cellular β– glucosidases also detected.	69

E

Source		Properties	Substrates	Observations	Ref.
FUNGI IMPERFECTI					
Arthrobotrys superba					
Aspergillus aureus		Opt. pH 5.0.	C.M.C.	Used in studies of tobacco leaf degradation.	49
			C.M.C., cellophane.		4
A. flavipes	1.		Cotton linters.	'S' factor present in filtrate.	63
A. flavus			C.M.C.	Studied cellulase production from various growth media.	49
	2.	Thermostable; boiling for 3 min. does not completely inactivate.	C.M.C., acid-swollen cellulose, alkali cellulose.		70
	3.		C.M.C.		71
A. fumigatus	1.		C.M.C.	Studied cellulase production from various growth media.	49
	2.	Opt. pH 4·6-5·1, stable over range pH 4·0-8·0. Heating for 3 min at 70° partially inactivates.	C.M.C. etc. (Ch. VI.)		61
	3.		C.M.C.	Products of hydrolysis studied.	71
A. luchuensis	1.		C.M.C.	Studied cellulase production from various growth media.	49
	2.		C.M.C. etc. (Ch. VI.)		61
A. nidulans	1.		C.M.C.		49
	2.		C.M.C., alkali cellulose.		70
A. niger	1.		C.M.C.	Studied cellulase production from various growth media.	49
	2.	Opt. pH 4·5. Inhibited by thymol, toluene, alkyldimethylbenzylammonium chloride.	H_3PO_4-swollen cellulose.		72
	3.	Opt. pH 3·5 to 5·5, stable over range pH 3·0-6·5. Inactivated by heating at 70° for 15 min.	C.M.C., alkali-swollen cellulose.	Purification using chromatographic, precipitation and electrophoretic techniques (Ch. IV).	73, 120
	4.	Opt. pH 4·5. Glucose formation at maximum at 60°.	H_3PO_4-swollen cellulose.	Partially purified (Ch. IV).	74
	5.		Cellodextrins, cellulose.	Some purification (Ch. IV).	75
A. oryzae	1.	Opt. pH 4·7.		Partial separation (Ch. IV).	2

Organism	No.	Cell walls of plants	Range of activity	Remarks	Ref.
	2.		Opt. pH 5·2, range of activity pH 2–8.	Hemicellulase also present.	77
	3.	C.M.C.		Multicomponent nature of cellulase demonstrated by electrophoresis.	78
	4.		Opt. pH 4·5.		79
	5.	C.M.C., repptd. cellulose, cellodextrin D.P. c. 100.	Opt. pH 3·5, activity affected by organic bases, notably caffeine and quinine; also by Fe^{+++}.	Crude culture filtrate degraded many β-glucosides.	80
A. rugulosus	1.	C.M.C.			49
A. sydowi	1.	C.M.C.		Studied cellulase production from various growth media.	49
	2.	C.M.C.			71
A. tamarii	1.	C.M.C.			49
	2.	C.M.C.			71
A. terreus	1.	C.M.C., H_3PO_4–swollen cellulose, cotton linters.		Produced large amounts of 'swelling factor'.	81
	2.	C.M.C.			71
A. unguis	1.	C.M.C.			70
A. ustus	2.	C.M.C.			70
	1.	C.M.C.			71
Botrytis cinerea	1.	C.M.C.		Studied cellulase production from various growth media.	49
	2.	C.M.C. and cellophane.		Used for studies of degradation of tobacco leaf.	4
Cladosporium cucumerinum		C.M.C.	Opt. pH 6·0, active range pH 4·0–8·0. Hg^{++} inhibitory.	Greater cellulase production at 23° than at 28°. Causes cucumber scab; relation of enzyme to this disease discussed.	82
C. herbarum	1.	C.M.C.		Produced only at 25°, not at 30°.	49
	2.	Cotton linters.		'S' factor present in filtrate.	63
Coccospora agricola					49
Curvularia lunata		C.M.C., H_3PO_4–swollen cellulose.		Studied effect of shaking on cellulase action.	64
Fusarium sp.		C.M.C.		Studied C_x production in filtrate in response to growth on various media.	49

Source	Properties	Substrates	Observations	Ref.
F. bulbigenum, F. equiseti, F. laterium, F. lini, F. oxysporum, and F. vasinfectum. F. dinerum, F. javanicum, F. scirpi and F. solani.	All opt. pH 5.5.	Repptd. cellulose.		83
1.	All opt. pH 6.5.	Repptd. cellulose.		83
2.		Cotton linters.		63
3. Fusarium moniliforme	Opt. pH 5.5.	Repptd. cellulose. C.M.C., F.P.	'S' factor present in filtrate. Partially purified by ethanol precipitation.	83 84
F. roseum 1.		C.M.C.	Studied C_x production in filtrate in response to growth on various media.	49
2.		F.P. C.M.C., H_3PO_4-swollen cellulose cotton linters.		84 81
3.		C.M.C., H_3PO_4-swollen cellulose, cotton linters.	Grown on esparto xylan.	81
Helminthosporium sp.	Opt. pH 5.5–6.0, opt. temp. 35°.			85
H. oryzae		C.M.C.		49
Humicola fuscoatra		C.M.C.		49
H. grisea 1.		C.M.C.		49
Memnoniella echinata 2.	Inhibited by cellobiose.	C.M.C.	Studied C_x production during growth on various media.	86
Monilia sitophila 1. 2.		C.M.C.	Cellulase found intracellularly. Growth studies.	49 87
Monotospora brevis Myrothecium verrucaria 1.	Opt. pH 5.6, opt. temp. 35°. Stimulated by proteins, basic dyes, and neutral salts; inhibited by heavy metal salts, oxidizing and reducing agents, iodoacetate and p-chloromercuribenzoate.	C.M.C., cotton linters. Swollen linters, repptd. cellulose.	Enzyme purified (Ch. IV) and properties studied (Ch. V). Mode of action on a number of substrates studied (Ch. VI).	81 88

62

No.	Properties	Substrates	Notes	Ref.
2.		C.M.C., H_3PO_4-swollen cellulose, cotton fibre.	Some purification (Ch. IV).	81
3.	Enzyme very thermostable.	Cotton fibres (beaten, ball milled), ground viscose rayon, bacterial cellulose, acid and alkali-swollen cellulose, repptd. cellulose, cellodextrins.		89
4.	Opt. pH of unheated enzyme, using C.M.C. as substrate 6·5; of heated enzyme (with C.M.C.) 6·0, (with ball milled cotton) 5·5. Opt. temp. of unheated enzyme 55°, of heated enzyme 42–45°.	C.M.C., ball milled cotton.	Studied action on other polysaccharides.	70
5.	Partially inactivated on heating at 50° for 30 min, some activity retained at 100°. Opt. pH 4·6–5·0. Inhibited by KCl, NaCl, CaCl₂, MgSO₄.	Cotton.	'S' factor studied.	63
6.	Opt. pH 5·5, opt. temp. 40°. Rapidly inactivated above 50° and beyond pH limits of 5·0 to 9·0.	Cotton.		90
7.	Stable over pH range 4·5 to 6·0. Opt. temp. 53°, partially inactivated on heating at 70° for 30 min.	C.M.C.		71
8.		Cotton cellulose, C.M.C.	Effect of pH value on inhibition and stimulation.	86
9.		C.M.C.		91
10.		C.M.C.	Studied C_x production on various media.	49
11.		Cellulose sulphate, cellodextrin, C.M.C., alkali cellulose, viscose rayon, linters.	Hydrolysis products studied particularly.	61

Source		Properties	Substrates	Observations	Ref.
Myrothecium verrucaria (continued).	12.	Partially inactivated on heating at 60° for 10 min. Activity on methyl cellulose not completely destroyed by boiling.	Cotton wool, F.P. powder, regenerated cellulose, soluble methyl cellulose.	Produced cellobiose and glucose on hydrolysis of cellulose	92
	13.		Sodium cellulose sulphate, insoluble cellulose preparation.	Partial separation by electrophoresis	93
	14.		Sodium cellulose sulphate, wheat straw cellulose, hemicelluloses.	Partial separation by electrophoresis	94
	15.		C.M.C.	Partial separation by chromatography on cellulose column (Ch. IV).	95
	16.		C.M.C.	Partial separation by electrophoresis (Ch. IV).	96
	17.		H_3PO_4–swollen cellulose.	Glucose, cellobiose and a higher oligosaccharide formed on hydrolysis.	97
	18.		Cotton, viscose and Bemberg rayon.	Studied early stages of enzymic attack.	98
	19.		Native cotton, ground cellophane, ball milled cotton.		62
	20.		Dewaxed cotton fibre, ball milled cotton, ball milled cellophane.		99
	21.		C.M.C., H_3PO_4–swollen cellulose.	Studied effect of shaking on cellulases.	64
	22.	175 compounds tested for inhibitory properties. Effective inhibitors include Ag^+, Hg^{++}, Mn^{++}, halogens, halogen releasers, phenol derivatives, octyl gallate, 2:3–dichloro–1:4–naphthoquinone, organic	C.M.C.		100

Organism	Details	Substrate	Remarks	Ref.
	23. mercury salts, nitrosopyrazoles, ethylenebisdithiocarbamates, methocel. (As Whitaker's cellulase, No. 1 above).	C.M.C.	Purified cellulase caused wilt in tomato cuttings.	101
Papulaspora sp. *Penicillium* sp.	Opt. temp. 55°, stable over pH range 6·0–7·0.	C.M.C.		49 102
P. capsulatum, P. chrysogenum, P. frequentans, P. janthinellum, P. luteum, P. piscarium, P. soppi, P. spinulosum, and *P. turbatum.* *P. digitatum* and *P. expansum*		C.M.C.	Studied production of C_x on various media (in some cases only).	49
P. pusillum	1. Opt. pH 4·0 and 6·8, inhibited by cellobiose.	C.M.C., cellophane. C.M.C., cotton.	Effect of pH value on inhibition and stimulation studied.	4 86
	2.	C.M.C., H_3PO_4–swollen cellulose, cotton linters.	Partial separation of enzymes by chromatography.	81
P. rubrum and *P. wortmanii*		C.M.C., H_3PO_4–swollen cellulose.	Studied effect of shaking on cellulases.	64
Pestalotia palmarum	1.	C.M.C.		86
	2.	C.M.C., H_3PO_4–swollen cellulose, cotton linters.	Partial separation of enzymes by chromatography.	81
Pestalotiopsis westerdijkii	3. 175 compounds tested for inhibitory properties. (Similar to *M. verrucaria* 22 above).	C.M.C. C.M.C.		49 100
Phoma sp. *Schizophyllum commune*	1.	C.M.C. C.M.C.	Studied C_x production on various media.	49 49
	2.	C.M.C., H_3PO_4–swollen cellulose, cotton linters.		81
Scopulariopsis brevicaulis	1.	C.M.C., H_3PO_4–swollen cellulose, cotton linters.		81
	2.	C.M.C.	Studied C_x production on various media.	49

65

Source		Properties	Substrates	Observations	Ref.
Sporotrichum carnis S. pruinosum			C.M.C.	Studied C_x production on various media.	103 49
Stachybotrys atra	1.		C.M.C., H_3PO_4-swollen cellulose, cotton linters.	Partial separation of enzymes by chromatography.	81
	2.	Opt. pH 6·0-7·5, and 8·0. Active over range pH 4·0-9·0. Inhibited by mercuric acetate, lead acetate, cupric sulphate and KCN.	C.M.C., ethylhydroxyethylcellulose, cellophane, ground F.P., H_3PO_4-swollen cellulose, various other glycosides.		104
Torula sp.			C.M.C.	Studied C_x production on different media.	49
Trichoderma viride ($\equiv T.$ koningi.)	1.	Inhibited by methocel.	C.M.C., H_3PO_4-swollen cellulose of differing D.P.'s, cotton linters.	Enzymes partially separated by chromatography.	81, 61
	2.		C.M.C.	Studied C_x production on various media.	49
	3.		Treated cotton, hydrocellulose.	Studied effect of cellulase on D.P. of cellulose and hydrocellulose (Ch. VI).	105
	4.	Partially inactivated by heating at 70° for 30 min.	C.M.C.		71
	5.		Cotton cellulose, C.M.C.	Influence of pH value on inhibition and stimulation studied.	86
	6.	Opt. temp. 40-45°, inactivated at 55°; opt. pH 4·0 to 5·0. Inhibited by Ag, Mn, Zn and Cu salts.	C.M.C., F.P., Bemberg rayon.	Enzyme partially purified.	106
	7.	175 compounds tested for inhibitory properties (similar to M. verrucaria 22 above).	C.M.C.		100
Verticillium albo-atrum				Effect of medium on production of cellulase studied. Glucose inhibitory in presence of cellulose.	107

66

ACTINOMYCETES

Source		Properties	Substrates	Observations	Ref.
Actinomyces sp.	1.		C.M.C.	Studied C_x production in different media.	49
	2.	Opt. pH 6·4–7·2, active over range pH 4·0–8·0. Max. activity at over 60°; destroyed on heating at 70° for 30 min.	C.M.C.		71
	3.		C.M.C.	Studied influence of pH value on inhibition and stimulation.	91
Streptomyces sp.	1.		C.M.C.		86
	2.		Cellulose sol.	Structural studies on cellulose.	48

BACTERIAL CELLULASES

Source	Properties	Substrates	Observations	Ref.
Bacillus hydrolyticus	Activity tested at pH 7·0 and 50°.	F.P.	Cellulase of 'weathering' type rendering substrate fragile and acid-labile. Some purification (Ch. IV).	108
Cellulobacillus mucosus and C. myxogenes	Opt. pH 6–7, opt. temp. 37°.			109
Cellulomonas sp. 1.		C.M.C., ball milled cotton, repptd. cellulose.	Enzyme 'constitutive' rather than 'adaptive'.	110
2.		C.M.C.		49
Cellvibrio fulvus		C.M.C.	Studied cellulase production from various growth media.	49
Cellvibrio vulgaris 1.		C.M.C.	Studied cellulase production from various growth media.	49
2.		C.M.C., H_3PO_4-swollen cellulose, cotton.		81
Clostridium thermocellulaseum	Opt. pH 5–8, opt. temp. 57–58°.	Ethylhydroxyethylcellulose.	Some properties studied (Ch. V).	111

67

Source	Properties	Substrates	Observations	Ref.
C. thermocellum		Ball milled cotton, repptd. cellulose, soluble derivatives.	Enzymes produced when grown on non-cellulosic media.	110
Corynebacterium sp. C. fimi (≡Cellulomonas fimi or C. liquata)	1. Opt. pH 6–7 depending on buffer solution used; opt. temp. 40°. Inhibited by cellobiose.	C.M.C.	Enzymes separated (Ch. IV).	49, 112
	2. Opt. pH 7·0, opt. temp. 36°. Inhibited by glucose, toluene, chloroform.	C.M.C. Lichenin, cellophane.	(Ch. IV and V).	49, 113
Cytophaga globulosa (≡Sporocytophaga myxococcoides.)	2.	C.M.C., cellulose sulphate, cellulose dextrins, linters, rayon.		61
	3.	C.M.C., H_3PO_4—swollen cellulose, cotton.		49, 81
Pseudomonas fluorescens	Opt. pH 6·5, opt. temp. 37°. Inactivated by heating at 70° for 10 min., or holding below pH 4·3 or above pH 9·0 for 1 hr.		Some purification (Ch. IV).	114
P. solanacearum	Opt. pH 7·0, active over range pH 4·0–9·0. Slightly activated by NaCl, KCl. Inhibited by heavy metal salts (e.g. Cu, Hg, Zn).	C.M.C.	Causal agent of certain wilts in plants.	101
Rumen micro-organisms	1. Opt. pH 5·5, opt. temp. 40–50°.	C.M.C., powdered cellulose.	Cell free extract from mixture of organisms ground with alumina, and extracted with saline solution.	115
	2. 3. Opt. pH 5·5–6·0.	C.M.C., powdered cellulose. Powdered cellulose, C.M.C.		116 117
	4. Opt. pH 6·0–6·5. Inhibited by gluconolactone.	C.M.C.	Butanol and alumina extracts (Ch. IV).	119

REFERENCES

1. ZIESE, *Hoppe-Seyl. Z.* 1931, **203**, p. 87.
2. FREUDENBERG AND PLOETZ, *Hoppe-Seyl. Z.* 1939, **259**, p. 19.
3. HOLDEN AND TRACEY, *Biochem. J.* 1950, **47**, p. 407.
4. HOLDEN, *Biochem. J.* 1950, **47**, p. 427.
5. HELFERICH AND GOERDELER, *Ber. Verhandl. sächs Akad. Wiss., Leipzig, Math.-phys. Klasse*, 1940, **92**, p. 75.
6. KARRER, SCHUBERT AND WEHRLI, *Helv. chim. Acta*, 1925, **8**, p. 797.
7. KARRER, *Kolloidzschr.* 1930, **52**, p. 304.
8. KARRER AND ILLING, *Kolloidzschr.* 1925, Special No., p. 91.
9. MYERS AND NORTHCOTE, *Biochem. J.* 1959, **71**, p. 749.
10. DE STEVENS, *Methods in Enzymology*, ed. Colowick and Kaplan, 1955, Vol. I, p. 173, Academic Press, New York.
11. HOLLÓ AND SZILAGYI, *Ind. agr. et aliment. (Paris)*, 1957, **74**, p. 131.
12. HASHIMOTO AND ONOMA, *Bull. Japan Soc. Sci. Fisheries*, 1949, **15**, p. 253.
13. NEWELL, *J. Marine Biol. Assoc.* 1953, **32**, p. 491.
14. PURCHON, *J. Marine Biol. Assoc.* 1941, **25**, p. 1.
15. MEEUSE AND FLUEGEL, *Nature, Lond.* 1958, **181**, p. 699.
16. YONGE, *Biol. Abstracts*, 1934, **8**, p. 9790.
17. FISH, *Nature, Lond.* 1955, **175**, p. 733.
18. LAVINE, *J. Cell. Comp. Physiol.* 1946, **28**, p. 183.
19. HULTIN AND LUNDBLAD, *Expt. Cell. Res.* 1952, **3**, p. 427.
20. BOYNTON AND MILLER, *J. biol. Chem.* 1927, **75**, p. 613.
21. NAIR, *Current Sci. (India)*, 1955, **24**, p. 126.
22. GREENFIELD AND LANE, *J. biol. Chem.* 1953, **204**, p. 669.
23. GREENFIELD, *Proc. Soc. Expt. Biol. Med.* 1955, **89**, p. 241.
24. HUNGATE, *Biol. Bull.* 1942, **83**, p. 303.
25. TRAGER, *Biochem. J.* 1932, **26**, p. 1762.
26. TRACEY, *Nature, Lond.* 1955, **175**, p. 815.
27. TRACEY, *Congr. intern. biochim., Résumés communs.*, Paris, 1952.
28. MISRA AND RANGANATHAN, *Proc. Indian Acad. Sci.* 1954, **39B**, p. 100.
29. LASKER AND GIESE, *J. Exp. Biol.* 1956, **33**, p. 542.
30. RIPPER, *Z. vergleich. Physiol.* 1930, **13**, p. 314.
31. TRACEY AND YOUATT, *Enzymologia*, 1958, **19**, p. 70.
32. MANSOUR AND MANSOUR-BEK, *Enzymologia*, 1937, **4**, p. 1.
33. BELEHRÀDEK, *Arch. intern. phys.* 1922, **17**, p. 260.
34. RAY AND JULIAN, *Nature, Lond.* 1952, **169**, p. 32.
35. TRACEY, *Nature, Lond.* 1951, **167**, p. 776.
36. TRACEY, *Biochem. J.* 1950, **47**, p. 431.
37. BARRETT, *J. Agric. Food Chem.* 1957, **5**, p. 220.
38. MASSART, *Intern. Tijdschr. Brouw. en Mout*, 1955, **15**, p. 6.
39. GOERDELER, *Hoppe-Seyl. Z.* 1948, **283**, p. 262.
40. ENEBO, SANDEGREN AND LJUNGDAHL, *J. Inst. Brewing*, 1953, **59**, p. 205.
41. PRINGSHEIM AND BAUR, *Hoppe-Seyl. Z.* 1928, **173**, p. 188.
42. KRISTIANSSON, *Svensk. Kem. Tid.* 1950, **62**, p. 133.
43. VAN SUMÈRE, *Naturwiss.* 1953, **40**, p. 582.

44. PREECE AND AITKEN, *J. Inst. Brewing*, 1953, **59**, p. 453.
45. DUNCAN, MANNERS AND ROSS, *Biochem. J.* 1956, **63**, p. 44.
46. KUPREVICH AND MOISEEVA, *Doklady Akad. Nauk S.S.S.R.* 1957, **115**, p. 1138.
47. ASCHAN AND NORKRANS, *Physiol. Plant.* 1953, **6**, pp. 564, 829.
48. NORKRANS AND RÅNBY, *Physiol. Plant.* 1956, **9**, p. 198.
49. REESE AND LEVINSON, *Physiol. Plant.* 1952, **5**, p. 345.
50. KILROE-SMITH, *J. South African Chem. Inst.* 1957, **10**, p. 29.
51. NISIZAWA, *J. Biochem. (Japan)*, 1955, **42**, p. 825.
52. FUKOMOTO AND KISHI, *Sci. Ind.* 1952, **26**, p. 295.
53. PLOETZ, *Hoppe-Seyl. Z.* 1939, **261**, p. 183.
54. HIGA, O'NEILL AND JENNISON, *J. Bact.* 1956, **71**, p. 382.
55. NARAYANAMURTI AND VERMA, *Holz. Roh u. Werkstoff*, 1953, **11**, p. 7.
56. SISON, SCHUBERT AND NORD, *Arch. Biochem. Biophys.* 1957, **68**, p. 502.
57. VAN SUMÈRE, VAN SUMÈRE-DE PRETER AND LEDINGHAM, *Canad. J. Microbiol.* 1957, **3**, p. 761.
58. NORKRANS, *Symbolae botan. Upsalienses*, 1950, **11**, p. 5.
59. HUSAIN AND DIMOND, *Proc. Nat. Acad. Sci. U.S.A.* 1958, **44**, p. 594.
60. BECKMAN, *Phytopathol.* 1956, **46**, p. 605.
61. LEVINSON, MANDELS AND REESE, *Arch. Biochem. Biophys.* 1951, **31**, p. 351.
62. ABRAMS, *Text. Res. J.* 1950, **20**, p. 71.
63. MARSH, *Plant Disease Rept.* 1953, **37**, p. 71.
64. BASU AND PAL, *Nature, Lond.* 1956, **178**, p. 312.
65. HIRSCH, *Experientia*, 1954, **10**, p. 80.
66. HUSAIN, *Phytopathol.* 1958, **48**, p. 338.
67. SAKSENA AND JAFRI, *Proc. Nat. Acad. Sci. India*, 1950, **20 B**, p. 49.
68. MEHROTRA, *J. Indian Bot. Soc.* 1949, **28**, p. 108.
69. BHARGAVA, *J. Indian Bot. Soc.* 1943, **22**, p. 85.
70. KOOIMAN, *Enzymologia*, 1957, **18**, p. 371.
71. LEVINSON AND REESE, *J. gen. Physiol.* 1950, **33**, p. 601.
72. WALSETH, *Tech. Pap. Pulp Pap. Ind., N.Y.* 1952, **35**, pp. 228, 233.
73. STONE, Ph.D. Thesis, University of London, 1954.
74. WHISTLER AND SMART, *J. Amer. chem. Soc.* 1953, **75**, p. 1916.
75. GRASSMANN, ZECHMEISTER, TOTH AND STADLER, *Annalen*, 1933, **503**, p. 167.
76. NISIZAWA AND KOBAYASHI, *Symp. Enzyme Chem. (Japan)* 1953, **8**, p. 123.
77. GRASSMANN AND RUBENAUR, *Münch. med. Wochschr.* 1931, **78**, p. 1817.
78. GILLESPIE AND WOODS, *Austr. J. Biol. Sci.* 1953, **6**, p. 447.
79. GRASSMANN, STADLER AND BENDER, *Annalen*, 1933, **502**, p. 20.
80. JERMYN, *Austr. J. Sci. Res.* 1952, **B5**, p. 409.
81. GILLIGAN AND REESE, *Canad. J. Microbiol.* 1954, **1**, p. 90.
82. HUSAIN AND RICH, *Phytopathol.* 1958, **48**, p. 316.
83. VENKATA RAM, *Proc. Nat. Inst. Sci. India (Biol. Sci.)*, 1956, **22B**, p. 204.
84. GASCOIGNE AND GASCOIGNE, unpublished results.
85. AKAI, *Ann. Phytopathol. Soc. Japan*, 1951, **14**, p. 97.
86. REESE, GILLIGAN AND NORKRANS, *Physiol. Plant.* 1952, **5**, p. 379.

87. AKAKI, *J. Ferment. Technol.* (*Japan*), 1950, **28**, p. 24.
88. WHITAKER, *Arch. Biochem. Biophys.* 1953, **43**, p. 253.
89. KOOIMAN, ROELOFSEN AND SWEERIS, *Enzymologia*, 1953, **16**, p. 237.
90. SAUNDERS, SIU AND GENEST, *J. biol. Chem.* 1948, **174**, p. 697.
91. REESE, SIU AND LEVINSON, *J. Bact.* 1950, **59**, p. 485.
92. AITKEN, EDDY, INGRAM AND WEURMAN, *Biochem. J.* 1956, **64**, p. 63.
93. GRIMES, DUNCAN AND HOPPERT, *Arch. Biochem. Biophys.* 1957, **68**, p. 412.
94. GRIMES, *Diss. Abstracts*, 1956, **16**, p. 643.
95. VAN HAGA, *Nature, Lond.* 1958, **182**, p. 1232.
96. MILLER AND BLUM, *J. biol. Chem.* 1956, **218**, p. 131.
97. HASH AND KING, *Science*, 1954, **120**, 1033.
98. BLUM AND STAHL, *Text. Res. J.* 1952, **22**, p. 178.
99. GREATHOUSE, *Text. Res. J.* 1950, **20**, p. 227.
100. REESE AND MANDELS, *Rept. Q.M. Res. and Dev. Centre, U.S.A.*, *Microbiology Ser.*, 1957, No. 17.
101. HUSAIN AND KELMAN, *Phytopathol.* 1958, **48**, p. 377.
102. SAVUR, *J. Indian Chem. Soc., Ind. and News Ed.* 1957, **20**, p. 62.
103. VARTIOVAARA, *Acta Agralia Fennicae*, 1935, **32**, p. 1.
104. THOMAS, *Austr. J. Biol. Sci.* 1956, **9**, p. 159.
105. REESE, SEGAL AND TRIPP, *Text. Res. J.* 1957, **27**, p. 626.
106. TOYAMA, *J. Ferment. Technol.* (*Japan*), 1953, **31**, p. 315; 1955, **33**, p. 266; 1956, **34**, pp. 274, 281; 1957, **35**, p. 362.
107. TALBOYS, *Brit. Mycol. Soc. Trans.* 1958, **41**, p. 242.
108. TERUI AND FUJIWARA, *J. Ferment. Technol.* (*Japan*), 1948, **27**, p. 203.
109. SIMOLA, *Ann. Acad. Sci. Fennicae*, 1931, **A6**, p. 1.
110. HAMMERSTROM, CLAUS, COGHLAN AND MCBEE, *Arch. Biochem. Biophys.* 1955, **56**, p. 123.
111. ENEBO, *Studies in Cellulose Decomposition*, 1954, Stockholm.
112. MATTHIJSSEN, *Diss. Abstracts*, 1957, **17**, p. 2141.
113. FÅHRAEUS, *Symbolae botan. Upsalienses*, 1947, **9**, p. 1.
114. OKAMOTO AND ASAI, *J. Agric. Chem. Soc. Japan*, 1952, **26**, p. 137.
115. KITTS AND UNDERKOFLER, *J. Agric. Food Chem.* 1954, **2**, p. 639.
116. STANLEY AND KESLER, *J. Dairy Sci.* 1959, **42**, p. 127.
117. HALLIWELL, *J. gen. Microbiol.* 1957, **17**, p. 166.
118. NISIZAWA AND HASHIMOTO, *Arch. Biochem. Biophys.* 1959, **81**, p. 211.
119. FESTENSTEIN, *Biochem. J.* 1958, **69**, p. 562.
120. STONE, *Biochem. J.* 1957, **66**, p. 1P.

IV

PURIFICATION OF CELLULASES

AN account of sources of cell-free cellulolytic enzymes and some of their properties has been given in Chapter III; of recent years more and more attention has been given to the concentration and purification of this type of enzyme, using techniques which have found wide application in the field of protein chemistry (e.g. electrolyte and solvent precipitation, chromatographic and electrophoretic methods) and this has resulted in the production of relatively pure and highly active enzymes from plant, animal and microbial sources.

PREPARATION OF CRUDE EXTRACTS

The preliminary extraction of the enzyme follows a general pattern, and a summary of methods for obtaining these extracts is given by Weidenhagen[1]. With snails and other animal sources the appropriate part of the organism is dissected out[59] and ground with sand, this is then extracted with water or other solvent and submitted to filtration or centrifugation; Karrer[2] and others[3,4] obtained their extracts in this way. Alternatively a homogenizer may be used[5]. From plant sources the enzyme may be found in the cell-sap, following maceration of the tissues[6], or the plant components may be extracted with water or sodium chloride solution; in such ways cellulolytic extracts from sprouted barley have been obtained[7-9]. The cellulolytic enzymes of fungi are mostly present in the liquid in which the organism has been grown; the fungus is usually cultured on a liquid medium containing cellulose and mineral salts, followed by filtration or centrifugation to remove the cells and residual cellulose, and most workers using fungi have obtained their initial preparations in this way[10-16]. The cellulolytic activity of micro-organisms is greatly influenced by external conditions (e.g. pH, temperature, presence of trace elements, carbon and nitrogen sources) and has been discussed in detail elsewhere[17,18]. Similarly these factors affect enzyme production, and when large quantities of enzyme are required it is useful to ascertain the best conditions for maximum enzyme yield.

The names of ion-exchange resins mentioned in this chapter are proprietary names. Zeo-Karb resins are manufactured by The Permutit Company Ltd., London; Amberlite resins by Rohm and Haas Co., Philadelphia, U.S.A.; Nalcite resins by the Dow-Chemical Co., Inc., Midland, Michigan, U.S.A.

Aeration of the liquid medium appears to increase the concentration of enzyme produced, and this may be achieved by using shake culture or submerged, aerated culture techniques. Where large amounts of enzyme are required for further study it is essential to employ a technique of this type. Diagrams of typical fermenters, as used by Thomas[10] and Whitaker[11], are given in *Figures 1* and *2*.

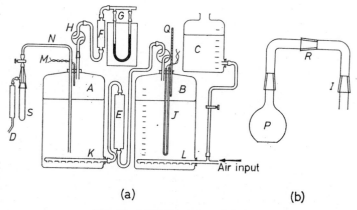

(a)   (b)

Figure 1—(a) Bulk culture apparatus.

A, Fermentation bottle; *B*, Bottle for saturating air entering *A*; *C*, Water reservoir for B; *D*, Sampling device; *E*, Input filter; *F*, Output filter; *G*, Sharp-edged orifice attached to water manometer; *H*, Splash head; *J*, Heating element; *K, L*, Aeration tubes; *M*, Thermistor; *N*, Glass tube leading to sampling tube *S*; *Q*, Thermometer; (b) *I*, Inoculating orifice; *P*, Inoculating flask; *R*, Ground-glass joint

(by courtesy, *Australian Journal of Biological Sciences*, 1956, **9**, p. 159)

Description of apparatus and procedure used by Thomas[10].

A 15-litre Pyrex aspirator was used as the fermentation vessel *A*, which contained the medium (10 l.). A perforated glass tube *K*, in the base of the fermentation vessel, acted as the air inlet, the agitation produced being sufficient to keep the medium well mixed. The air flow-rate was measured by the drop in pressure across a sharp-edged orifice *G* using a water manometer previously calibrated against a standard flowmeter; the air input and output filters (*E* and *F*) were packed with non-absorbent cotton wool. The whole apparatus was operated in a constant temperature room and saturated air at the required temperature was passed into the output filter from an aspirator *B* containing water. The temperature drop in *B*, due to latent heat of evaporation losses, was compensated by a heating element *J*. The outgoing air temperature from *B* was measured by a thermometer *Q* inserted in the neck of *B*. The level of water in *B* could be readjusted as necessary from the aspirator *C*. Sampling was achieved by means of the device *D*, which consisted of a tube S, joined through a ground glass joint and filter assembly and a short piece of rubber tubing to the glass tube N, inserted into the fermentation vessel. Sterile samples could be drawn over into S which could then be replaced by another sterile tube. A starter culture consisting of an 8-day shake culture of the fungus on a cellulose medium in a 500–ml ground glass-jointed flask was used for inoculation of the fermentation vessel through the inoculating port I, to which it was attached by means of two right-angled ground glass joints, as shown in *Figure 1*(b). On rotation of the flask P through 180° about joint R the culture was transferred to the fermentation vessel, the inoculating device was replaced at joint I by the sterile splash head H, attached to the output filter F, and aeration was commenced. The whole apparatus could be easily dismantled for sterilization of individual parts.

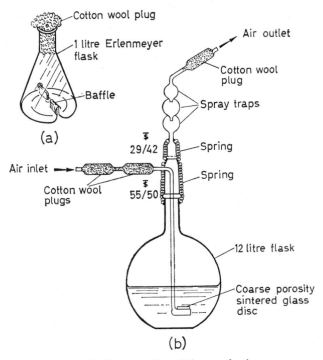

Figure 2—Flasks used in cellulase production.
(a) Shake culture flasks; (b) Submerged culture flasks
(by courtesy, *Archives of Biochemistry and Biophysics*, 1953, **43**, p. 253)

Description of apparatus and procedure used by Whitaker[11].

Starter cultures were grown on a cellulose-containing medium (300 ml) in 1-litre flasks which were baffled as shown in *Figure 2* (a), each baffle being about 1·5 in. long and 0·5 in. high, in order to increase agitation during shaking. Seven-day shake cultures were used to inoculate 12-litre flasks containing medium (6 litres), shown in *Figure 2* (b). These flasks were incubated, usually in batches of six, with vigorous aeration and rotary shaking. Prior to passing into the flasks the air was washed and partially saturated with water by passage through a coarse porosity sintered-glass disc at the bottom of a 9-litre bottle containing $0.02N$ sulphuric acid (6 litres), and then passed through a spray trap to a manifold connected to the flasks. The air to each flask then passed through a cotton-wool filter and was distributed in the 12-litre flask by means of a sintered-glass disc. The air outlet was guarded by a series of spray traps and a cotton wool air filter.

The composition of the medium varies according to the fungus employed. Some form of cellulose is usually used as the sole carbon source; ground cotton linters[11], Whatman cellulose powder[10], phosphoric acid swollen Whatman cellulose powder[19] and filter paper[12] have all been employed. A nitrogen source, usually inorganic, in the form of ammonium salts or nitrate, magnesium sulphate, a source of potassium and of phosphorus are all essential; growth factors and trace elements may be added. Media used by various workers and the organisms grown are listed in *Table 1*. Cellulase production is also dependent on the temperature of growth and pH value of the medium. The optimum conditions for cellulolytic enzyme production vary with the organism used, and in any study of cellulase production by fungi the most suitable conditions for the particular organism in question should be ascertained[10,20,40].

The technique for obtaining active enzyme extracts from bacteria is more complicated, often involving extraction of bacterial cells. Active preparations from *Cytophaga* spp., grown on filter paper in a mineral salts medium, were obtained both from the culture liquor and by extraction of the dry bacteria with borate buffer solution[21], while enzyme extracts from rumen micro-organisms were prepared by extraction with *n*–butanol, or by grinding with alumina and extracting the ground powder[22–24]. It is interesting to note that while Halliwell[22] failed to detect any cellulolytic activity in the supernatant liquid obtained after centrifugation of rumen fluid, other workers have been able to prepare active, cell-free extracts of rumen fluid after agitation in a Waring blender, followed by centrifugation[25]. Attempts to prepare active extracts from rumen organisms by supersonic vibration were unsuccessful[23]. Active preparations have been derived from the medium in which the bacterium is grown, after centrifugation or filtration to remove the cells and the residual cellulose[26]. Factors affecting production of cellulases by bacteria are as critical as for fungi and some detailed studies have been made[26–28].

Table 1. Composition of Media (in g./litre) Used for the Production of Fungal cellulases

Myrothecium verrucaria[11]	Irpex lacteus[12]	Many fungi[13]	Stachybotrys atra[10]	Fusarium moniliforme[19]
Cotton linters, 30·0	Filter paper, 17·33	Cellulose*, 4–5	Whatman cellulose powder, 10·0	H_3PO_4 swollen Whatman powder, 10·0
NH_4NO_3, 0·60	NH_4NO_3, 3·33	NH_4NO_3, 1·0	$(NH_4)_2HPO_4$, 2·50	$(NH_4)_2HPO_4$, 2·50
$NaNO_3$, 3·80				
$MgSO_4, 7H_2O$, 0·30	$MgSO_4, 7H_2O$, 0·40	$MgSO_4, 7H_2O$, 0·20	$MgSO_4, 7H_2O$, 0·50	$MgSO_4, 7H_2O$, 0·50
NaH_2PO_4, H_2O, 2·0				NaH_2PO_4, H_2O, 0·50
Na_2HPO_4, 1·50				
KH_2PO_4, 0·20		KH_2PO_4, 1·40		
K_2HPO_4, 0·15	K_2HPO_4, 1·665			
			KCl, 0·50	KCl, 0·50
Glucose, 1·0	Lactic acid, 0·866	Difco yeast extract 0·10		
mg/litre			mg/litre	mg/litre
$FeSO_4$, $7H_2O$, 0·054			$CaCl_2$, 20·0	$CaCl_2$, H_2O, 10·0
H_3BO_3, 0·06			$FeSO_4$, $7H_2O$, 10·0	$FeSO_4$, $7H_2O$ 10·0
$CuSO_4, 5H_2O$, 0·20			$ZnSO_4, 7H_2O$, 2·0	$ZnSO_4, 7H_2O$, 2·0
$ZnSO_4, 7H_2O$, 2·0			$MnCl_2, 4H_2O$ 1·0	
$MnCl_2, 4H_2O$, 0·08				
$CoCl_2, 6H_2O$, 0·40		pH 6·1–6·3	pH 7·1–7·3	pH 6·5
$Ca(NO_3)_2$, $4H_2O$, 1·20				
NH_4molybdate, 0·04				

*Used ground dewaxed cotton, two types of wood cellulose, Na salt of CMC, alkali cellulose.

PRELIMINARY TREATMENTS

Initial treatments of crude cellulolytic extracts may include concentration and de-ionization by various methods, followed by one or two solvent or salt precipitations[10,14,29–31]. These merely serve as an initial concentration and purification procedure and no claims to have obtained thus a purified cellulase have been made, the presence of mixtures of enzymes being openly acknowledged. However, some extensive purification studies of cellulases have been made and some account of this work will be given here.

Concentration Procedures

Where large volumes of culture medium containing active cellulolytic enzymes have to be processed some form of concentration of the bulk of the liquid is essential to facilitate handling and to obtain satisfactory concentrates of protein for any purification methods tested during later work. Various methods of concentration have been used satisfactorily by different workers, apart from precipitations; a combination of vacuum evaporation using a Bartholomew evaporator and concentration by slow freezing gave a final concentration of about 10 : 1, losses of up to 5 per cent in enzyme activity being reported during vacuum evaporation carried out at 35°–39°, with no losses in the slow freezing procedure[11]; a concentration of 20 litres to about 600 ml achieved in a climbing film vacuum evaporator below 30° followed by electrodialysis and final freeze-drying gave a powder having at least 95 per cent of the original activity[10]. Evaporation using a cyclone evaporator operating below 30°, followed by freeze-drying has been used successfully, and in fact an apparent increase in enzyme activity was noted after concentration by this means[19]; similar effects have been noted elsewhere[32,33]. No logical explanation has been given for this but it may be due to an increase in concentration of an activator present in the medium in small amounts.

De-ionization of Cellulolytic Enzyme Preparations

De-ionization procedures for enzyme solutions have been described by Stauffer[34]. Dialysis techniques and ion-exchange resins are the two most widely used processes for the removal of ions from solution in modern times. Dialysis of cellulolytic enzyme preparations presents an unusual problem because the widely used dialysis membrane, which is cellulosic in nature, is attacked and weakened by the enzymes, which may also be adsorbed on it with consequent loss in activity. Alternative methods of de-ionization and different membranes are available, however, and have been used satisfactorily by different workers.

Electrodialysis procedures, between cellophane membranes against a continuous flow of distilled water, have been developed in the isolation of cellulolytic enzymes from *Aspergillus oryzae*[41] and *Stachybotrys atra*[10]. In the latter case dialysis was continued until the conductivity of the solution was constant (*c.* 10 hours). The resultant powder obtained after lyophilization of the de-ionized

77

enzyme solution retained at least 95 per cent of the original activity and contained no ash or ammonium salts. However, other workers[19], using a crude enzyme preparation from *Fusarium moniliforme*, lost only 45 per cent by weight of total solids after electrodialysis for 8 hours across cellulosic membranes, and the final preparation retained only 75 per cent of the activity of the original solution. Nitrocellulose films have been used for dialysis causing no loss in enzymic activity and allowing a satisfactory rate of dialysis[36,37]. The preparation of these films has been described[38]. However, other workers[21,76] have reported that the use of nitrocellulose results in loss of enzyme activity. Vellum and rabbit bladder membranes are said to be satisfactory[76].

Another protein membrane which has been widely used is goldbeaters' skin. This has been used in the preparation of cellulase from *Myrothecium verrucaria*[11]; however, before use care must be taken to ascertain that there are no pinholes in the membrane. The removal of 80 to 90 per cent by weight of total solids of crude cellulolytic preparations, with no loss in activity has been achieved by dialysis for 72 hours against running tap water over this membrane[19]. The use of acetylated cellulosic dialysis tubing has recently been developed[39]. This membrane appears to be unsusceptible to enzymic attack, to cause little loss in enzymic activity, and to allow a satisfactory rate of dialysis (over 90 per cent by weight of total solids removed in 72 hours' dialysis against running tap-water[19]). The membrane is prepared by acetylation of cellophane tubing at room temperature using a mixture of benzene, acetic anhydride and pyridine, followed by thorough washing of the membranes with water. Nylon membranes have been found unsatisfactory for dialysis due to swelling of the membrane pores in electrolyte solutions. In view of the ease of preparation and the satisfactory results obtained, it would appear that acetylated dialysis tubing is the most suitable membrane for dialysis of cellulolytic enzyme preparations.

The use of ion-exchange resins has been attempted by some workers[41]. Cellulolytic preparations from *Hydnum henningsii* were desalted by passage down an ion-exchange resin column (1 part Deacidite E : 1 part Zeo-Karb 225); however, there was a considerable loss in activity after this treatment[42]. Similar results were obtained when extracts from *F. moniliforme* were passed down columns containing mixed beds of the following resins (a) Amberlite IRA–400(OH) a strongly basic anion exchanger and Amberlite IR–120(H) a strongly acidic cation exchanger, (b) Amberlite IR–4B(OH) a weakly basic anion exchanger and Amberlite IR–120(H), (c) Amberlite IRA–400(OH) and Amberlite IRC–50(H) a weakly acidic cation exchanger[19]. In contrast to all these results Roth[78] successfully de-ionised a culture filtrate from *M. verrucaria* by passage through a mixed bed column of Amberlite IR–120(H) and Amberlite IRA–400(OH); there was a 35 to 50 per cent loss in total protein, but no loss in cellulase activity of the protein which passed through. However the use of a 'buffered' ion-exchange resin column has proved highly satisfactory[43,44]. The preparation of this is described below:—

(i) Place Amberlite IR–120 (H) (*ca* 600 ml) in a column and back wash with water. Regenerate the column with hydrochloric acid (10%) by downward flow and wash with water until the eluate is of constant pH value. Treat Dowex 2 (*ca* 600ml) similarly using sodium hydroxide solution (4%) in place of hydrochloric acid.

(ii) Wash approximately 400 ml of Amberlite IR–120 (H) with ammonium hydroxide (N solution) to replace H^+ by NH_4^+, and then with water.

(iii) Wash approximately 400 ml of Dowex 2 with acetic acid (N solution) to replace OH^- by $(OAc)^-$, and then with water.

(iv) Combine the remaining portions of the untreated resins (H and OH forms), and mix thoroughly.

(v) Pack the fractions into a column as shown in *Figure 3*. During passage of salt solutions through the column, the cations are exchanged for

Solution in
↓

R SO_3^-.NH_4^+

R R^1_3 N^+.OAc^-

Mixed bed
R SO_3^-.H^+
R R^1_3 N^+.OH^-

↓
De-ionized
solution out

Figure 3—Packing of 'buffered' ion-exchange column.

ammonium ions, and the anions are exchanged for acetate ions; this is followed by an exchange of the ammonium and acetate ions for the hydrogen and hydroxyl ions respectively. In this way exposure of the enzyme to strong acid and alkali during de-ionization is avoided.

This technique readily de-ionized a crude enzyme extract from *M. verrucaria* (after partial dialysis) without loss, but with the pure enzyme, resulted in some adsorption but no deactivation. These results have been confirmed using crude, partially dialysed extracts from *F. moniliforme*.

The use of nitrocellulosic or acetylated cellulosic membranes and 'buffered' ion exchange columns for de-ionization of cellulolytic enzyme extracts give very satisfactory results.

Purification by Precipitation Techniques

These techniques include precipitation using salts such as ammonium sulphate, lead acetate and rivanol, and solvents, including ethanol, acetone and ether. A general account of these techniques is given elsewhere[35]. Extensive work using these precipitants has been done, resulting in the preparation of highly active cellulolytic enzymes from various sources, having varying degrees of purity.

Using crushed green malt as their enzyme source Enebo *et al.*[7] obtained a preparation, after precipitation with ammonium sulphate followed by dialysis and final precipitation with acetone, which had a nitrogen content of 12 per cent and was about forty times as active as the original material. A protocol of their purification procedure is given in *Figure 4*. Data concerning the concentration and purification of cellulases of animal origin are, again, relatively few except in the case of the snail. However, an enzyme preparation has been obtained from the insect silver-fish[30] by fractionation of an extract of the mid-gut with ammonium sulphate, cellulase being precipitated at a concentration of 60 to 70 per cent saturation. A cellobiase was also present. Details are also available of a method of the concentration of cellulolytic enzymes from the ship-worm *Teredo*[45]. This involved autolysis of a homogenate of digestive tracts, dissected from intact specimens obtained from infected wood, in pentachlorophenol solution at a low temperature followed by centrifugation; the supernatant solution thus obtained was mixed with a cellulose substrate, prepared from a cellulose gum and aluminium sulphate, to allow the enzyme to be adsorbed, followed by further centrifugation. The adsorbed enzyme was recovered by dissolution of the deposit in a buffered sodium chloride solution followed by dialysis of the redissolved material and fractionation of the dialysate with ammonium sulphate. Most of the cellulolytic activity was recovered in the fraction precipitated at 100 per cent saturation, which had an activity approximately twice that of the original digestive tracts.

Over the years extensive studies have been made on the purification of cellulolytic enzymes from fungi. The closely related enzymes

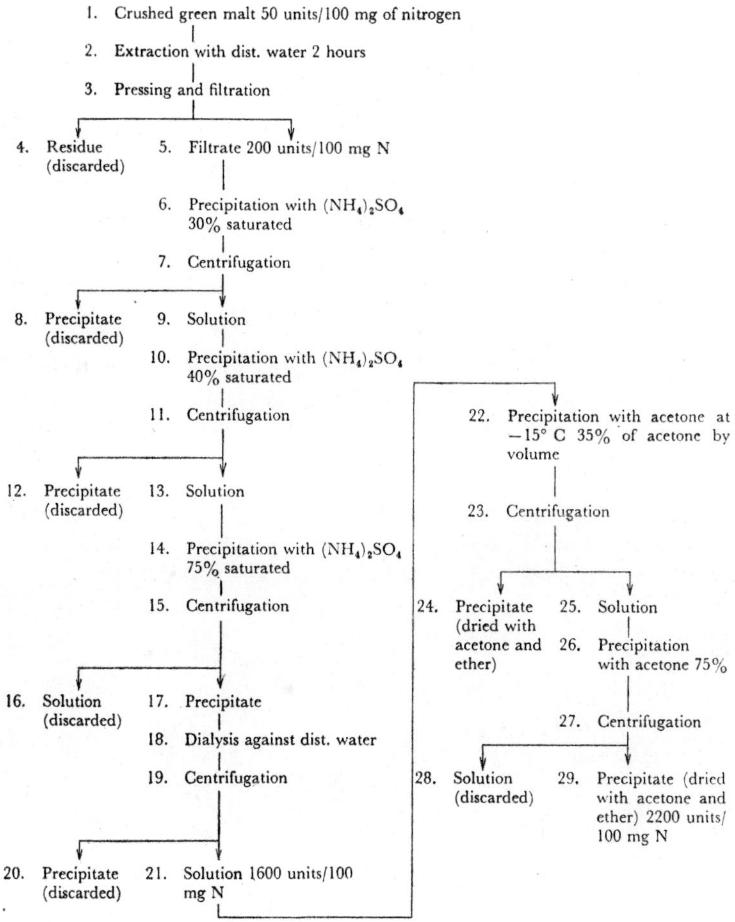

1. Crushed green malt 50 units/100 mg of nitrogen

2. Extraction with dist. water 2 hours

3. Pressing and filtration

4. Residue (discarded)

5. Filtrate 200 units/100 mg N

6. Precipitation with $(NH_4)_2SO_4$ 30% saturated

7. Centrifugation

8. Precipitate (discarded)

9. Solution

10. Precipitation with $(NH_4)_2SO_4$ 40% saturated

11. Centrifugation

12. Precipitate (discarded)

13. Solution

14. Precipitation with $(NH_4)_2SO_4$ 75% saturated

15. Centrifugation

16. Solution (discarded)

17. Precipitate

18. Dialysis against dist. water

19. Centrifugation

20. Precipitate (discarded)

21. Solution 1600 units/100 mg N

22. Precipitation with acetone at $-15°$ C 35% of acetone by volume

23. Centrifugation

24. Precipitate (dried with acetone and ether)

25. Solution

26. Precipitation with acetone 75%

27. Centrifugation

28. Solution (discarded)

29. Precipitate (dried with acetone and ether) 2200 units/100 mg N

Figure 4—Preparation of cellulase from green malt
(by courtesy, *Journal of the Institute of Brewing*, 1953, **59**, p. 207)

81

cellulase and lichenase, obtained from *Aspergillus oryzae* were separated by fractional precipitation with ethanol–ether mixtures, similar results also being obtained with enzymes from the digestive juices of the snail *Helix pomatia*[46]. By a similar technique, separation of these enzymes was achieved from cultures of the wood-rotting fungus *Merulius lacrymans*[47]. In this case, however, β–glucosidase was precipitated at a lower concentration of added solvents than lichenase, cellulase requiring the highest concentration for precipitation; this behaviour was the reverse of the same enzymes from *A. oryzae* and *H. pomatia*. Karrer[2] records that solvent precipitations are of little use for the separation of these enzymes from snail-gut juice.

A highly active preparation was obtained from a culture of *Trichoderma koningi* (*T. viride*)[48] grown on wheat bran by extraction with water at room temperature and filtration, the filtrate then being subjected to the following purification procedure; treatment with lead acetate solution (1%) and sodium pentachlorophenate solution (0·05%) followed by filtration; the filtrate thus obtained was precipitated by adding ammonium sulphate to 30 per cent saturation, the precipitate discarded and the filtrate further precipitated with ammonium sulphate to 70 per cent saturation. The precipitate thus obtained was dialysed, the residue was treated with ethanol to 70 per cent concentration; this precipitate, after centrifugation was washed with ether and dried to give a brown cellulase preparation which showed one hundred times the activity of the original. Alternative treatment of the residue after dialysis involved treatment with rivanol (1%), removal of the precipitate and further precipitation of the filtrate with ethanol to 70 per cent concentration and, as final purification, two precipitations with acetone. This method was later modified[77] and after treatment of the crude extract with lead acetate and ammonium sulphate, treatment with rivanol resulted in the precipitation of a rivanol-enzyme complex, which contained the major portion of cellulase of the original extract. The complex was dialysed, the residue dissolved and then treated with acetone to precipitate a free enzyme preparation, which con-contained only a single component on ionophoresis, and hydrolysed cellulose, carboxymethylcellulose, starch and cellobiose. Further separation of these enzymes using ion-exchange resins is discussed later.

Preparations have been made from various wood-rotting fungi: The purification of a cellulase from *Irpex lacteus* by salting out with ammonium sulphate, followed by dialysis and precipitation from acetone has been reported[49]. Concentrates were prepared from

Hydnum henningsii by precipitation with ammonium sulphate; further concentration by vacuum evaporation, followed by saturation with magnesium sulphate, the resultant precipitate being extracted with water and desalted by passage through an ion-exchange column, resulted in considerable loss in activity[42]. Partial purification of a cellulase from *Polyporus palustris*[16] was made following growth on a synthetic medium in submerged culture for fifteen days, by passing the cell-free culture filtrates through a cation exchange resin (Nalcite HCR), dialysing the effluent over a collodion membrane and evaporating it to one-fortieth of its original volume in a forced air-draught at 25°. The sediment obtained at this stage was discarded after centrifugation, and the enzymically active fraction was precipitated from the concentrate using ethanol (3 volumes cooled to −15° to 1 volume of concentrate cooled to 2°). After centrifugation this precipitate was taken up in Clark and Lubs' phthalate buffer at pH 4·4 at 4°, followed by evaporation in a forced air-current in the cold, yielding two crystalline forms, one large and irregular, the other small, rectangular and uniform. The former was soluble in cold distilled water and was shown to contain buffer salts, while the latter was insoluble in cold distilled water and retained much of the cellulolytic activity of the original filtrate. In an attempt to obtain enzymes which, when allowed to act on wood, would remove cellulose leaving large amounts of chemically unchanged lignin, the isolation of a cellulolytic enzyme preparation from *Poria vaillantii* was achieved[15]. Six week-old cultures of the fungus were used, and following filtration, concentration of the culture filtrates and isolation of the enzyme by precipitation with cold acetone were effected. The purification scheme is shown in *Figure 5*. The preparation showed two main peaks on electrophoresis in acetate buffer at pH 5·3, and as fractionation proceeded the concentration of the faster moving component, the cellulase fraction, increased compared with the slow moving component.

Attempts to purify a commercial cellulase preparation, derived from *Aspergillus niger*, to obtain an extract giving cellobiose as the end-product of cellulose hydrolysis, through acetone and ammonium sulphate fractionations were unsuccessful[50]. Fractional precipitations of a similar enzyme preparation with ammonium sulphate indicated that most of the activity was precipitated in the range 45 to 60 per cent saturation[37]. However, in this latter work it should be noted that no attempt was being made to produce a 'cellobiose-producing' fraction. A 'cellobiose-producing' fraction has been produced from culture filtrates of *Fusarium moniliforme* by ethanol

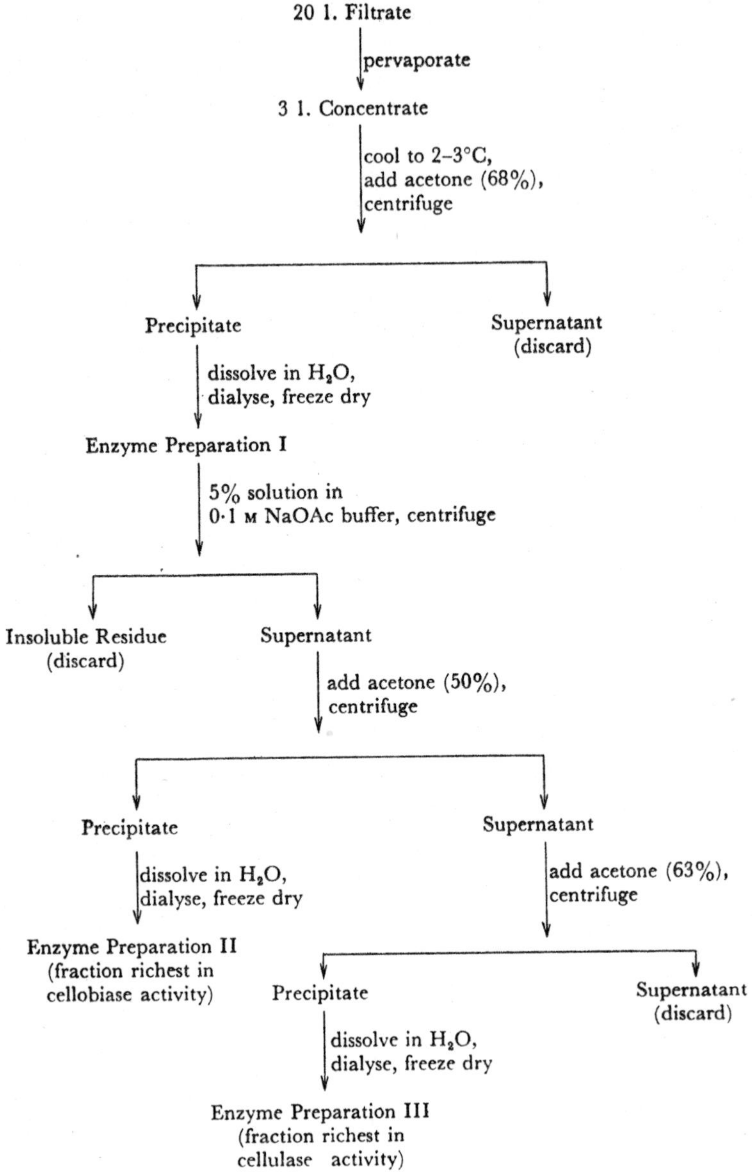

Figure 5—Purification of cellulase from *Poria vaillantii*
(by courtesy, *Archives of Biochemistry and Biophysics*, 1958, **75**, p. 262)

precipitation[19]; it was obtained by precipitation between 55 and 78 per cent by volume ethanol concentrations.

In an effort to obtain a mild treatment for the release of active constituents from plant drugs the use of enzymic means was considered to break down the plant cell wall[78]. This led to the development of a method for the purification of *M. verrucaria* cellulase which consisted of de-ionization of the culture filtrate using ion-exchange resins, followed by concentration at 25° to 30° and finally freeze-drying. The freeze-dried material was dissolved in 0·01M acetate buffer at pH 5·0, to give a protein concentration of one per cent; this solution was fractionated by alcohol precipitation, fractions with high cellulase activities being obtained between 30 and 50 per cent alcohol concentrations. Further purification was carried out by dissolution of the active fraction in acetate buffer (0·01M, pH 4·35) to give a one per cent solution of protein, and precipitation with an equal volume of polymethacrylic acid (0·25 per cent) in the same buffer. The precipitate thus obtained was dissolved in acetate buffer (0·05M, pH 6·5) and polymethacrylic acid removed by precipitation with barium chloride solution (10 per cent). The purified cellulase thus obtained was shown by electrophoresis to contain one major component, with traces of two others. A preparation containing only two components was obtained by cooling the liquid after concentration to 0° to 2° and removing the precipitate of low activity thus formed; after freeze-drying the remainder it was precipitated using an alcohol concentration of 20 per cent, and this low activity precipitate discarded; the final precipitate was obtained at an alcohol concentration of 50 per cent. The 50 per cent alcohol fraction was used unsuccessfully in attempts to facilitate the extraction of strychnine from *Nux vomica*.

Two claims have been made that 'pure' cellulases have been produced. Nisizawa[12] obtained a cystalline preparation from *Irpex lacteus*; after growth in submerged culture, followed by dialysis and seven precipitations using acetone, crystals were obtained the specific activity of which remained unchanged on further recrystallization from acetone. These crystals are claimed to be crystals of pure cellulase and are active towards CMC and *p*–nitrophenyl–β–cellobioside; a threefold purification was achieved. The purification procedure is reproduced in *Figure 6*.

Claims to have prepared a pure cellulase have also been made by Whitaker[11] who obtained the only electrophoretically homogeneous preparation. Using cell-free culture filtrates from the highly cellulolytic fungus *Myrothecium verrucaria*, the enzyme was purified by a sequence of concentration, precipitation by ammonium sulphate,

```
                    Starting solution (5·51)
                        │ Concentrate, dialyse for 4 days
                    150 ml.
                  (Enzyme solution 1)
                        │ Add acetone (68%), centrifuge
          ┌─────────────┴──────────────────┐
     Supernatant                        Precipitate
                                            │ Dissolve in 100 ml
                                            │ water, centrifuge
                   ┌────────────────────────┴───────────┐
              Supernatant                          Insoluble residue
           (Enzyme solution 2)
                   │ Add acetone (50%), centrifuge
          ┌────────┴───────────────┐
      Precipitate              Supernatant
           │ Dissolve in          │ Add acetone (63%),
           │ 100 ml water         │ centrifuge
   (Enzyme solution 2')    ┌───────┴──────────────┐
                       Precipitate            Supernatant
                           │ Dissolve in 100 ml
                           │ water, centrifuge
                ┌──────────┴────────────┐
       Insoluble residue          Supernatant
                                 (Enzyme solution 3)
                                      │ Add acetone (60%), centrifuge
                          ┌───────────┴────────────┐
                      Precipitate              Supernatant
                          │ Dissolve in 50 ml water,
                          │ centrifuge
                ┌─────────┴───────────────┐
        Insoluble residue            Supernatant
                                   (Enzyme solution 4)
                                        │ Add acetone (58%), centrifuge
                      ┌─────────────────┴───────────┐
                 Precipitate                    Supernatant
                      │ Dissolve in 50 ml water,
                      │ centrifuge
          ┌───────────┴──────────────┐
  Insoluble residue             Supernatant
  (very small amount)         (Enzyme solution 5)
                                    │ Add acetone (61%), centrifuge
                        ┌───────────┴────────────┐
                    Precipitate              Supernatant
                 (somewhat crystalline)
                        │ Dissolve in 30 ml water*
                 (Enzyme solution 6)
                        │ Add acetone (70%), centrifuge
            ┌───────────┴────────────┐
        Precipitate              Supernatant
         (crystals)
            │ Dissolve in 20 ml water*
   (Enzyme solution 7)
            │ Add acetone (75%), centrifuge
    ┌───────┴────────────────┐
Precipitate              Supernatant
    │ Dissolve in 10 ml water*
(Enzyme solution 8)
   *No insoluble matter remained.
```

Figure 6—Purification of cellulase from *Irpex lacteus*
(by courtesy, *Journal of Biochemistry* (*Japan*), 1955, **42**, p. 827)

	Protein mg	Swollen linters cellulase units	Precipitated cellulose cellulase units
A. Precipitation with $(NH_4)_2SO_4$			
Concentrated culture filtrate 1990 ml, pH 6·5, 1°C.	4240	4060	4060
100 ml 1 M phosphate, pH 6·8			
900 ml satd. $(NH_4)_2SO_4$			
Centrifuged.			
Sediment	304	36	**37**
Supernatant saturated with $(NH_4)_2SO_4$ by dialysis. Centrifuged. Supernatant discarded.			
Sediment			
Extracted twice with water (200 ml, 50 ml). Centrifuged after each extraction; supernatants combined.			
Initial extract	3650	3690	3780
Sediment	215	56	59
Total	4170	3780	3880
B. Fractionation with ethanol			
2·8 g. Initial extract protein (dialysed against 0·01 M phosphate, pH 6·8) Vol. 95 ml.	2800	2830	2900
pH to 4·95			
Ethanol to 5% (v/v) at 1°C. Centrifuged, sediment washed and recentrifuged.			
Sediment	659	401	387
Combined supernatants			
Ethanol to 25% (v/v) at −7°C.			
Sediment A	1762	2210	2110
Supernatant	309	151	169
Total	2730	2760	2670
C. Fractionation with PMA			
1·62 g. Sediment A protein	1620	2030	1940
Dissolved in 162 ml of 0·01 M sodium acetate at 1°C. Glacial acetic acid added by capillary inflow to pH 4·35. Centrifuged, sediment washed, and re-centrifuged.			
Sediment	100	81	78
Supernatants			
162 ml of 0·25% PMA in 0·01 M sodium acetate at pH 4·35. Centrifuged, washed, and re-centrifuged.			
Supernatant	510	73	80
Sediment			
Dissolved in 80 ml of 0·05 M sodium acetate at pH 6·5; 6 ml 10% $BaCl_2$ added; centrifuged and sediment (Ba PMA) discarded.			
Supernatant (Purified cellulase)	724	1620	1640
Total	1430	1770	1800

Figure 7—Purification of cellulase from *Myrothecium verrucaria*
(by courtesy, *Archives of Biochemistry and Biophysics*, 1953, **43**, p. 262)

fractionation with ethanol and finally precipitation with poly-methacrylic acid. Details of the final method of purification together with the activity of each fraction are shown in *Figure 7*. The final preparation was twice as active as the original culture fluid. It is interesting to note that Thomas[10], using a cellulolytic extract of different origin, from the fungus *Stachybotrys atra*, was unable to repeat this purification procedure.

Until recently few attempts have been made to purify bacterial cellulases extensively by precipitation methods. Cellulolytic preparations obtained from aerobic spore-forming bacteria and from aerobic bacteria of the *Cytophaga* group have been used by Simola[51] and Fåhraeus[21] respectively, in their work on cellulose degradation by bacteria, and the action of the cellulase from *Clostridium thermo-cellulaseum*[26], obtained by the concentration of centrifuged fermentation liquid followed by precipitation with ethanol, has also been studied. A cellulase preparation was obtained from a cell-free enzyme solution derived from *Pseudomonas fluorescens* var. *cellulosa* by salting out with ammonium sulphate[53], while the 'weathering' cellulase of *Bacillus hydrolyticus*[54] has been obtained in cell-free solution by autolysis of cells with toluene or sodium cyanide at 50°, followed by precipitation of the autolysate with ethanol and extraction with water. This enzyme preparation caused the cellulose to become fragile and more acid-labile.

Of all bacterial cellulolytic enzymes the most extensive purification studies have been made on the enzyme system from *Coryne-bacterium fimi*[28]. The enzyme preparations obtained from this organism were fractionated by the use of increasing concentrates of ammonium sulphate, ethanol and acetone, and by different precipitants used in succession. The β–glucosidase activity present in the crude preparations was removed during precipitations with ammonium sulphate, but was retained on precipitation with ethanol.

No universal method of purification of cellulases by precipitation techniques is yet available, even amongst enzymes derived from similar types of organisms, while even such steps as the elimination of β–glucosidases from crude enzymic mixtures is not achieved at the same level of precipitant concentration. Considerably more work will be necessary before a standard method becomes available.

Purification by Adsorption Techniques

The application of adsorption techniques to the problem of concentration, separation and purification of cellulolytic enzymes, either separately or in conjunction with precipitation or other methods has been widely practised. In fact, many earlier workers achieved separation of the closely related enzymes cellulase, cello-biase, hemicellulase, lichenase and xylanase by these means.

Cellulases of plant origin.—Otto[56] found that the cellulase of malt, could be adsorbed on aluminium hydroxide, while some separation and purification of enzymes present in aqueous extracts of malt was achieved by adsorption on and elution from kaolin and aluminium β–hydroxide[57]. Van Sumère[8] found a very active hemicellulase in extracts of sprouted barley, which attacked the mannogalactan from St. John's bread. Attempts to separate this enzyme from the cellulolytic enzyme, also present, by fractional precipitation with ammonium sulphate were unsuccessful, and a procedure involving the elution of a column containing the precipita-ted enzymes in the presence of an inert carrier and a medium of high salt concentration, with a solution of diluted salt concentration was derived. Sprouted barley was extracted with sodium chloride solution (0·6%), filtered, centrifuged, and the mother liquor concentrated by lyophilization. Saturated ammonium sulphate solution was added to the powder and the solution treated with Celite (Johns-Manville); this mixture was poured into a column and eluted with 33 per cent saturated ammonium sulphate solution. This procedure allowed complete separation of the enzymes manno-galactanase and cellulase.

Cellulases of animal origin.—Accounts of the separation and purifica-tion of cellulases of animal origin by adsorption techniques are rather sparse, but these methods were extensively used by Karrer *et al.*[58] in their studies with snail cellulase. This enzyme was adsorbed by various aluminiferous earth preparations and by basic aluminium sulphate, but not by kaolin. A two-step purification of *Helix* cellulase, based on adsorption on alumina preparations was carried out by de Stevens[59]; however the most extensive purification of this enzyme has been made by Myers and Northcote[5] who obtained a five-fold purification. The enzyme was not adsorbed on calcium phosphate gel or on aluminium metahydroxide and was denatured by ethanol and acetone; it was precipitated over a wide range of ammonium sulphate concentrations and the final purification was carried out by a combination of lead acetate and ammonium sulphate precipita-tion and column chromatography using cellulose powder and an ion-exchange resin. A protocol of the method is shown in *Figure 8*. It will be seen that use is made of a cellulose column; of recent years much use has been made of cellulose as a carrier for separation of cellulolytic enzymes, and the recovery of enzymic activity from it is discussed in Chapter VI. In the above purification of *Helix* cellulase it was the only method capable of separating the enzyme

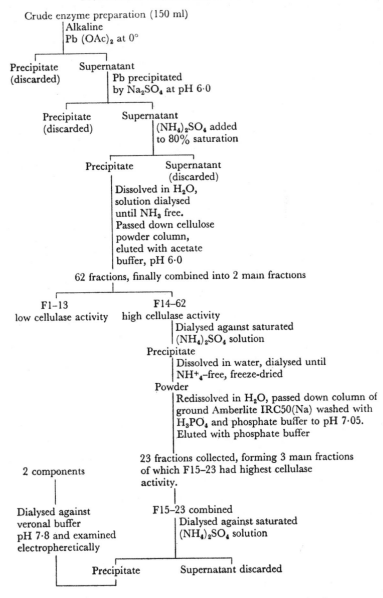

Figure 8—Purification of *Helix pomatia* cellulase (abridged).

from the accompanying pigments. From the final separation on an ion-exchange resin column, three fractions were obtained (by combination of fractions from the column), all having cellulase activity of the same order. Since the proteins had different chromatographic mobilities it was suggested that there are at least three enzymes involved in cellulose decomposition in the digestive tract of *Helix*. The most active fraction, examined electrophoretically, showed two components. It has been shown that the cellulase obtained from the flagellate *Trichomonas termopsidis*[3] can be adsorbed on aluminium hydroxide and eluted with potassium dihydrogen phosphate solution (3%). This enzyme could also be precipitated with acetone, but much activity was lost in the process.

Fungal cellulases.—Adsorption techniques have been applied to the separation of fungal cellulases more widely than to cellulases of either plant or animal origin, both for the separation of distinct enzymes and of components of the cellulolytic complex.

(i) *Separation of carbohydrases.* Grassmann et al.[60] studied the action of an enzyme solution on celluloses and hemicelluloses; separation of xylanase from cellulase was achieved by adsorption of the former on charcoal, while cellobiase was removed from the mixture by the use of an aluminium hydroxide. The same workers[61] separated a cellulase and a cellobiase from *Aspergillus niger* by means of an aluminium hydroxide and the minerals diaspore and bauxite, cellobiase being adsorbed in each case, leaving cellulase in solution. More recently separation of cellobiase from cellulolytic enzymes has been achieved by adsorption of the latter on alkali cellulose[62]. Separation of cellulolytic enzymes from amylase in a preparation from *Trichoderma koningi* has been achieved by paper chromatography (ascending technique), when cellulase remained near the origin, and amylase was located near the solvent front[63]. Pentosanase, cellulase and polygalacturonase from a fungal enzyme preparation have been partially resolved by paper chromatographic techniques[64]. The mobility of the enzymes was controlled by varying the hydrogen ion concentration and the composition of solvent; at pH 4·5 the enzymes had low mobility, while at pH 6·5 they were found near the solvent front; high concentrations of salt (30% ammonium sulphate) and of acetone (40%) gave low mobility. The best separations were obtained with 20 to 22 per cent aqueous ammonium sulphate solutions at pH 4·6, when two separate fractions were obtained, one of low mobility containing cellulase and pentosanase activity, the other of high mobility containing polygalacturonase activity. However, elution of the cellulase-pentosanase fraction from the paper was incomplete with acetate and phosphate buffers over a pH value range of 4·5 to 7·5.

(ii) *Resolution of cellulolytic enzymes.* The purification of cellulase from *Irpex lacteus* by chromatography on an alumina preparation has been reported[65]. Extracts from *A. niger* have been used by several workers. Attempts were made to separate an enzyme preparation which hydrolysed cellulose to cellobiose[50]. No fractionation was achieved by sorption on ion-exchange resins, charcoal, wheat starch, kaolin, Super-Cel, bauxite or aluminium hydroxide. However, after sorption of the crude extract, at pH 3·0, on a column of powdered cellulose, and elution with borate buffer at pH 9·0, a preparation was obtained which was adjusted to pH 6·0 and brought to 80 per cent saturation with ammonium sulphate; the precipitate obtained, after centrifugation, was dissolved in water, dialysed and freeze-dried. This preparation catalysed the hydrolysis of swollen cellulose to produce cellobiose as the major product for the first three hours of the reaction. The presence of two cellulolytic components in an *A. niger* preparation[37] was indicated by adsorption on and elution from cellulose (Whatman filter paper powder and Solka floc) at both acidic and alkaline pH values; however, on gradient elution of the enzyme from a calcium phosphate gel-Celite column it was possible to separate three main components showing cellulolytic activity. Later results[66] obtained using a similar separation technique (i.e. gradient elution from a calcium phosphate gel column using phosphate buffer of increasing molarity), showed that a component eluted at 0·0075M concentration was enzymically active towards both sodium carboxymethylcellulose (CMC) and phosphoric acid swollen cellulose, while a second component eluted between 0·03 and 0·05M phosphate concentrations was considerably more active towards CMC than cellulose, and a third component eluted between 0·055M and 0·07M concentrations was again active towards both cellulosic substrates. During his extensive studies on the purification of *M. verrucaria* cellulase Whitaker[11] attempted the purification of the crude enzyme by adsorption on calcium phosphate gel, eluting the adsorbed protein with phosphate buffer. Studies of the fractions collected indicated that the protein was eluted at a very sharp concentration front, followed by a long continuously decreasing tail. The ratio of cellulase activity to protein concentration was found to be greatest for the first protein fraction, and decreased with later fractions, the highest activity obtained being approximately twice that of the starting product. He recorded elsewhere[67] that the most active fraction was obtained by adsorption at a protein concentration of one per cent in 0·001M phosphate buffer at 1°, and elution with 0·05M phosphate buffer, but again total recoveries were low on account of the tailing effect.

The most extensive and detailed work on the chromatographic separation of cellulolytic enzymes has been carried out by Reese et al.[68,69], who applied this method in an attempt to answer the question whether the polysaccharase acting on the (1→4) β linkage of cellulose is a single enzyme or a group of similar enzymes. Other hydrolytic enzyme systems have been studied by this method[70-72] and evidence for multiple components has been obtained. Reese and co-workers used sheets of filter paper (Whatman No. 1), pre-treated by immersion in zein solution (4%) in ethanol (75%) at pH 4·0 and air dried. The crude enzyme solutions (previously concentrated by an acetone precipitation) were applied to strips of this paper which were then irrigated by the descending technique for 16 to 24 hours at 8°, using 0·3M sodium chloride in 0·05M citrate buffer solution at pH 5·4. The papers, after air-drying, were cut into small strips; the activity of each strip or an eluate from it was assayed by incubation with a CMC-buffer mixture followed by estimation of the reducing sugar produced, which latter is a function of the enzyme concentration on the strip; a typical enzyme pattern showing the activity plotted against the number of the fraction is shown in *Figure 9a*. It is evident from this that the organism used (*A. terreus*) gave rise to an enzyme complex containing three cellulolytic components of differing mobilities, as indicated by the three peaks in the diagram. The enzyme patterns obtained were said to be highly reproducible, and it was possible to obtain up to three cellulolytic components from filtrates of cellulolytic organisms, depending on the species and conditions of growth. Some separation of cellulolytic components was also obtained by differential adsorption on cellulose and kaolin. In addition to this paper strip technique these workers also applied column chroma-tography using cellulose and calcium phosphate gel columns. For the latter the gel was prepared by the method of Swingle and Tiselius[73], and diluted with 10 parts of Celite 545. The column was washed with water and sodium chloride solution (2%) prior to the addition of dialysed enzyme solution, and separation was achieved by gradient elution with increasing concentrations of potassium phosphate buffer (0·002M to 0·02M, pH 7·0) in sodium chloride solution (2%); aliquot eluates, which varied in volume with column size, were collected and assayed for activity by measur-ing the production of reducing sugar on incubation with *Walseth* cellulose (i.e. phosphoric acid swollen cellulose) and CMC under standard conditions. A typical enzyme pattern, thus obtained, is shown in *Figure 9b*. From *Trichoderma viride* culture filtrate eluted from a calcium phosphate gel column evidence for the presence of at least three enzymic components (A,B and CD) may be inferred. Measurements of protein in the eluates can also be made, and in the case of *T. viride* it was shown that movement of protein coincided

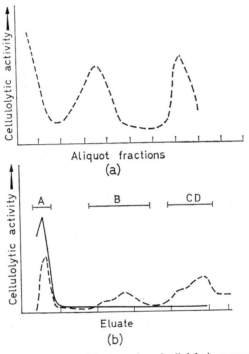

Figure 9—Chromatographic separation of cellulolytic components.

(a) Filtrate from *Aspergillus terreus*, activity measured by production of reducing sugar from CMC (by courtesy, *Archives of Biochemistry and Biophysics*, 1955, **45**, p. 77)

(b) Filtrate from *Trichoderma viride*, activity measured by production of reducing sugar from *Walseth* cellulase (broken line), 'swelling factor' activity (solid line) (by courtesy, *Canadian Journal of Microbiology*, 1954, **1**, p. 97)

with the movement of enzyme. Measurements of the 'swelling factor' (the action of which is said to cause increased swelling of cotton in alkaline solution) were also made and are recorded in *Figure 9b*. The presence of several cellulolytic components in the extracellular filtrates of various micro-organisms, including *T. viride* and *M. verrucaria*, which differed in their relative activities towards native cotton, *Walseth* cellulose and CMC was shown. These workers state that the best separations were obtained using calcium phosphate gel columns, and emphasize that the method found capable of separating components from filtrates of one organism may be invalid when applied to another organism. Reference to the mode of action of some of these components is made later (Chapter VI). It should be realized that the cellulolytic components separated thus are not necessarily free from other materials; the presence of traces of a β–glucosidase in the culture filtrate of *T. viride* which, following concentration and passage down the column was present only in fraction A (*Figure 9*), was noted; similarly an amylase present in the original filtrate was found in fraction A, but it had a lower mobility than the cellulolytic component (cellulase peak in eluate 4, amylase peak in eluate 5).

Other workers have used similar techniques to study the multi-enzymatic nature of cellulolytic enzymes. Columns of alkali-swollen cellulose powder were used by Hash and King[74], who eluted an *M. verrucaria* enzyme concentrate with phosphate-citrate buffers of increasing hydrogen ion concentration and ionic strength, fifty 50 ml fractions being collected in all; the activities of these towards CMC, insoluble and soluble cellodextrins, cellobiose and an aryl β–glucoside were determined. Cellobiase activity was found to be restricted to the first few fractions, and enzymes attacking substrates of increasing chain length were eluted progressively more slowly, the fractions acting on the longest chains being eluted last. In contrast to this, Gilligan and Reese[69] found no such correlation between chain length of substrates and elution of fractions; fraction A (*Figure 9*) was equally active on celluloses of high and low degrees of polymerization (D.P.), fraction B was more active on cellulose of high D.P. and fraction CD was more active on cellulose of low D.P. In an effort to explain the divergent results of Whitaker[11], who isolated a homogeneous protein exhibiting all the properties of the crude product with the consequence that cellulase appeared to be a single enzyme, and others who postulate a multienzymatic system it was proposed[75] that in crude filtrates the cellulolytic enzymes might complex with a number of metabolic products, giving rise to a large number of complexes with cellulolytic activity. (It has been shown that cellulase proteins complex with carbohydrate moieties.) Attempts were made to devise a method to split these bound forms of cellulase. Portions of a freeze-dried powder, obtained after concentration and dialysis of a crude culture filtrate from *M. verrucaria*, were passed through a cellulose powder column using water adjusted to pH 11·0 with sodium hydroxide; the eluate was collected in 2 ml portions and assayed for activity. Two fractions were obtained, the second of which showed a four-fold increase in activity; 75 per cent of the original activity was recovered. No such separation occurred in the presence of small amounts of sodium chloride, using starch columns, or on elution at pH values of 5 to 9, while at pH 12·0 great losses in activity were experienced. It was emphasized that the question of how far the activity of the free enzyme was affected by complex formation required further investigation.

In addition to the use of aluminiferous earths, cellulose and calcium phosphate gel, as carriers in the chromatographic separation of cellulases, a recent development has been the use of ion-exchange resins. An account of their use for de-ionization purposes has been given earlier in this chapter when it was seen that the strongly acidic cation exchanger Amberlite IR–120(H) and the strongly basic anion exhanger Amberlite IRA–400(OH) were used successfully in a mixed bed column, and Amberlite IR–120(H) and Dowex 2, a strongly basic anion exchanger were used successfully in a 'buffered' column. In IR–120(H) the functional groups are sulphonic acid groups and in IRA–400(OH) and in Dowex 2 the functional groups are quaternary ammonium groups. Certain resins have been used for preparative purposes as opposed to being used purely for de-ionization. A method for the purification of *M. verrucaria* cellulase by a one-step process on an ion-exchange column has been worked out[79], but no further details are available at the moment. The use of Amberlite IRC 50 (a weakly acidic cation exchanger) in the purification of *Helix* cellulase has been mentioned, where it formed the third stage of the purification process and good recoveries were obtained. Use of this resin has also been made to separate individual enzymes present in a preparation obtained from *T. koningi*[77]. This preparation, which on ionophoresis was shown to contain a single component, showed the presence of saccharase, amylase, cellulase, carboxymethylcellulase, maltase and cellobiase activities. Treatment with Amberlite IRC–50 (H form) separated saccharase activity from carboxymethylcellulase and amylase, while treatment with Amberlite IRA–400 (Cl form) separated amylase from carboxymethylcellulase and saccharase. By ion-exchange treatment it was shown that cellobiase and carboxymethylcellulase had the same activity peaks, as also had amylase and maltase. Amberlite IRC–50 is a cross-linked methacrylic acid resin, and its functional groups are carboxylic acid groups.

No general conclusions can be reached regarding methods for the purification and separation of cellulase and related enzymes. Methods found satisfactory by one worker have been shown to

96

be of little use by other workers, even using preparations derived from the same organism. It has been shown that it is possible to alter the number of components of the cellulolytic complex by alteration of growth conditions, and it is not feasible at the present time to attempt to lay down a standard method for the purification of these enzymes. A general account of the preparation of enzymes by adsorption techniques is given elsewhere[162].

Purification by Electrophoresis

As proteins are ampholytes they migrate to one electrode or the other in an electric field; however, at a particular hydrogen ion concentration, *the isoelectric point*, no such migration occurs in the protein solution. With materials of low molecular weight (e.g. amino-acids, sugar phosphates, sugar-borate complexes) the migration is spoken of as 'ionophoresis', but in the case of the high molecular weight proteins the term 'electrophoresis' is generally used. As the various proteins have different structures and the array of component amino-acids present differing overall ionic characteristics, each protein migrates at a characteristic rate at certain pH values; it is possible, therefore, to analyze a mixture of proteins by electrophoresis, and also to carry out the analysis in a medium of almost constant composition. The classical work of Tiselius[80] has enabled proteins of closely similar compositions to be separated, although it is often necessary to investigate the electrical migration at a range of hydrogen ion concentrations. Two common methods of fractionating proteins result in either *zone* or *boundary* separation.

For the observation of the boundary separation, the protein dissolved in a buffer solution is placed in a U-tube and above it are carefully introduced layers of the buffer solution alone; the protein concentration should not be below 0·01 per cent. The electrophoresis cell is maintained at a temperature just above 0° in order to minimize the convection currents caused by the heating effects of the electrical current. The ends of the U-tube, frequently of rectangular cross section, are connected to electrode compartments containing reversible electrodes immersed in the buffer solution. The migration of the boundaries of the protein solution may be observed visually (or photographically), by ultra-violet light absorption methods in a quartz U-tube, or by observation of the refractive index of the solution as in the Toepler–Schlieren method[81], or by the Antweiler interferometry technique[82]. A beam of light passing through the U-tube horizontally will be deflected downwards at a boundary, and a camera equipped with a horizontal edge diaphragm will collect light from all parts of the U-tube except where this downward deflection falls below the diaphragm edge, so that the image of the boundary appears as a dark band. Thus, by coupling the movement of the photographic plate with that of the diaphragm edge, a record of the refractive index gradient of the whole boundary region can be obtained.

In zone electrophoresis the migrating zones are located by staining or analytical methods. The protein is adsorbed on a finely

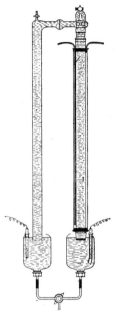

Figure 10—Porath's zone electrophoresis apparatus
(by courtesy, *Biochimica et Biophysica Acta*, 1956, **22**, p. 153)

divided powder in order to stabilize the zones during electrophoresis on a column packed with the powder. Some gels form suitable stabilizing media, but it is often difficult to elute the separated proteins from the gel if isolation of particular fractions of a mixture is required. The apparatus of Porath[83] (*Figure 10*), using a column length of 150 cm, can be used to separate a mixture containing 20–30 g of protein. The zone method does not lend itself to precise measurements of mobility, but the fractions may be collected in the order expected from their mobilities, when the latter are measured in *free* solution (i.e. without stabilizing medium), by the use of an automatic fraction collector.

The analysis of mixtures by paper electrophoresis has found widespread use in carbohydrate, amino-acid and protein fields[84]. A length (often about 30 cm) of filter paper is spotted with drops of the protein solution along an origin line about midway along and perpendicular to its length, and is then impregnated with a buffer solution. The strip of paper is then supported between two glass plates on either side of which are fitted water-cooled copper plates and a clamping device. The ends of the strip are allowed to hang over the ends of the glass plates into troughs containing the buffer solution and platinum electrodes. A direct current (of 100 to 1000 volts) is applied to the electrodes, whereupon the components of the mixture migrate along the paper strip; some electroendosmotic flow towards the cathode also occurs and the extent of this flow is measured by applying spots of a non-ionic compound (e.g. trinitrobenzene or o–nitroaniline[55]) to the origin line, and observing its migration. After a certain time (depending on the potential difference across the paper strip and the current density) the strip is removed, dried and sprayed with a specific reagent (e.g. ninhydrin solution for proteins), followed by gentle heating to reveal coloured spots. Placing the mixture on the origin line in two zones will enable the finished electrophoretogram to be cut longitudinally, one half being sprayed as above, while from the other half the areas corresponding to the detected components may be eluted or treated with some reagent in order to measure the enzyme activity present in each area. In some cases, a vertical apparatus has been used[85], simple forms of the horizontal apparatus can be recommended[86,87], while the use of such techniques in enzymology has been reviewed by Laurell[88]. It is important to choose the buffer solution carefully, too high an ionic strength may well lead to overheating of the paper strip, but on the other hand, adequate buffering capacity must be ensured during the whole period of the electrophoresis.

Electrophoresis has been applied to cellulolytic enzymes for two principal purposes:

(a) the determination of the number and enzyme activity of components in a comparatively crude preparation, and

(b) the demonstration that a purified enzyme preparation consists of a single protein, and hence it may be regarded as a 'pure' enzyme.

No extensive studies of the action of electrophoretically separated fractions on a range of substrates have been reported, and it cannot be claimed that the method has been used preparatively; however, where it is possible to remove the separated enzyme proteins from the stabilizing medium, the method could be scaled-up for use in cellulase preparation. The second purpose (*b*) will be discussed later. Free boundary electrophoresis of one per cent solutions of acetone-precipitated fractions from a culture of *Poria vaillantii* in acetate buffer (0·1M, pH 4·6 and 5·3) at 150 volts, 10 mA for 45 minutes enabled Sison, Schubert and Nord[15] to show that the fractions consisted principally of two components, one of which was practically immobile at the pH values used. The faster moving component had larger cellulase activity, while the slow component contained a cellobiase. The patterns obtained showed that, after a series of acetone fractionations, the faster moving component increased in concentration relative to the slow component; the ratio of the cellulase activities, using a CMC substrate, of the two components is shown in *Table 2*. However, it was not possible to de-

Table 2. Cellulase Activities of Electrophoretic Components

Enzyme Fraction	Component	Activity	Ratio Fast : Slow
I	Fast Slow	12·5 4·1	3·05
II	Fast Slow	4·7 1·3	3·61
III	Fast Slow	37·0 3·2	11·6

termine whether another enzyme existed with a specificity intermediate between those of cellulase and cellobiase; it must be noted that the short time period and rather high ionic strength of the buffer solutions employed may have led to some blurring of components. The free boundary method has also been used to examine the components present in an enzyme preparation from *Aspergillus oryzae*, using a veronal buffer at pH 8·6 for 3 hours with a current of 15 mA[41].

Zone electrophoresis for the separation of the cellulase components of *Myrothecium verrucaria* has been used by Miller and Blum[89] who ingeniously used a block of potato starch as the stabilizing medium in an apparatus similar to that described by Kunkel and Slater[90]. Changes in pH value at the electrodes were eliminated by circulating the cathode solution into the anode vessel by means of a pump and arranging a return flow through a siphon; the siphon consisted of an inverted-V, at the top of which a tube was attached to enable electrolysis gas to be drawn off, and so obviate the possibility of gas locks in the siphon. The crude enzyme (100 mg) in a buffer solution (usually phosphate of ionic strength 0·05 at pH 7) was placed in a slit cut crosswise near the anode end of the starch block (of size 50 × 10 × 1·3 cm); the electrophoresis was carried out at 5° for 42 hours using a potential difference across the block of 400 volts. The components separated into curved zones, and in order to overcome this difficulty in the overlapping of zones, the

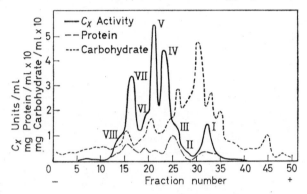

Figure 11—Distribution of protein, carbohydrate and activity in zone electrophoresis of crude cellulase at pH 7 for 42 hours at 400 volts (by courtesy, *Journal of Biological Chemistry*, 1956, **218**, p. 131)

outer 2 cm from each side of the block was cut off and discarded. The centre strip was then cut crosswise into sections one centimetre wide. Each section was extracted with buffer solution, the extracts were divided into aliquot volumes and were each assayed for protein and carbohydrate contents, and for cellulase (C_x) activity (using CMC as a substrate and the determination of reducing sugar). The distribution of these factors is shown in *Figure 11*, from which it will be observed that at least eight distinct enzyme components were present, one of which was completely separated from the others. A more extended electrophoresis was made possible, after the first run described above, by removing the anode section of the block (up to and including Component I), moving the cathode end of the block up to the anode, and adding a fresh starch block to the incomplete cathode end. Thus, there was no increase in the block length, but electrophoresis could now be continued for a further 40 hours, after which time analysis showed that Components VII and VIII were almost completely separated from the others. Improved resolution was not obtained at different pH values in the range pH 3 to 10, although at pH 3 it was suggested that none of the carbohydrate and only a fraction of the protein present in the crude enzyme extract were associated with the cellulase activity. It was observed that the removal of the 2cm edge strips brought about poor recoveries of protein and enzyme activity from the centre section, whereas carbohydrate recovery was quite high; this latter recovery was traced to the presence of amylase in the crude enzyme, and its action on the starch block. This careful work merits special consideration, and it is hoped that preparative designs of zone electrophoresis apparatus[91,92] will be utilized for the complete separation of cellulolytic components, although some prior precipitation or chromatographic procedure may still be necessary. It has been possible by zone electrophoresis to separate as many as sixteen components having cellulase (C_x) activity.

The paper electrophoresis technique has been applied by Gillespie and Woods[41,93] to the separation of the enzymes of *Aspergillus oryzae* into at least seven cellulolytic components; the movement of protein along the filter paper strip was demonstrated by staining with bromophenol blue[94]. The strip was cut into segments 1 cm wide, each segment was eluted with water, and the enzyme activity of the eluate was determined. Hash and King[74] also applied this method to culture filtrates from *Myrothecium verrucaria*, using a barbital buffer at pH 8·55 for 6 to 7 hours at a potential difference of 500 volts. Although the pattern of separation was reproducible for each filtrate, there was a large variation in both the number of cellulase components and their activities between different batches of crude enzyme. It was suggested that this variation arose from:

(i) synthesis of varying proportions of the components by the fungus due to peculiar conditions of growth,

(ii) selective adsorption of some of the enzymic components on the residual cellulose of the culture medium,

(iii) partial denaturation of some or all of the components during the preparation of the filtrate.

Electrophoresis for longer periods effected no improvement in the resolution, and some activity was lost due to the prolonged exposure to the alkaline buffer solution; however, electrophoresis at pH values of 7 or below did not permit any separation of cellulolytic components.

102

The polysaccharase activities of the Enzyme 19 (a crude extract from *Aspergillus niger*, prepared by Rohm and Haas Company, Philadelphia, U.S.A.) have been investigated recently[64]; among the methods of fractionation used was electrophoresis on strips of thick filter paper (Whatman 3 MM) impregnated with a 4 per cent alcoholic zein solution. The dialysed, lyophilized crude enzyme (30 mg) was placed on the origin line, the paper strip was impregnated with a diluted McIlvaine buffer at pH 5·5, placed between a pair of Teflon films, and covered with a water-cooled glass plate. Electrophoresis was carried out at voltages between 225 and 400 volts (the maximum being *c.* 8V/cm) for 6 to 7 hours with a current in the range 3·5 to 5·0 mA. The distribution of enzymes on the dried strip was found by placing narrow strips, cut lengthwise from the electrophoretogram, in contact with substrate agar plates; for cellulase action, CMC of DS 0·84 was used as substrate. The agar plates were incubated at 37° for 18 hours; liquefaction of the gel enabled the cellulolytic components to be recognized, and the corresponding sections could be cut from the remainder of the electrophoretogram. The enzymes were eluted from the paper with acetate or phosphate buffer solutions, their activities being then determined by both the agar cup-plate method[95] and reducing sugar estimation after incubation of the eluate with CMC at pH 4·5. Complete separation of a given enzyme component from all others (e.g. *a*–amylase, cellulase, pentosanase, polygalacturonase, and protease) was not obtained, but the best patterns were obtained using buffer solutions of acid pH values in which most of the components were either immobile or negatively charged. The cellulases present were resolved into two components, one of which did not migrate on electrophoresis, while the other occurred in an elongated region which was composed of a negatively charged fraction. It was noted that cellulase migrated more rapidly on zein-impregnated paper than on untreated paper. The method enabled the almost clear separation of cellulase and pentosanase from polygalacturonase to be accomplished. Excellent accounts of the different methods of electrophoresis have been given in the recent book edited by Bier[96].

DEGREE OF PURIFICATION

The course of purification of any enzyme must be followed by determinations of the amount of enzymic activity at each stage, and an estimation of the total recovery of activity during the overall purification procedure. The amount of enzyme used in such analyses must, of course, vary with both source and stage of purification;

as cellulases are principally (or even wholly) protein in nature, the activity determined is referred to unit weight of protein or of protein nitrogen. The enzyme extract must therefore be analysed for protein content, frequently by the classical Kjeldahl nitrogen analysis; as most proteins contain approximately 16 per cent nitrogen, the protein content is calculated by multiplying the Kjeldahl nitrogen value by 6·25[52]. It must be emphasized that this method is not absolute as the nitrogen content of proteins varies considerably. Another method, which depends on the intense ultra-violet absorption of the aromatic amino-acids of proteins at 260 and 280 mμ, has been used frequently provided that nucleic acids are absent; otherwise, the equation given by Layne[97] should be used to determine the protein content:

$$\text{Protein concentration (mg/ml)} = 1·55D_{280} - 0·76D_{260},$$

where D_{280} and D_{260} are the optical densities of the solution at 280 and 260 mμ respectively. Again, the method depends on the composition of the protein examined. Chemical methods for protein estimation are the biuret method[98], the Folin-Ciocalteu biuret–phosphotungstate–phosphomolybdate reaction (determining 70 to 700 μg protein per ml)[99], and the turbidimetric methods, notably the potassium ferrocyanide–acetic acid precipitation[100]; however, turbidimetric methods do not differentiate between protein and nucleic acids and care must be exercised in their use, particularly when examining intracellular enzymes. Indeed, any technique used for protein analysis must be carefully considered, especially for interference occurring from the presence of precipitants and other reagents used in the purification procedure; for example, incomplete removal of widely-used precipitants, such as ammonium sulphate, will totally invalidate protein values based on many nitrogen analyses; (de-ionization and dialysis methods have been discussed earlier in this chapter).

Few complete schedules for the enhancement of cellulase purity at each stage and the recovery of activity have been reported; the protocol of Whitaker given earlier in *Figure 7* is a model for the tabulation of such data; Nisizawa[12], and also Myers and Northcote[5] have recorded the enrichment of cellulase obtained during fractionation. Many different substrates have been used in the determination of cellulase activity, including insoluble materials like plant, animal and bacterial celluloses, swollen and regenerated celluloses, and cellodextrins; soluble substrates have included the sodium salt of carboxymethylcellulose (CMC), hydroxyethylcellulose (HEC), ethyl hydroxyethylcellulose (EHEC), methylcellulose, sodium cellulose sulphate and lower cellodextrins. The principal substrates have been recorded in Chapter III, but this list is by no means exhaustive. The most common method for the determination of of activity, with practically all substrates, is the determination of the reducing sugar liberated during enzymic hydrolysis, while the hydrolysis of soluble substrates, which form viscous solutions in water, lends itself to viscometric study. The number of assay methods is legion, but most of them are based on the following procedures:

1. Increase in reducing sugar value.
2. Effect on viscosity of soluble cellulose derivatives.
3. Loss in weight of insoluble substrates.
4. Turbidimetry with a cellulose suspension.
5. Oxygen uptake during the enzymic oxidation of glucose produced by hydrolysis.
6. Decrease in mechanical properties of fibres or films.
7. Changes in bi-refringence of films.

Increase in Reducing Sugar Value

The methods of determining reducing end-groups in sugars are nearly all empirical, the reactions occurring being generally poorly understood and frequently non-stoichiometric. The reducing value of cellulose itself is small, and in the case of insoluble substrates, the degraded polymer can be removed from the enzyme assay system by centrifugation or filtration. In some cases, the protein must be removed also, often by precipitation with trichloroacetic acid or a zinc sulphate-barium hydroxide treatment[101]. Both volumetric and colorimetric methods have been used in the study of cellulase activity; classical methods, like the Willstätter-Schudel hypoiodite oxidation[102] and the Benedict copper method[103], have formed the basis of many recent modifications. Hypoiodite oxidation of the reducing sugars formed from the enzymic hydrolysis of CMC has been used by Jermyn[104], who noted that the total hydrolysis of 1 ml of a one per cent CMC solution would liberate reducing groups equivalent to 1 ml $0 \cdot 1$N iodine solution. Hence, the iodine consumed by a hydrolysate under alkaline conditions would lead to an approximate estimate of the percentage of glycosidic linkages in the substrate broken during hydrolysis. Other modifications of the hypoiodite method[105] have been used by Holden and Tracey[76] and by Festenstein[24]. The importance of standardizing the alkaline conditions has been emphasized[106,107], while the method has been studied further by Colbran and Nevell[108]; this method demands the presence of rather large amounts of reducing sugar (e.g. 0·1 to 4 mg/ml glucose).

The reduction of alkaline ferricyanide, originally Folin's method[109], has been applied as a colorimetric method[110] to study the action of *Teredo* cellulase on a regenerated cellulose. Protein was removed from the enzyme–cellulose–phosphate buffer digest by precipitation with trichloroacetic acid, while salts and glycogen (arising from the *Teredo* extract) were precipitated with ethanol before analysis of the final supernatant liquid; the colouration obtained in the ferricyanide method, measured at 690 mμ, was compared with that given by solutions containing 1–9 μg glucose[111]. The final Prussian blue precipitate often requires stabilization, and both Gum Ghatti and sodium monolauryl sulphate have been used; a typical procedure has been given in an account of the determination of reducing end groups in amylose[112]. Another similar method[113] has been applied to the determination of reducing sugar produced by the action of rumen cellulolytic enzymes on CMC[24]. The yellow-orange colour produced in the phenol-sulphuric acid reaction with sugars is stable for several hours; the absorption value can be measured at 490 mμ for hexoses and at 480 mμ for pentoses, and the method has been recommended for use at glucose concentrations of 5 to 35 μg/ml with an accuracy of more than 5 per cent[114]. The assay of reducing end groups by cyanohydrin formation has not been applied to cellulase-produced hydrolysates, although the determination of radioactivity of the resultant cyanohydrin prepared from Na[14]CN is a promising procedure, the accuracy of which approaches that of the copper reduction methods[115]. Where enzymic hydrolysates contain mixtures of sugars (e.g. glucose and cellobiose), the interpretation of results from periodate oxidation and borohydride reduction methods becomes very difficult. In all colorimetric finishes the intensity of the colour produced must obey Beer's law, although it is frequently found that this simple check has been overlooked or only assumed. In general, the reducing sugars are produced in dilute aqueous solution and the application of methods requiring known and often very low water contents does not produce the required accuracy; for qualitative tests, many such reagents are available, and have been reviewed by Hough[116].

Copper Reduction Methods.—The reduction of cupric salts to cuprous oxide by aldehydes has been utilized by many workers for the estimation of reducing sugars. Since the advent of the well-known Fehling's solution, much effort has been directed to produce a stable copper solution and to the composition of the several reagents. Stability of the copper solution has been conferred, to some degree,

106

by preparing the cupric solution from either sulphate or acetate with the addition of potassium hydroxide, carbonates, citrates, tartrates, phosphates or ammonia. The extent of the reduction is affected by the alkalinity; although lower alkalinities give higher reducing values and so enable smaller amounts of sugar to be detected, the rate of oxidation declines, and so the time of heating of the solution is prolonged. Other factors affecting the extent of reduction are the nature of the sugar, the temperature and time of heating, the degree of aeration (stirring), and even the type of stabilizing agent (e.g. D–, L– or *meso*-tartrate). Shaffer and Somogyi[117] studied these variables, and suggested several reagents for the iodometric determination of reducing sugars; a further review of these variables and the many copper reagents available has been given by Noggle[118]. The original Shaffer-Hartmann technique[119] has now been largely superseded by methods drawn up by Somogyi, who has made a detailed study of the alkaline copper reagent, finally recommending a mixture of cupric sulphate, sodium carbonate, sodium bicarbonate, sodium sulphate and Rochelle salt, in which the quantity of the last-named salt is kept low, in order to minimize both the reducing effect of tartrate in hot solutions and the deviation from Beer's law produced by tartrate[120]. The colorimetric method devised by Nelson[121] and revised by Somogyi[120] is capable of detecting as little as 5 μg of glucose, while the iodometric method of Somogyi[120] is slightly less sensitive; both methods can be used in the range 0·01 to 3·0 mg of reducing sugar (as glucose). The following principal cuprimetric procedures have been used in cellulase studies:

  (i) Benedict's method[103] used by Hirsch[122],
 (ii) Shaffer-Hartmann method[119] used by Nisizawa[123], Kilroe-Smith[42], and Whistler and Smart[50],
(iii) Shaffer-Somogyi method[117] used by Duncan et al.[29], in the form of a further modification[124],
 (iv) Somogyi method[125] used by Duncan et al.[29], and Whitaker[11].
  (v) Somogyi method[120] used by Aitken et al.[126],
 (vi) Nelson's method modified by Somogyi[120] used by Thomas[10], Duncan et al.[29], and Festenstein[24].

Comparisons of some of these methods have been made; the presence of sugars other than glucose has a profound effect on the reducing values obtained. With both cuprimetric and hypoiodite methods the reducing value for cellobiose was approximately 53 per cent of that obtained for an equal weight of glucose, whereas a ferricyanide method[113] gave the much higher value of 86 per cent. The enzymic hydrolysis of CMC was assayed by both cuprimetric and hypoiodite methods giving similar results in terms of glucose produced, but the ferricyanide method gave values two or three times higher[24]. This rejection of ferricyanide methods has been justified by the work of Holden, Pirie and Tracey[76,127]. In general, the best of these methods appears to be the Nelson-Somogyi colorimetric procedure.

It is sometimes important to measure the total carbohydrate content, especially where it is felt that the enzyme extract itself may contain carbohydrate associated with the enzyme protein. Hash and King[128] used the anthrone method[129] for total sugars, and the Nelson-Somogyi procedure for reducing sugar values. Another occasionally used procedure[89] is the colorimetric method based on the reaction of glucose with orcinol in the presence of sulphuric acid[130].

Reduction of Dinitrosalicylic Acid.—The final reducing sugar determination to be discussed is the colorimetric procedure based on the reduction of 3:5–dinitrosalicyclic acid by sugars giving rise to a brown colour. The method was first used in enzyme work by Sumner and Howell[131,132], but it has been applied extensively to the enzymatic hydrolysis of cellulose. A typical procedure for this assay is given below using a soluble substrate, but precipitated celluloses, alkali-swollen cotton linters, ground cotton sliver, and phosphoric acid swollen filter paper powder have all been used[133,134]; in general, each assay should contain approximately 50 mg substrate per 10 ml digest; after incubation the digest is filtered and aliquot volumes (1 ml) are removed from the filtrate for reducing sugar determinations.

Reagents

McIlvaine buffer solution of suitable pH value (e.g. pH 5·0 (see *Table 4* later)).

Sodium carboxymethylcellulose (CMC) solution (1% w/v), filtered through a sintered glass crucible (No. 1 porosity). Suitable sources of CMC are CMC 50T (Hercules Powder Co. Inc.), or Cellofas B low viscosity grade (Imperial Chemical Industries Ltd.); these have degrees of substitution of *c.* 0·52 and 0·46 respectively.

Enzyme Extract: usually a cell-free culture filtrate or a partially purified enzyme; nitrogen content (protein) is determined as described earlier.

DNS Solution: add 3:5–dinitrosalicylic acid (6·3 g) and sodium hydroxide solution (262 ml, 2N) to a hot solution of Rochelle salt (182 g) in water (500 ml). The mixture is stirred and heated until DNS is dissolved, when redistilled phenol (5 g) and anhydrous sodium bisulphite (5 g) are added. The solution is cooled and the volume brought to one litre with water. This solution will remain stable for many months if protected from light and carbon dioxide in a cool place.

Method

(*a*) To 100 ml CMC solution add 20 ml buffer solution and 60 ml water, mix well. Transfer 9 ml volumes of the mixture to test tubes containing 1 ml of enzyme extract. Mix and immediately remove 1 ml portion (in duplicate) to a dry test tube for immediate reducing sugar determination (as in *C*) at zero time.

(*b*) Incubate the remainder of the solution at a suitable temperature; for example, 50° for 2 hours.

(*c*) To the portions taken at zero time (immediately after mixing as in *A*), and to 1 ml volumes from the incubated digest add 1 ml water, cool quickly to room temperature and add 1 ml DNS solution. Mix and place the tubes in a boiling water bath for 5 minutes. Cool the tubes and make up with water to a suitable volume.

(*d*) Measure the optical density at 540mμ of the solutions photometrically (using a green filter, as filter No. 540 in an Evelyn colorimeter, No. 54 in a Klett-Summerson colorimeter, or an Ilford No. 605 in the Hilger Spekker absorptiometer).

(*e*) Construct a calibration curve using an aqueous solution of glucose (0·05 to 1 mg in 1 ml) and applying the above procedure, replacing the digest by the glucose solution.

(*f*) Record the quantity (in mg) of reducing sugar produced during the incubation period, allowing for any present at zero time.

The activity (C_x enzyme when CMC is used as a substrate) is recorded as the amount of reducing sugar produced (as glucose, in mg) per unit volume (ml) of enzyme extract, or per unit weight of protein or of protein nitrogen. For example, Reese and Levinson[13] define a C_x unit as the amount of enzyme which catalyses the production of 0·40 mg of reducing sugar, as glucose, per ml of the reaction mixture under specified conditions. The enzyme extract, after testing for inhibition, may be preserved by the addition of Thiomersalate* solution (1 ml 1% w/v per 100 ml enzyme solution), and storage at 2° until required. If the enzyme extract has a deep colour the DNS method is unsuitable, but lightly coloured solutions can sometimes be assayed, provided that a blank experiment containing the enzyme extract with its activity destroyed (e.g. by boiling) can be carried out at the same time.

Effect on Viscosity of soluble Cellulose Derivatives

Although many water soluble cellulose derivatives have been used in the determination of cellulase activity, the procedure employed must take into account the following factors:

(i) the degree of substitution (DS) of the derivative, and its effect on activity; this aspect is discussed in Chapter VI,

(ii) the influence of buffer solutions on the viscosity of a solution of the derivative,

* sodium ethyl mercurithiosalicylate.

109

(iii) the possibility of applying a second method of measuring the extent of hydrolysis (e.g. reducing sugar value) to the same derivative,

(iv) the influence of concentration of the derivative on the relative viscosity of its solution,

(v) the effect of other substances present in either enzyme extract or cellulose derivative (e.g. other proteins, trace metals, electrolytes, peptising agents) on the viscosity.

In many cases these effects have not been studied, but the method has been widely used to measure the C_x activity of enzyme extracts. Often a compromise between utility and accuracy has to be made; for example, the viscosity of CMC is dependent on the ionic strength of the solution, whereas the viscosity of ethylhydroxyethylcellulose solutions is not so dependent[10]. Methylcellulose does not accord with factor (iii) above, the conventional methods of reducing sugar determination not being applicable[135]. A wide range of viscometers are available, but convenient types are the No. 2 Ostwald U-tube (to BS 188:1957), the PCL Suspended Level Viscometer (Polymer Consultants Ltd., Colchester, England), or the Hoeppler Falling-ball Viscometer.

The viscosity (η) of the solution can be calculated from the known constants of the viscometer used and can be compared with the viscosity (η_o) of the solvent (i.e. the buffer solution):

$$\text{Specific viscosity} = \eta_{sp} = \frac{\eta - \eta_o}{\eta_o} = \frac{\eta}{\eta_o} - 1,$$

$$\text{then specific fluidity} = \phi_{sp} = \frac{1}{\eta_{sp}}$$

For determinations of the degree of polymerization, the intrinsic viscosity will be required:

$$[\eta] = \left(\frac{\eta_{sp}}{C} \right)_{c \to 0}$$

where C = concentration of substrate.

However, for comparative measurements during enzyme fractionation or among different enzyme sources, the course of hydrolysis is given by the relation between specific fluidity and time, since during the first few hours of hydrolysis this relationship is linear. Hultin[136,137] has derived, on theoretical grounds, the following expression for the enzyme hyaluronidase:

$$E = C^2 \frac{d\phi_{sp}}{dt}$$

110

where E = enzyme concentration in units per g reaction mixture and C = substrate concentration in g per g reaction mixture. Thus, in the presence of excess substrate a linear relationship between E and the rate of change of specific fluidity is to be expected. However, Thomas[10] found an appreciable deviation from linearity, and showed that

$$E \propto \left(\frac{d\phi_{sp}}{dt}\right)^x$$

and thus $x = \dfrac{d \log E}{d \log \dfrac{d\phi_{sp}}{dt}}$

From studies of the cellulase-catalysed hydrolysis of various substrates the values of x derived by various workers are shown in *Table 3*.

Table 3. Fluidity equation $E \propto \left(\dfrac{d\phi_{sp}}{dt}\right)^x$ — values of *x*

Enzyme source	Substrate	x	Reference
Stachybotrys atra	CMC	$1 \cdot 11 \pm 0 \cdot 01$	10
S. atra	EHEC	$1 \cdot 48 \pm 0 \cdot 05$	10
Barley	EHEC	$1 \cdot 5$	7
Barley	Barley β–glucan	$1 \cdot 0$	138

A major difficulty in these methods is the preparation of solutions of reproducible concentration and initial specific viscosity. To this end, Thomas[10] modified Hultin's equation to

$$E = \left(\eta_{sp}\right)^y_{t=0} \left(\frac{d\phi_{sp}}{dt}\right)^x$$

and determined x as $1 \cdot 11$ and y as $1 \cdot 25 \pm 0 \cdot 07$ for CMC solutions, or x as $1 \cdot 5$ and y as $1 \cdot 5$ for EHEC solutions. Although such relationships permit a reasonable comparison of cellulase activities even when assayed at different substrate concentrations, in view of the complexity of the calculations required it is preferable to compare activities at a single substrate concentration where possible; this procedure has been followed by Levinson and Reese[139], and by Enebo[26]. The latter worker has also investigated the influence of enzyme concentration, and found that it was desirable to work with an enzyme concentration resulting in the value of $\dfrac{d\phi_{sp}}{dt}$ being as close to $0 \cdot 01$ as possible.

111

Using CMC solutions as substrates, the choice of buffer solution has varied, but in general McIlvaine's citrate-phosphate buffer is a good first choice, but care must be taken to examine the effect of ionic strength and the components of the buffer solution on the cellulase activity; the composition of this buffer solution is given in *Table 4*, and covers the range pH 2·6 to 7·0[140]. A higher pH value

Table 4. *McIlvaine's Buffer Solutions*
(by courtesy, *Journal of Biological Chemistry*, 1921, **49**, p. 183)

pH value	A	B	pH value	A	B
7·0	43·6	6·5	4·6	23·3	26·7
6·8	40·9	9·1	4·4	22·2	27·8
6·6	36·4	13·6	4·2	20·6	29·4
6·4	34·6	15·4	4·0	19·3	30·7
6·2	33·1	16·9	3·8	17·7	32·3
6·0	32·1	17·9	3·6	16·1	33·9
5·8	30·3	19·7	3·4	14·1	35·9
5·6	29·0	21·0	3·2	12·3	37·7
5·4	27·8	22·2	3·0	10·2	39·8
5·2	26·7	23·3	2·8	7·8	42·2
5·0	25·7	24·3	2·6	5·4	44·6
4·8	24·8	25·2			

Solution 1: 0·2M solution of disodium hydrogen phosphate.
Solution 2: 0·1M solution of citric acid.
Mix A ml of solution 1 with B ml of solution 2, and dilute to 100 ml with water.

range can be obtained by the use of phosphate buffer (pH 5·7 to 8·0). The use of preservatives during enzymic hydrolysis also requires some consideration; the inhibition of certain cellulases[141] by organic mercury compounds makes it imperative to question the use of such compounds as sodium ethyl mercurithiosalicylate (*Merthiolate, Thiomersalate*). Where short periods of incubation are envisaged, the preparation of buffer and CMC solutions with sterile water in sterile apparatus is probably the best procedure. The volumes of solutions to be used will depend on the enzymic activity of the extract to be tested, but the following example presents the essential details:

Reagents

CMC solution: suitable substrates are Cellofas B (Imperial Chemical Industries Ltd.) (available in high, medium or low viscosity grades) or NaCMC 70M (Hercules Powder Co. Inc.). The degree of substitution of these substrates can be determined by a colorimetric method[142]. A stock solution containing CMC (1–1·5% w/v) is prepared by shaking an aqueous suspension of the powder for 6 hours, removing any undissolved material by filtration through glass wool under reduced pressure. This solution is stable for several weeks, stored at 2°. Depending on the viscometer to be used, the stock solution is diluted with buffer solution, so that, when the mixture (100 ml) is added to the enzyme solution, the viscosity can be measured conveniently (e.g. a flow time of approximately 100 seconds in the Ostwald No. 2 viscometer).

Enzyme solution: the cell-free culture filtrate or other enzyme source, diluted with water, if necessary, to produce suitable changes in viscosity of the CMC solution under the conditions chosen by prior experiment.

Method

CMC solution (100 ml) is mixed with the enzyme solution (1 ml); a a sample is immediately withdrawn and its viscosity (at 25°) is determined, giving a zero time value. The remainder of the solution is incubated at the required temperature (e.g. 35°), and aliquot volumes are removed at 1 hour, 2 hours, and every hour up to 8 hours, cooled, and the viscosity determined. The course of the hydrolysis is plotted as the specific fluidity $\left(\dfrac{1}{\eta_{sp}}\right)$ against time. The slope of this line (linear during short incubation periods) is taken as a measure of the enzymic activity. If possible, it should be arranged that the initial specific viscosity (at zero time) is the same in each series of experiments.

Loss in Weight of Insoluble Substrates

The hydrolysis of partially crystalline celluloses leads to a crystalline residue (crystallites) and the production of reducing sugars. In the case of the enzymic attack on cotton, ramie, bacterial or animal celluloses the amount of reducing sugar produced is small; it may therefore be more convenient to remove the unattacked material by a standard procedure, and to find the weight of the dried residue. Thus, changes in cotton have been investigated by the action of a commercial preparation (Enzyme 19AP, Rohm and Haas, Philadelphia, U.S.A.) from *Aspergillus niger* on ground samples of purified and crude cotton[143]. In this study the following conditions were considered optima:

> Substrate concentration (cotton) 100 mg
> Enzyme preparation concentration 6 g per 100 ml
> pH value of solution (acetate buffer) 4·5
> Incubation conditions 5 hr/50°

The unattacked residue was filtered on to a fine porosity sintered glass crucible, water washed, and dried at 105° ± 1° for at least 4 hours; it was found that the addition of a wetting agent (Aerosol) before enzymic attack had no effect on cellulase activity, but the addition enabled more reproducible values to be obtained.

Walseth[144] used a similar method in examining the cellulase activities of eleven commercial preparations at two pH values using acid-swollen cotton linters (swollen for 2 hours at 2° in 85% H_3PO_4 followed by extensive washing) as a substrate. A suitable antiseptic for use during incubation was 2–chloro–4–phenylphenol (*Dowicide D*) at a final concentration of 0·01 per cent. Walseth devised 5 hour- and 16 hour-tests using the conditions shown in *Table 5*. The enzyme extracts were prepared from the commercial

Table 5. *Walseth's Conditions for Cellulase Determination*
(by courtesy, *Technical Association of the Pulp and Paper Industry*, 1952, **35**, p. T.229)

	5 hr. test	16 hr. test
Cellulose (oven dry weight) g	0·58–0·60	0·28–0·30
Cellulose concentration g/100 ml soln.	3·00	1·00
Enzyme concentration g solids/100 ml soln.	1·00	0·60
pH value (Walpole acetate buffer)	4·5	4·5
Ionic strength (acetate)	0·160M	0·133M
Temperature of incubation	47°	47°
Time of incubation	5 hr.	16 hr.

samples by dissolution in cold water and filtration, and the solids content of the solutions was determined by drying small aliquot volumes over calcium chloride *in vacuo*. If only one test was envisaged, a sealed bottle was used for the incubation, otherwise the antiseptic was added. The bottle was rotated in a thermostat bath, and after the appropriate time the contents were filtered on to a tared sintered glass crucible (porosity M or C); after washing, the residue was dried at 105°, cooled and weighed. The loss in weight of acid-swollen cotton varied from 1·4 to 44 per cent at pH 4·5 and from 0·7 to 15·9 per cent at pH 6·5, using the 5-hour test. It was suggested that the 5-hour test was useful as an index of the activity of extracts, while the 16-hour test gave an indication of the reactivity of various celluloses.

The cellulolytic activity of rumen micro-organisms has been determined by Halliwell using a weight-loss method[22]; dewaxed cotton fibres, filter paper powder, a hydrocellulose, and phosphoric acid swollen cotton were used as substrates. The insoluble cellulose (30 to 50 mg) was added to a carbon dioxide-saturated sodium bicarbonate and salts buffer solution to give a pH value of 6·8 in an assay tube which could be closed with a Bunsen valve. The total volume (8 ml), containing the enzyme solution (1 ml), was incubated statically at 37° for about 40 hours. The residual cellulose was removed by filtration on to a sintered glass crucible (porosity 3), and was washed successively with 5 ml volumes of 3·8N hydrochloric acid, 0·7N ammonia solution, 1% (w/v) Teepol XL*, and distilled ethanol (10 ml), with a water wash between each solvent; finally, the residue was dried at 100° for 16 hours, cooled and weighed. Corrections were applied, where necessary, for apparent 'endogenous cellulose' of the enzyme source; in the case of rumen precipitated organisms, this was less than 4 per cent of the weight of the cellulose used as a substrate. The washing procedure employed overcame the difficulties usually encountered in the slow filtration of such solutions. Careful choice of substrate must be made for weight-loss determinations, as cellulose containing other insoluble polysaccharides may lead to erroneous cellulase activities; in such cases, however, the reducing sugar methods may give even more spurious results, the small overall amounts of reducing sugars produced possibly having their origin in non-cellulosic materials, such as other glucans, mannans or xylans. The occurrence of water soluble pentosans in such common substrates as filter paper powder has been noticed[22,145]. In this connection, it must also be noted that some enzyme stimulators or inhibitors (e.g. sodium fluoride) may have an action on polysaccharases present other than cellulase, and again a false impression of the degree of cellulolysis is obtained. The cellulase unit of Halliwell[22] was defined as *the minimum amount of enzyme which in an extract or suspension* produces *c. 70% cellulolysis under standard conditions*. The temperature and time of drying both the original cellulose and the final residue are very important in view of the hygroscopic nature of cellulosic substrates; in general, the oven-drying procedure (e.g. 105° for 4 hours) is to be recommended.

The weight-loss method has been extended by Halliwell[146] to give a colorimetric finish. The residual cellulose, after washing as described above, is dissolved in acid dichromate solution under standard conditions, and the excess dichromate is determined colorimetrically against carefully prepared 'blank' solutions; alternatively, the excess dichromate may be determined iodometrically. These methods make it possible to determine cellulose equivalent to 0·1 to 1·4 mg glucose; an even more sensitive method has been developed by Dearing[147].

Turbidimetry

The gradual hydrolysis of insoluble substrates gives rise to suspensions with decreasing optical densities, and the turbidimetric method,

* Teepol XL—a registered trade mark of Shell Chemicals Ltd.

together with reducing sugar and weight-loss determinations, has been used by Newell[148] in a study of the cellulases of certain *Mollusca*. The cellulolytic activities of culture filtrates from several *Fusaria* were assayed by their action on regenerated filter paper[149] suspended in Sørensen's phosphate buffer at 37° and between pH 5·0 and 7·5. Estimations of the density of the suspension were made after incubation for 0, 4, 16, 22, 28 and 40 hours with the aid of the Hilger Spekker Absorptiometer using H2 neutral filters. The increase in percentage light transmission with time was taken as an indication of the cellulase activity of the culture filtrate tested[150]. Using a similar procedure with cellulose precipitated from cuprammonium hydroxide solution as a substrate and incubation with culture filtrates from various *Tricholoma* species, Norkrans[151] correlated changes in the extinction values, determined in white light, with the amounts of reducing sugar produced and the changes in the degree of polymerization of the cellulose residue.

Other Methods for Estimating Cellulase Activity

The dehydrogenation of glucose in the presence of the enzyme *notatin* (see Chapter I) can be used to measure the rate of formation of reducing sugar; a suitable method has been described by Levinson, Mandels and Reese[152], and this paper also demonstrates the method for determining the individual sugars in a cellobiose-glucose mixture with the aid of notatin and a β–glucosidase. Other very sensitive procedures have been described utilising notatin[153,154]. The decrease in certain mechanical properties caused by the hydrolysis of insoluble substrates has been used in cellulase work, notably by Fåhraeus[155] who measured the tensile strength of a cellophane strip before and after enzymic attack; other workers[156] have determined the decrease in bursting strength of a cellophane film. The measurement of the breaking strength of cellulosic fibres and of the extension at break has been used frequently in the examination of the rotting of textile fibres[157–159]; in enzyme studies this method has been applied to cotton[160], although such methods are not as sensitive to small changes in the substrate as the reducing sugar and viscosimetric procedures.

In cellulose films the orientation of the cellulose chains is not completely random and the film exhibits bi-refringence, and some change in this property would be expected during hydrolysis. Thomas[10] examined this change as a possible method for assaying cellulase preparations. The cellophane film was placed in a glass dish and was brought to focus in the eyepiece of a polarizing microscope fitted with a Berek compensator. The compensation angles (a and b) were measured and the difference ($2i$) was used to calculate the retardation (Γ), enabling the bi-refringence (B) to be determined from the equation

$$\log \Gamma = \log Bl = \log C + \log f(i)$$

where l = thickness of the film, C = compensator plate constant and $\log f(i)$ is the logarithmic function of the semi-difference (i) found from the manufacturer's tables. Using culture filtrates from *Stachybotrys atra*, the rate of change of birefringence was very low, and this was overcome, to some extent, by shaking the cellophane disc during incubation with the enzyme solution. The method requires only very small amounts of both substrate and enzyme, and as the cellophane disc is not damaged in the assay procedure, progressive changes in the same disc can be followed. The technique is relatively insensitive, and the difficulties associated with obtaining a disc of uniform thickness or of measuring compensation angles on exactly the same very small area of disc do not commend the method. However, it is one of the few techniques in which one of the earliest changes in decomposition, the breakdown in the orientation of cellulose chains, may be observed and measured.

CRITERIA OF ENZYME PURITY

In view of the wide range of possible substrates for cellulases, the criterion of 'one substrate–one enzyme' cannot be applied directly. However, many cellulases have a specificity of a higher order than that of the β–glucosidases, although the exact point at which a β–glucosidase can also be regarded as a cellulase is not well defined. The crystallization of enzymes in recognizable crystal form has long been a method of assessing purity. Relatively few crystalline cellulases are known and the modern techniques of electrophoresis and ultracentrifugation supply other criteria necessary for ascertaining if cellulase is a single protein, and whether highly purified preparations contain only a single entity. The action of cellulases on various substrates is discussed in Chapter VI, but, in general, very few such enzymes exhibit a high degree of specificity. Indeed, of recent years, only one cellulase devoid of action in the hydrolysis of xylan has been recorded[5], and even the pure cellulases of Whitaker[11] and Nisizawa[12] catalyse a wide range of hydrolyses.

Electrophoretic Studies

Whitaker[11] found that his 'initial extract' (see *Figure 7*, p. 87) showed several components on moving boundary electrophoresis at pH 6·8 in phosphate buffer of ionic strength 0·2, using a protein concentration of 0·61 per cent; one component moved very slowly, another had intermediate mobility, while at least two minor components migrated rapidly. After purification to give a specific activity twice as great as in the initial extract, he found that the cellulolytic protein was electrophoretically homogeneous at pH values of 6·82, 5·03 and 4·33; these pH values were above, close to, and below the isoelectric point of the protein, respectively. The time of electrophoresis to obtain these sharp boundaries was around 200 minutes. This evidence for the existence of a single cellulolytic component has been the subject of much controversy. The snail cellulase of Myers and Northcote[5] had a specific activity five times as great as that of the starting material, but this enzyme was not electrophoretically homogeneous, in spite of such closely related substrates to cellulose as xylan and methyl–β–cellobioside not being hydrolysed. Miller and Blum[89] felt that the most probable reason for Whitaker's observation of a single component, as compared with the multiple components found by them, was the use of short distances of migration. It will be recalled that Miller and Blum used zone electrophoresis in a starch block, and here the distance moved by the enzymes was some forty times that observed by Whitaker. They regarded as less likely the possibility that Whitaker's single component arose from different conditions under which the enzyme was synthesized; less likely, too, was the possibility that the enzyme was fractionated by the precipitation methods used, since such procedures do not usually succeed in bringing about a sharp separation of closely related enzyme proteins.

In reply to these contentions, Thomas and Whitaker[161] carried out zone electrophoresis on both glass fibre paper and filter paper supports using quantities up to 5 mg of protein from Whitaker's purified and crude enzymes at pH 7 in phosphate buffer of ionic strength 0·2, and with potential differences around 350 volts for periods up to 270 minutes. At least seven protein components were located in the crude enzyme, but only one of these had cellulolytic activity; although this component exhibited some 'tailing' on filter paper, it occurred as a compact zone on glass fibre paper. The purified enzyme, on paper electrophoresis, also showed only one cellulolytic protein component. This component was active in the hydrolysis of cello-oligosaccharides containing two to six glucose units, of a cellodextrin with a degree of polymerization (DP) of 24, and also of a swollen cellulose of average DP 1000. The enzyme preparations of Miller and Blum contained approximately equal amounts of protein and an electrophoretically heterogeneous polysaccharide, and Whitaker advances this as a reason for their multiplicity of enzymes. Thomas[10] submitted a cellulase preparation from

Stachybotrys atra to paper electrophoresis at five pH values, and reached the conclusion that his enzyme concentrate consisted of at least three proteins, and one or possibly two carbohydrates. The neutral, cellulolytic protein component was shown to be associated, probably in the form of a complex, with the non-adsorbed carbohydrate; the complex showed no mobility between pH 3 and 10. Moving boundary electrophoresis at pH 8·54 in a veronal buffer solution of ionic strength 0·22 showed a similar heterogeneity in the enzyme concentrate; in addition to some immobile component, at least three anodic components could be distinguished. It may be that the cellulase of *Myrothecium verrucaria*, like that of *Stachybotrys atra*, forms stable complexes with polysaccharides and other metabolic products in the culture medium. Enebo[26] has carried out electrophoresis of a freeze-dried preparation from an ethanol fractionation of the culture medium of *Clostridium thermocellulaseum* on a starch column; among the five protein components detected, only one showed cellulase activity; however, the adsorption of this enzyme on filter paper led to the conclusion that although the major part of the enzyme preparation was easily adsorbed, some part of the enzyme cannot be adsorbed, even on excess filter paper. From this work it cannot be said that Enebo advances satisfactory evidence for or against Whitaker's unienzymatic hypothesis. In conclusion, the proof of the multiplicity of enzymes in purified preparations must await the complete separation of components from each other, and from contaminants, such as polysaccharides, which may not be entirely inactive towards the enzyme proteins.

Ultracentrifuge Studies

In this field, only one report has been noticed, and again Whitaker[11] showed that his purified cellulase gave a single component in the pattern obtained in the ultracentrifuge (Spinco Model E) at a speed of 60,000 r.p.m. for 32 mins., using an acetate buffer solution of the enzyme at pH 5·03 and an ionic strength of 0·2. The controversy between multi-enzymatic and uni-enzymatic mechanisms for the catalysis of cellulose hydrolysis still goes undetermined, but it is to be hoped that mutual practical collaboration between the various workers may overcome this dilemma.

REFERENCES

1. WEIDENHAGEN, *Methoden der Fermentforschung*, ed. Bamann and Myrbäck, 1941, p. 1903, Georg Thieme, Leipzig.
2. KARRER, *Kolloidzschr.* 1930, **52**, p. 304.
3. TRAGER, *Biochem. J.* 1932, **26**, p. 1762.

4. BOYNTON AND MILLER, *J. biol. Chem.* 1927, **75**, p. 613.
5. MYERS AND NORTHCOTE, *Biochem. J.* 1959, **71**, p. 749.
6. TRACEY, *Biochem. J.* 1950, **47**, p. 431.
7. ENEBO, SANDEGREN AND LJUNGDAHL, *J. Inst. Brewing*, 1953, **59**, p. 205.
8. VAN SUMÈRE, *Naturwiss.* 1953, **40**, p. 582.
9. GOERDELER, *Hoppe-Seyl. Z.* 1948, **283**, p. 262.
10. THOMAS, *Aust. J. Biol. Sci.* 1956, **9**, p. 159.
11. WHITAKER, *Arch. Biochem. Biophys.* 1953, **43**, p. 253.
12. NISIZAWA, *J. Biochem. (Japan)*, 1955, **42**, p. 825.
13. REESE AND LEVINSON, *Physiol. Plant.* 1952, **5**, p. 345.
14. NORKRANS AND RÅNBY, *Physiol. Plant.* 1956, **9**, p. 198.
15. SISON, SCHUBERT AND NORD, *Arch. Biochem. Biophys.* 1958, **75**, p. 260.
16. HIGA, O'NEILL AND JENNISON, *J. Bact.* 1956, **71**, p. 382.
17. SIU, *Microbial Decomposition of Cellulose*, 1951, p. 176, Reinhold Publishing Corporation, New York.
18. SIU AND SINDEN, *Amer. J. Bot.* 1951, **38**, p. 284.
19. GASCOIGNE AND GASCOIGNE, unpublished results.
20. MANDELS AND REESE, *J. Bact.* 1957, **73**, p. 269.
21. FÅHRAEUS, *Symbolae botan. Upsalienses*, 1947, **9**, p. 1.
22. HALLIWELL, *J. gen. Microbiol.* 1957, **17**, pp. 153, 166.
23. KITTS AND UNDERKOFLER, *J. Agric. Food Chem.* 1954, **2**, p. 639.
24. FESTENSTEIN, *Biochem. J.* 1958, **69**, p. 562.
25. STANLEY AND KESLER, *J. Dairy Sci.* 1959, **42**, p. 127.
26. ENEBO, *Studies in Cellulose Decomposition*, 1954, Victor Pettersons Bokindustri Aktiebolag, Stockholm.
27. PORTER, *Diss. Abstracts*, 1958, **18**, p. 761.
28. MATTHIJSSEN, *Diss. Abstracts*, 1957, **17**, p. 2141.
29. DUNCAN, MANNERS AND ROSS, *Biochem. J.* 1956, **63**, p. 44.
30. LASKER AND GIESE, *J. Exp. Biol.* 1956, **33**, p. 542.
31. HUSAIN AND DIMOND, *Prac. Nat. Acad. Sci. U.S.A.* 1958, **44**, p. 594.
32. HAMMERSTROM, CLAUS, COGHLAN AND MCBEE, *Arch. Biochem. Biophys.* 1955, **56**, p. 123.
33. GRIMES, DUNCAN AND HOPPERT, *Arch. Biochem. Biophys.* 1957, **68**, p. 412.
34. STAUFFER, *Technique of Organic Chemistry*, ed. Weissberger, 1950, Vol. III, p. 313 *et seq.*, Interscience, New York.
35. GREEN AND HUGHES, *Methods in Enzymology*, ed. Colowick and Kaplan, 1955, Vol. I, p. 67, Academic Press, New York, U.S.A.
36. SIU, as ref. 17, p. 268.
37. STONE, Ph.D. Thesis, University of London, 1954.
38. STONE, *Biochem. J.* 1957, **66**, p. 11P.
39. WHITAKER, private communication.
40. ASCHAN AND NORKRANS, *Physiol. Plant.* 1953, **6**, p. 829.
41. GILLESPIE AND WOODS, *Aust. J. Biol. Sci.* 1953, **6**, p. 477.
42. KILROE-SMITH, *J. South African Chem. Inst.* 1957, **10**, p. 29.
43. ONCLEY AND DINTZIS, Abstracts of Papers, 122nd Amer. chem. Soc. Meeting, 19C, 1952.

44. THOMAS, private communication.
45. GREENFIELD, *Proc. Soc. Exp. Biol. Med.* 1955, **89**, p. 241.
46. FREUDENBERG AND PLOETZ, *Hoppe-Seyl. Z.* 1939, **259**, p. 19.
47. PLOETZ, *Hoppe-Seyl. Z.* 1939, **261**, p. 183.
48. TOYAMA, J. *Ferment. Technol. (Japan)*, 1955, **33**, p. 260.
49. FUKOMOTO AND KISHI, *Sci. Ind.* 1952, **26**, p. 295.
50. WHISTLER AND SMART, J. *Amer. chem. Soc.* 1953, **75**, p. 1916.
51. SIMOLA, *Ann. Acad. Sci. Fennicae*, 1931, A34, p. 1.
52. BALLENTINE, as ref. 35, Vol. III, p. 984.
53. OKAMOTO AND ASAI, J. *Agric. Chem. Soc. Japan*, 1952, **26**, p. 137.
54. TERUI AND FUJIWARA, J. *Ferment. Technol. Japan*, 1948, **27**, p. 203.
55. JERMYN AND THOMAS, *Nature, Lond.* 1953, **172**, p. 728.
56. OTTO, *Biochem. Z.* 1929, **209**, p. 276.
57. PRINGSHEIM AND BAUR, *Hoppe-Seyl. Z.* 1928, **173**, p. 188.
58. KARRER, SCHUBERT AND WEHRLI, *Helv. chim. Acta*, 1925, **8**, p. 797.
59. DE STEVENS, as ref. 35, p. 174.
60. GRASSMANN, ZECHMEISTER, TOTH AND STADLER, *Naturwiss.* 1932, **20**, p. 639.
61. GRASSMANN, ZECHMEISTER, TOTH AND STADLER, *Annalen*, 1933, **503**, p. 167.
62. KOOIMAN, *Enzymologia*, 1957, **18**, p. 371.
63. TOYAMA, J. *Ferment. Technol. (Japan)*, 1956, **34**, p. 274.
64. WOLF, JURKOVITCH AND MACMASTERS, *Arch. Biochem. Biophys.* 1959, **81**, p. 15.
65. NISIZAWA AND KOBAYASHI, *Symp. Enzyme Chem. Japan*, 1953, **8**, p. 123.
66. STONE, *Biochem. J.* 1957, **67**, p. 1P.
67. WHITAKER, *Nature, Lond.* 1951, **168**, p. 1070.
68. REESE AND GILLIGAN, *Arch. Biochem. Biophys.* 1953, **45**, p. 74.
69. GILLIGAN AND REESE, *Canad. J. Microbiol.* 1954, **1**, p. 90.
70. GIRI, PRASAD, DEVI AND RAM, *Biochem. J.* 1952, **51**, p. 123.
71. CABIB, *Biochim. Biophys. Acta*, 1952, **8**, p. 607.
72. REID, *Nature, Lond.* 1950, **166**, p. 569.
73. SWINGLE AND TISELIUS, *Biochem. J.* 1951, **48**, p. 171.
74. HASH AND KING, J. *biol. Chem.* 1958, **232**, p. 381.
75. VAN HAGA, *Nature, Lond.* 1958, **182**, p. 1232.
76. HOLDEN AND TRACEY, *Biochem. J.* 1950, **47**, p. 407.
77. TOYAMA, J. *Ferment. Technol. (Japan)*, 1957, **35**, p. 356.
78. ROTH, *Diss. Abstracts*, 1956, **16**, p. 1591.
79. WHITAKER, Review of the National Research Council, 1958, Ottawa, Canada, p. 41.
80. TISELIUS, as ref. 35, Vol. IV, p. 3.
81. TISELIUS, *Trans. Faraday Soc.* 1937, **33**, p. 524.
82. ANTWEILER, *Kolloidzschr.* 1949, **115**, p. 130.
83. PORATH, *Biochim. Biophys. Acta*, 1956, **22**, p. 151.
84. LEDERER, *An Introduction to Paper Electrophoresis*, 1955, Elsevier Publishing Company, London.
85. WILLIAMS, PICKELS AND DURRUM, *Science*, 1955, **121**, p. 829.

86. FOSTER, *Chem. and Ind.* 1952, p. 1050.
87. VALMET AND SVENSSON, *Science Tools*, 1954, **1**, p. 3.
88. LAURELL, as ref. 35, Vol. IV, p. 21.
89. MILLER AND BLUM, *J. biol. Chem.* 1956, **218**, p. 131.
90. KUNKEL AND SLATER, *Proc. Soc. Exp. Biol. Med.* 1952, **80**, p. 42.
91. BRADISH AND SMART, *Nature, Lond.* 1954, **174**, p. 272.
92. SVENSSON AND BRATTSTEN, *Arkiv. Kemi*, 1949, **1**, p. 401.
93. WOODS AND GILLESPIE, *Aust. J. Biol. Sci.* 1952, **6**, p. 130.
94. DURRUM, *J. Amer. chem. Soc.* 1950, **72**, p. 2943.
95. DINGLE, REID AND SOLOMONS, *J. Sci. Food Agric.* 1953, **4**, p. 149.
96. BIER (ed.), *Electrophoresis, Theory, Methods, and Applications*, 1959, Academic Press, New York.
97. LAYNE, as ref. 35, Vol. III, p. 447.
98. GORNALL, BARDAWILL AND DAVID, *J. biol. Chem.* 1949, **177**, p. 751.
99. LOWRY, ROSEBROUGH, FARR AND RANDALL, *J. biol. Chem.* 1951, **193**, p. 265.
100. HEEPE, KARTE AND LAMBRECHT, *Hoppe-Seyl. Z.* 1951, **286**, p. 207.
101. SOMOGYI, *J. biol. Chem.* 1945, **160**, p. 69.
102. WILLSTÄTTER AND SCHUDEL, *Ber. dtsch. chem. Ges.* 1918, **51**, p. 780.
103. BENEDICT, *J. Amer. Med. Soc.* 1911, **57**, p. 1193; *J. biol. Chem.* 1911, **9**, p. 57.
104. JERMYN, *Aust. J. Sci. Res.* 1952, **B5**, p. 409.
105. JANSEN AND MacDONNELL, *Arch. Biochem.* 1945, **8**, p. 97.
106. MARTIN, SMITH, WHISTLER AND HARRIS, *J. Res. Nat. Bur. Stand.* 1941, **27**, p. 449.
107. CHANDA, HIRST, JONES AND PERCIVAL, *J. chem. Soc.* 1950, p. 1289.
108. COLBRAN AND NEVELL, *J. chem. Soc.* 1957, p. 2427.
109. FOLIN, *J. biol. Chem.* 1929, **81**, p. 231.
110. PARK AND JOHNSON, *J. biol. Chem.* 1949, **181**, p. 149.
111. GREENFIELD AND LANE, *J. biol. Chem.* 1953, **204**, p. 669.
112. NUSSENBAUM AND HASSID, *Anal. Chem.* 1952, **24**, p. 501.
113. LEVVY, *Biochem. J.* 1946, **40**, p. 396.
114. DUBOIS, GILLES, HAMILTON, REBERS AND SMITH, F., *Nature, Lond.* 1951, **168**, p. 167.
115. ISBELL, *Science*, 1951, **113**, p. 532.
116. HOUGH, *Methods of Biochemical Analysis*, Vol. I, p. 205, 1957, Interscience, New York.
117. SHAFFER AND SOMOGYI, *J. biol. Chem.* 1933, **100**, p. 695.
118. NOGGLE, *The Carbohydrates*, ed. Pigman, p. 612, 1957, Academic Press, New York.
119. SHAFFER AND HARTMANN, *J. biol. Chem.* 1921, **45**, pp. 349, 365.
120. SOMOGYI, *J. biol. Chem.* 1952, **195**, p. 19.
121. NELSON, *J. biol. Chem.* 1944, **153**, p. 375.
122. HIRSCH, *Experientia*, 1954, **10**, p. 180.
123. NISIZAWA, *J. Agric. Chem. Soc. Japan*, 1953, **27**, p. 239.
124. HANES AND CATTLE, *Proc. Roy. Soc.* 1938, **B125**, p. 387.
125. SOMOGYI, *J. biol. Chem.* 1945, **160**, p. 61.

126. AITKEN, EDDY, INGRAM AND WEURMAN, *Biochem. J.* 1956, **64**, p. 63.
127. HOLDEN, PIRIE AND TRACEY, *Biochem. J.* 1950, **47**, p. 399.
128. HASH AND KING, *Science*, 1954, **120**, p. 1033.
129. DIMMLER, SCHAFFER, WISE AND RIST, *Anal. Chem.* 1952, **24**, p. 1411.
130. RIMINGTON, *Biochem. J.* 1940, **34**, p. 931.
131. SUMNER, *J. biol. Chem.* 1924–5, **62**, p. 287.
132. SUMNER AND HOWELL, *J. biol. Chem.* 1935, **108**, p. 51.
133. REESE, SIU AND LEVINSON, *J. Bact.* 1950, **59**, p. 485.
134. SISON, SCHUBERT AND NORD, *Arch. Biochem. Biophys.* 1957, **68**, p. 502.
135. Letzig, *Z. Untersuch. Lebensmitt.* 1942, **84**, p. 289; 1943, **85**, p. 401.
136. HULTIN, *Svensk. Kem. Tidskr.* 1946, **58**, p. 198.
137. HULTIN, *Acta Chem. Scand.* 1949, **3**, p. 625.
138. PREECE AND AITKEN, *J. Inst. Brewing*, 1953, **59**, p. 453.
139. LEVINSON AND REESE, *J. gen. Physiol.* 1950, **33**, p. 601.
140. MCILVAINE, *J. biol. Chem.* 1921, **49**, p. 183.
141. BASU AND WHITAKER, *Arch. Biochem. Biophys.* 1953, **42**, p. 12.
142. EYLER, KLUG AND DIEPHUIS, *Analyt. Chem.* 1947, **19**, p. 24.
143. PESANT, FARQUHAR AND McLAREN, *Canad. Text. J.* 1955, **72**, p. 33.
144. WALSETH, *Tech. Ass. Pulp Pap. Ind.* 1952, **35**, p. T.228.
145. HUFFMANN, REBERS, SPRIESTERSBACH AND SMITH, F., *Nature, Lond.* 1955, **175**, p. 990.
146. HALLIWELL, *Biochem. J.* 1958, **68**, p. 605.
147. DEARING, *Nature, Lond.* 1957, **179**, p. 579.
148. NEWELL, *J. Mar. Biol. Assoc. U.K.* 1953, **32**, p. 491.
149. SCALES, *Science*, 1915, **41**, p. 662.
150. RAM, *Proc. Nat. Inst. Sci. India (Biol. Sci.)*, 1956, **22B**, p. 204.
151. NORKRANS, *Symbolae botan. Upsalienses*, 1950, **11**, p. 5.
152. LEVINSON, MANDELS AND REESE, *Arch. Biochem. Biophys.* 1951, **31**, p. 351.
153. KEILIN AND HARTREE, *Biochem. J.* 1948, **42**, p. 230.
154. EDWARDS AND LARRABEE, *J. Physiol.* 1955, **130**, p. 456.
155. FÅHRAEUS, *Experientia*, 1946, **2**, p. 413.
156. JENNISON *et al.*, *Physiology of Wood-rotting Fungi*, Final Rept. No. 8, Office of Naval Res., Syracuse University, 1952.
157. SIU, see ref. 17, p. 326.
158. BELL, RAMSEY AND WHEWELL, *J. Soc. Dyers and Col.* 1955, **71**, p. 660.
159. THOMAS, *Text. Res. J.* 1955, **25**, p. 559.
160. BLUM AND STAHL, *Text. Res. J.* 1952, **22**, p. 178.
161. THOMAS AND WHITAKER, *Nature, Lond.* 1958, **181**, p. 715.
162. COLOWICK, as ref. 35, Vol. I, p. 90.

V

PROPERTIES OF CELLULOLYTIC ENZYMES

THE influence of environmental conditions such as temperature, hydrogen ion concentration and presence of other substances has a profound effect on enzymic activity and, indeed, may totally change the mode of action of an enzyme. For instance the action of β–amylase under optimum conditions of pH and temperature was entirely single chain, but under adverse conditions (pH 10·0, 26°; pH 4·7, 70°) evidence of multienzymic activity was found[1]. In Chapter III a summary of cell-free cellulolytic extracts, together with some of their properties, has been made. In this chapter some of these properties will be examined in more detail, and it should be remembered that in many cases this work has been carried out using impure enzyme extracts, and other substances, often of unknown and diverse composition, were present. Relatively few studies have been made on the properties of purified cellulases.

INFLUENCE OF HYDROGEN ION CONCENTRATION

It is well known[2] that the activity of enzymes depends on the hydrogen ion concentration of the solution used. It is important to distinguish between the amount of acid or alkali present (e.g. found by titration) and the hydrogen ion concentration; it is the latter value, usually designated as 'pH value', that is the factor which must be considered when discussing enzyme activities. Enzymes are generally active only over a limited range of pH values and the activity of most enzymes shows a maximum at a definite pH value, referred to as the *optimum pH value*. This optimum value may be due to any one of three effects or even to a combination of these effects:

(i) a reversible effect on the maximum velocity of the reaction catalysed, obtained when the enzyme is saturated with its substrate,

(ii) a stability effect—the enzyme may undergo inactivation by denaturation or even destruction, and this effect may be irreversible, when the enzyme is maintained above or below the optimum pH value,

(iii) the effect of hydrogen ion concentration on the affinity between the enzyme and its substrate; at pH values on either side of the optimum the enzyme may not be saturated with substrate.

The results of these effects can be seen from pH–activity curves. The derivation of such curves requires careful consideration; the activity of the enzyme can be measured at a number of pH values, or alternatively the enzyme may be exposed to one given pH value for a period and then its activity measured over a range of pH values. In the latter case, the enzyme may undergo a destruction progressive with time, so that an unreal or misleading optimum

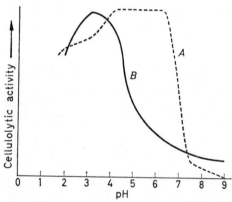

Figure 1—Effect of pH value on the activity of cellulase from *Poria vaillantii* (by courtesy, *Archives of Biochemistry and Biophysics*, 1958, **75**, p. 226)

value is recorded, as the enzyme is no longer undegraded. Few such studies have been made with cellulases, but the effect may be seen in *Figure 1*. Curve A shows the effect on the enzyme by holding it for 24 hours at the pH values shown in the graph, following which the enzyme activity was determined. The curve B shows the usual 'bell'-shaped curve where the activity was determined in solution at the pH values given[18]. Thus it will be seen that this cellulase undergoes an irreversible and progressive destruction at pH values on the alkaline side. The use of high concentration of substrate, sufficient to saturate the enzyme at all pH values, eliminates the effect of pH value on enzyme-substrate affinity. A study of enzymic reactions reveals an essential condition for the exact definition of these pH value-activity effects. Sufficient experimental data must be obtained at each pH value to determine the maximum velocity of the reaction and also *Km*, the Michaelis constant for the reaction. Very few sets of complete data exist (e.g. [4,5]), and indeed, for cellulases what data do exist must be treated with caution. The pH value effects are due to changes in the ionization state of all the components of the reaction. There is little knowledge about the form of the cellulase-substrate complex, and as cellulases are proteins[6] they contain many groups capable of being ionized and there is a complete lack of data concerning these states of ionization. As will be seen, the catalytic activity of cellulases is confined (usually) to a relatively small range of pH values and therefore it would appear probable that the active centre of cellulase will not contain more than one of these ionizing groups; or to put this in another way, it seems that only one of the ionic forms of the active centre of cellulase is active in catalysed reactions[7].

Plant, Animal and Bacterial Cellulases

The optimum activity of the cellulase of crushed green malt occurs at pH 5·0 and this enzyme retains a part of its activity over the pH range 3·0–8·0 [8], whilst another report gives the optimum pH value of 4·0 for barley cellulase. Reference to Chapter III will show that most plant cellulases have pH optima in the region of 5·0. Tracey[9] has shown that cellulase-producing plants have saps with pH values of above 5·0; two plants with more acid saps did not contain cellulases. The snail has been accorded the most detailed study in the animal kingdom. The digestive juices of *Helix pomatia* contain the enzyme and its activity reaches a maximum around 5·3 [10,11]. The effect of the substrate was shown by the action of *Helix* cellulase on cellulose glycol ether and on cellophane where the optimum pH values were found to be 4·0 and 5·5 respectively[12,13]; however no such effect of substrate was noticed using a preparation which had an optimum value of 5·6 for both soluble and insoluble substrates[14]. *Helix* cellulase retains its activity over a wide range and limits have been given of pH 4·0 to 9·0 [13]. The marine borer, *Teredo*, has a wider spectrum for its enzyme pH optimum (pH 5·6–6·7)[15] (an effect also noted for crude preparations of *Helix* cellulase compared with a purified enzyme[14]); the activity of *Teredo* cellulase is retained in the range pH 5·0 to 7·6. As may be expected in a warm blooded host, the cellulase of a cattle ciliate, *Endoplodinum neglectum*, is active over a narrower range of hydrogen ion concentration; limits of pH 4·0 to 6·0 have been reported[16]. Whilst it is unsafe to generalize the pH optima for most animal cellulases are in the region pH 5·0 to 5·5.

The optimum pH values for most bacterial cellulases appear to lie between 5·8 and 7·0 (see Chapter III) and they are active over a comparatively wide range of pH values. An example of the surprising stability of some cellulases is afforded by the enzyme of *Pseudomonas fluorescens* which still retains some activity after being maintained at pH 4·3 or 9·0 for one hour. It will be seen that these few studies do not bring enlightenment on the reaction mechanism or on the form of the enzyme-substrate complex in the way that the work of Massey and Alberty[4] clarified the activity of the enzyme fumarase.

Fungal Cellulases

Although many crude enzyme extracts are listed in Chapter III, there is now considerable data concerning hydrogen ion concentration effects on partially purified fungal cellulases, and some of these are summarized in *Table 1*. While the optimum pH value for

Table 1. *pH Optima of Partially Purified Fungal Cellulases*

Source of partially purified fungal cellulase	Optimum pH value	Active pH range	pH stability	Reference
Aspergillus oryzae	4·7	—	—	11
Trichoderma koningi	5·0	4·0–6·0	—	17
	4·5	4·0–5·2	—	
Poria vaillantii	3·2	2·0–6·0	4·0–6·0	18
Aspergillus niger	4·5	—	—	19
Myrothecium verrucaria 1.	5·6	4·0–7·0	—	20
2.	5·7–6·5	—	—	72

Aspergillus niger is reported here as 4·5, it is interesting to note that Stone[21] showed a relationship between the length of incubation period and the optimal pH value for a similar enzyme from the same organism. After 2 hours there was little variation in optimum values over a range 3·5 to 5·5, while after 5 hours the optimum was 5·5, and after 15 hours this had dropped to 5·0; it was postulated that these changes may be due to the successive action of several enzymes, with varying specificity for different chain length dextrins produced as the hydrolyses proceeds. The effect of different substrates on pH optima is illustrated by the work of Toyama[17] who found that the enzyme from *Trichoderma koningi* degrading carboxymethyl-cellulose (CMC) showed maximum activity at pH 4·5, while the cellulose-degrading enzyme showed an optimum value of 5·0, and it was reported to show different values again when acting on Bemberg rayon fibre and on filter paper respectively. The crude enzyme from *Stachybotrys atra*[22] also showed different optima, using different methods for assaying activity. Measuring the reducing sugar produced from either powdered Whatman No. 1 paper or ethylhydroxethylcellulose (EHEC) the enzyme showed maximum activity between pH values of 6·0 and 7·5; however, when activity was measured by reduction in viscosity of EHEC an optimum value was obtained at pH 8·0. Measurements were made at 37° and 30° respectively, but this serves well to show the effect of different assay conditions upon such measurements as pH optima.

Optimal pH values vary widely for fungi over a range from pH 3·0 to pH 8·0, however, they are largely on the acid side of

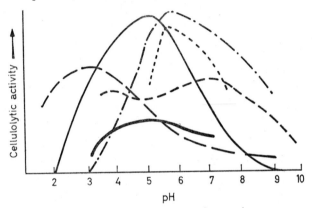

Figure 2—pH optima of cellulase activity from various sources.

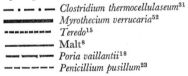

— · — · — *Clostridium thermocellulaseum*[31]
▬▬▬▬▬ *Myrothecium verrucaria*[52]
— — — — — *Teredo*[15]
———————— Malt[8]
— — — — *Poria vaillantii*[18]
— — — — — *Penicillium pusillum*[23]

neutrality, mostly between pH 4·0 and pH 7·0, and different results obtained by different workers using similar preparations derived from the same organism may be partially explained by widely differing conditions of assay. Bimodal pH curves have been reported[23,24] but appear to be rare cases, and a typical curve is shown in *Figure 2* (which also shows pH curves for several other enzyme preparations). They may be indicative of the presence of two cellulases having different pH optima.

Other pH considerations

Isoelectric point.—There appears to be little relationship between the isoelectric points of cellulolytic enzymes and their optimal pH values. The isoelectric point of barley cellulase, found to have an optimal pH value of 5·0, lies between pH values of 6·0 and 7·0[8], while the isoelectric point of purified *M. verrucaria* cellulase has been estimated to be approximately pH 4·7 [25], this enzyme having optimal activity at pH 5·6 [20].

Cellulase production.—The initial conditions of a medium in which a cellulolytic organism is grown have a profound effect on cellulase production by that organism; thus no cellulase was produced by *S. atra* in a medium in which the hydrogen ion concentration was outside the range 5·0 to 8·0 [22], similarly Reese and Gilligan[26] showed that, by variations of hydrogen ion concentration of the growth medium, production of one of the components of the cellulolytic complex obtained on chromatographic separation of crude culture filtrate could be suppressed. Similar effects have been noted with temperature changes, e.g. there was no production of cellulase by *Neurospara crassa* grown at 25°, but an extracellular enzyme was produced at 35° [27]. The temperatures and hydrogen ion concentrations used for the growth of various organisms, and the optimum temperatures and hydrogen ion concentrations for the cellulolytic preparations derived therefrom (or, alternatively, used in assays for enzymic activity) are shown in *Table 2*. There is little difference

Table 2. Comparison of Optimum Temperatures and pH Values of Enzyme Preparations from Different Organisms, and Temperatures and pH Values Used for their Growth

Organism	Temperature used for growth	Optimum temperature of enzyme	pH value used for growth	Optimum pH value of enzyme	Reference
Fungi					
Myrothecium 1.	30	40		5·5	28
verrucaria 2.	30	35*		5·6	6
Stachybotrys atra	28	28–37	7·1–7·3	6–7·5	22
Poria vaillantii	27–28	60		3·2	18, 29
		40 or room temperature*			
Trichoderma koningi	25	40	6·0	5·0	30
Bacteria					
Sporocytophaga	32–37	36	7·4	7·0	32
Clostridium thermocellulaseum	55–60	57–58	8·0	5·8	31
Corynebacterium fimi		40	6·0–7·0	6·0–7·0	60

*Temperature of assay. Temperatures given in °C.

129

between the hydrogen ion concentrations used, but more variations in the temperatures used.

Purification.—It has been shown in the previous chapter how critical hydrogen ion concentration is a factor in achieving chromatographic separations of cellulolytic enzymes, and it is emphasized that a difference in pH value of as little as one unit may make all the difference between successful and unsuccessful separations. This principle applies equally well to purifications by precipitation techniques, and the work of Whitaker[6] in the purification of *M. verrucaria* cellulase illustrates this well; thus, using ethanol as a protein precipitant, decreasing the pH value from 6·8 to 4·5 caused a decrease in the ethanol concentration required to initiate and complete protein precipitation. This pH dependence should be borne in mind when undertaking purification studies, and before the presentation of a complete purification protocol many detailed and careful studies of such factors as the dependence of separations upon pH value are necessary.

INFLUENCE OF TEMPERATURE

The influence of temperature upon enzyme reactions is complex, but it is the result of the effect of heat upon two factors, the velocity of the reaction and the destruction of the enzyme by heat. The changes produced in enzyme protein by the action of heat, causing inactivation, resemble closely changes produced in structure caused by the action of heat and other agents upon all protein molecules, known as denaturation, and a direct relationship between inactivation of enzyme and denaturation of protein has been shown for pepsin and trypsin[33,34]. In these cases denaturation can be reversed under certain conditions and a recovery of activity parallel with the renaturation of protein was obtained. The rate of thermal inactivation of enzymes is very dependent on other factors such as hydrogen ion concentration, ionic strength, protein concentration and the protective action of substrate, inhibitors and other substances. The concentration of water is also important and dried enzymes are comparatively heat stable; dry preparations of sucrase can be heated in boiling toluene without loss of activity, whereas aqueous solutions are rapidly inactivated at temperatures above 55°. The rate of inactivation in solution increases rapidly with a rise in temperature, in nearly all cases inactivation being instantaneous at temperatures well below 100°. The number of enzymes withstanding 100° is very small, the classic example being that of adenylate kinase which withstands prolonged heating at 100° at pH 1·0[35]. Pure ribonuclease can also be boiled for a short time while crystalline

130

trypsin in hydrochloric acid (0·1N), purified horse-radish peroxidase, hyaluronidase[36] and a pectolytic factor from tomatoes[37] are also very heat stable. The thermal stability of an enzyme can be studied by exposing it to definite temperatures for a definite period of time and then measuring its activity under standard conditions at a temperature at which it is known to be stable.

The general effect of increasing temperature on an irreversible reaction is to increase its velocity, and this also holds true for enzyme reactions provided that the products are continually removed. The influence of temperature on the velocity of enzyme reactions may be due to effects involving the catalysed reaction itself, that is

(i) an effect on enzyme stability,

(ii) an effect on the actual velocity of breakdown of the complex (determined by the heat of activation of the reaction),

(iii) an effect on the enzyme substrate affinity, which can be eliminated by using a sufficiently high concentration of substrate to saturate the enzyme,

(iv) a transfer of rate-limiting function from one enzyme to another, in a system involving two or more enzymes with different temperature coefficients.

Outside factors which influence the enzyme reaction in some way may themselves be influenced by temperature as

(i) an effect on the pH functions of any or all of the components (due to an alteration of their pK values which is determined by the heat of ionization),

(ii) an effect on the affinity of the enzyme for activators or inhibitors, a factor which can be eliminated by using a sufficiently high concentration to saturate the enzyme,

(iii) subsidiary causes such as change in concentration of dissolved oxygen due to a change of solubility, or a change in pH value of buffer used.

As the temperature is raised an acceleration of the enzyme catalysed reaction occurs and the amount of substrate reacted in any stated period of time at first rises, then falls, giving an apparent *optimum temperature*. This point is the point of balance between the effect of temperature on increasing the reaction velocity, and its effect on the rate of destruction of the enzyme, producing a gradual fall in the concentration of active enzyme. It is a value which varies considerably depending upon all sorts of factors such as impurities present, hydrogen ion concentration and length of time the reaction is run. It is difficult to generalize, but for animal enzymes it is often between 40° and 50°, while for plant enzymes it is usually between 50° and 60°.

Plant, Animal and Bacterial Cellulases

Few detailed studies have been made on the thermal relationships of cellulase and in the majority of cases only two values, that of the optimum temperature and the temperature of inactivation are recorded (see Chapter III). Typical results from stability studies using the cellulase of *H. pomatia*[14] are shown in *Table 3*. While other

Table 3. Temperature Stability of Cellulases

Organism	Time of heating (min)	Temperature of heating °C									Temperature of activity assay °C	Ref.
		30	40	50	60	65	70	80	90	100		
		Activity retained (per cent)										
Helix pomatia	5	53	—	12·5	—	—	0	—	—	—	25 or 37	14
Cytophaga	5	—	—	50	—	—	6	0	—	—		32
Clostridium thermocellulaseum	30	—	—	100	88	49	8	0	—	—	30	31
Poria vaillantii	10	—	100	90	86	—	56	7	0	0	40	18

results (see Chapter III) record inactivation of *Helix* cellulase at similar temperatures, two workers failed to obtain complete inactivation after holding a diluted enzyme solution at 100° for ten minutes, when soluble cellulose derivatives were used as substrates in assaying residual activity. No other heat-stable cellulases have been obtained from animal sources, but it has been reported that a preparation from barley required autoclaving at 105° before complete inactivation of its cellulolytic properties[38]; in contrast to this, while green malt itself retained some cellulolytic activity after kilning (at 85°) an extract from it was inactivated on heating at 60° for thirty minutes[8]. Other cellulolytic plant extracts are relatively heat sensitive with the exception of algal extracts, which are only slightly inactivated on heating at 60° for fifteen minutes (see Chapter III). Bacterial cellulases are inactivated under quite mild conditions, the stability of preparations from *Cytophaga*[32] and *Clostridium thermocellulaseum*[31] being shown in *Table 3*.

Little is known concerning the optimum temperatures of these enzymes. Data in Chapter III show that optimal temperatures for bacterial cellulases vary between 36° and 40°, but the enzyme from the thermophilic organism *C. thermocellulaseum* has optimal activity at 57° to 58°[31] (see *Figure 3*). Cellulases from animal sources (e.g. *Helix pomatia* and *Trichomonas termopsidis*) appear to act best from about 25° to 35°, while little is known of the optimal temperature conditions of cellulases of plant origin.

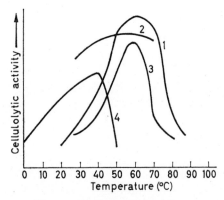

Figure 3—Influence of temperature on cellulase activity.
1. *Poria vaillantii*[18]
2. *Myrothecium verrucaria*[74]
3. *Clostridium thermocellulaseum*[31]
4. *Myrothecium verrucaria*[28]

Fungal Cellulases

Temperature relationships of purified fungal cellulases have not been studied in very great detail, and as with cellulases from other sources, for many fungal preparations only single figures are recorded and no further data are available; some of these are recorded elsewhere (see Chapter III). The effect of heat on the stability of the partially purified preparation from *Poria vaillantii* is shown in *Table 3*[18]. Similarly enzyme preparations from *Aspergillus niger*[21] and *Trichoderma koningi*[17] are inactivated after heating at 70° for relatively short periods of time. In contrast to these findings, and contrary to the results of Saunders *et al.*[28] who found that inactivation of unpurified *M. verrucaria* cellulase began at 50° and was completed on heating at 70° for ten minutes, Kooiman and his co-workers[39] found that holding a cellulolytic preparation from this organism at 110° for thirty minutes did not eliminate all the activity. Chromatographic analysis of the incubated solutions led to the conclusion that a thermosensitive cellobiase and transglycosylase and a thermoresistant cellulase were present in the solution. This cellulase

133

catalysed the hydrolysis of a group of substrates including native cellulose, cellotriose and carboxymethylcellulose (CMC).

Preferential destruction of cellobiase by heat has been reported elsewhere[40-42], while other workers[41,43] have also noted the presence of thermostable components in *M. verrucaria* culture filtrates, which were able to reduce the viscosity of CMC solutions after heating for periods varying from ten to thirty minutes at 95° to 100°, a treatment which did not completely destroy 'S' factor present in the same filtrate[43]. Results obtained by Whitaker[44] working with a purified preparation from this mould are more in agreement with those of Saunders *et al.*[28]. Heating the enzyme at 80° for five minutes caused an 87 per cent loss in activity towards cellopentaose. Using a series of oligoglucosides (cellobiose, cellotriose, cellotetraose and cello-pentaose) as substrates he observed that a pre-treatment resulting in a certain loss of enzymic activity towards one oligoglucoside may result in a different loss in activity towards another, the greater loss being shown towards the substrate having the lower degree of poly-merization (DP). These results may be explained by assuming that there are degrees of denaturation[45] and the enzyme undergoes changes in structure, the effect of which on activity varies with the DP of the substrate; the activity towards substrates of lower DP is more affected than that towards substrates of higher DP. An alterna-tive explanation would be possible, assuming the presence of four different enzymes each of which is denatured to a varying extent by heat treatment, cellobiase acting on the substrate of lowest DP being most susceptible, and the enzyme cleaving cellopentaose being the least susceptible. This is improbable in this case however, the preparation being shown to be homogeneous (by ultracentrifuge, diffusion and electrophoresis), in addition to which would be the assumption of a very high degree of enzyme specificity in relation to substrate DP. Varying results on thermostability of cellulases, especially of *M. verrucaria* cellulase, may be due to several factors. They may be the result of varying assay conditions; in the majority of cases the thermostable enzymes were shown to reduce the viscosity of soluble cellulose derivatives, a method which measures the ability of an enzyme to cleave long chains, and they were not assayed for production of reducing sugar, the method used by Whitaker and shown by him to be sensitive to the effect of slight changes in DP; the viscometric method may not be sensitive to measure such changes. Variances in hydrogen ion concentration, ionic strength and protein concentration may account for differing results, while high heat tolerance may be accounted for by the influence of non-enzymatic material in the medium, possibly introduced in the crude enzyme sources used in some of the studies. In general it can be said that thermostability of a true cellulase (i.e. an enzyme attacking native cellulose), is the exception rather than the rule.

Numerous temperatures have been quoted for optimal cellulase activity. These figures are also affected by differing assay conditions and this may explain such large variations. Temperature curves for the activity of two enzyme preparations derived from *M. verrucaria*[28,74] and *P. vaillantii*[18] are shown in *Figure 3* (page 133), maximum reducing sugar production for the latter enzyme occurring between 60° and 70°. It is interesting to note that determinations of activity of the enzyme from *P. vaillantii* were not performed at this temperature, but at a value 20° lower. Fåhraeus[32] stated that the optimum temperature for the action of *Cytophaga* enzyme preparations was 36°, but observed that at 42° hydrolysis was greater initially but considerably reduced later, and suggested that this effect was due to enzyme inactivation. In studies of this kind, where shorter incubation periods are employed, maximum hydrolysis may occur at higher temperatures (provided these are not sufficiently high to cause almost instantaneous inactivation in the period of time employed), however if incubation is prolonged maximum hydrolysis may occur at lower temperatures. It is important to state exactly how such measurements are made, for the benefit of other workers in the field, because in this way many anomalous results may be explained.

INHIBITION AND ACTIVATION

Inhibition and activation studies have always played an important part in enzyme work. Activation of enzymes may be of two types:

(i) the enzyme may occur in an inactive form or zymogen, which is activated on contact with a second substance known as a kinase; such an enzyme is trypsin, which is present in the pancreatic juice as trypsinogen, and meets enterokinase in the small intestine thus forming the active enzyme,

(ii) unspecific activation is said to occur when the enzyme alone has considerable activity which is increased by the addition of other substances. There are a variety of reasons for this increase in activity, which will be discussed as definite cases of activation arise.

Inhibition may also be classified as specific and non-specific. Practically all enzymes are proteins, which contain certain common groups, e.g. free carboxyl, amino, and thiol groups; any reagent blocking these groups causes non-specific inhibition of enzymic

135

activity; this inhibition may be reversible by the addition of other substances which react with the inhibitors, thus preventing their combination with the enzyme. The addition of substances blocking the active centres conferring specificity on an enzyme is known as specific inhibition. Enzyme specificity is only relative and an enzyme may be capable of reacting with substances which are structurally related to the substrate; for example the enzyme succinic dehydrogenase reacts with various analogues of succinic acid such as malonic acid, but it cannot activate these substances and inhibition is due to the fact that access to the active centres of the enzyme is blocked. Thus, enzymes are also inhibited by the products of their own reactions because of a structural analogy with the substrate and competition with the substrate for the active centres.

Data in the literature on the inhibition and activation of cellulases are very scattered. Interpretation of the results must be considered with caution bearing in mind the degree of purity of the enzyme preparation, the substrate and conditions of incubation. A summary of information on the inhibition of β–glucosidases has been made by Veibel[46], known inhibitors including heavy metals, oxidizing agents, formaldehyde and carbonyl reagents. Compounds which have been used in studies on cellulases may be classified into five main groups each of which will be considered in turn:

1. (a) Inorganic compounds including metallic and other ions, and salts.
   (b) Oxidizing and reducing agents.
2. Sugars.
3. Proteins and amino-acids.
4. Anionic and cationic compounds.
5. Miscellaneous substances (e.g. antiseptics).

As few studies have been made using purified cellulases, work using crude enzyme extracts will also be considered here.

1(a) Inorganic Compounds

Comparatively little is known concerning the activation and inhibition of cellulases of plant, animal and bacterial origin. The action of *Helix* cellulase[12] on hydroxyethylcellulose (HEC) was shown to be inhibited by a mixture of copper sulphate (1%) and hydrogen cyanide (3%) while much larger amounts of copper sulphate alone and of ferric chloride were needed to attain complete inhibition; the use of citrate buffer in place of phosphate buffer decreased the inhibitory effects. A similar enzyme preparation was reversibly inhibited by the commonly used enzyme precipitant ammonium sulphate[14]. Zinc and chromate ions (0·1M) caused a decrease in activity of a cellulase from the hind-gut of a termite *Termes obesus*[48], while trivalent chromium had a similar effect on the cellulolytic enzyme from the thermophilic bacterium *Clostridium thermocellulaseum*[31]. The addition of silver, cupric and ferric ions also affects this enzyme; the amounts of metal causing 25, 50 and 75 per cent inhibition using an ethylhydroxyethylcellulose (EHEC) substrate are shown in *Table 4*. The addition of peptone, which by itself

Table 4. Inhibition of Cellulase from Clostridium thermocellulaseum by Metallic Ions. (by courtesy, from L. Enebo, *Studies in Cellulose Decomposition by an Anaerobic Thermophilic Bacterium and Two Associated non-cellulolytic Species*. Victor Petterson's Bokindustri Aktiebolag, Stockholm 1954)

Per cent inhibition	Metals mg/litre			
	$AgNO_3$ (Ag^+)	$CuCl_2.2H_2O$ (Cu^{2+})	$KCr(SO_4)_2.12H_2O$ (Cr^{3+})	$FeCl_3.6H_2O$ (Fe^{3+})
25	0·012	0·16	1·7	0·9
50	0·044	0·29	3·2	2·6
75	0·260	0·88	5·8	6·6

had no stimulatory effect, counteracted this inhibition probably due to its capacity to adsorb heavy metal ions. Manganese and calcium had no stimulatory effect on this enzyme, confirming the results obtained by Fåhraeus[32] on the hydrolysis of cellophane and lichenin using *Cytophaga* preparations, a reaction which was stimulated by the addition of magnesium ions. In contrast to this it has been shown that magnesium ions had no effect on the enzymic hydrolysis of EHEC[31], or on the hydrolysis of a cellulose sol by a fungal enzyme preparation from *Tricholoma* sp.[49]. The effect of some salts and metallic ions on the action of fungal cellulases is summarized in *Table 5*. Particular attention is drawn here to the extensive work of Jermyn[50] and of Reese and Mandels[51] who tested wide ranges of compounds for their effect on cellulolytic action of *Aspergillus oryzae* and *Trichoderma viride*, *M. verrucaria* and *Pestalotiopsis westerdijkii* respectively.

A study of the influence of various metallic ions on the action of a purified cellulase[6] has been made by Basu and Whitaker[52], and their results are reproduced in *Table 6*. These experiments were carried out at pH 5·6, and the influence of a change in hydrogen ion

Table 5. *Effect of various Inorganic Substances on the Action of Fungal Cellulases*

Fungus from which enzyme preparation derived		Inhibitors	Activators	Reference
Aspergillus oryzae	1.	Zn^{2+}, Ag^+, Hg^{2+}, Cd^{2+}, HCN, H_2S, pyrophosphate		61
	2.	CN^-, K(SbO)tartrate, sulphide	Co^{2+}, Cd^{2+}, Ni^{2+} Fe^{3+}, Mg^{2+}, Cu^{2+} hexametaphosphate, boric acid, I_2, caused slight activation. MnO_4^-, MoO_4^{2-} more pronounced activation	50
Irpex lacteus			Mn^{2+}	62
Myrothecium verrucaria	1.	CN^-, $Na_2S_2O_5$		51
	2.	Hg^{2+}, Cu^{2+} (inhibit 'S' factor)		43
Pestalotiopsis westerdijkii		CN^-, $KMnO_4$	NaF	51
Poria vaillantii		Ag^+, Pb^{2+}, Ca^{2+}, Cr^{2+}, Cd^{2+}, Zn^{2+} $NaNO_3$, Cu^{2+}	Mn^{2+}, Co^{2+}	18
Puccinia graminis		Ag^+, Cu^{2+}, Zn^{2+}, Pb^{2+}, Hg^{2+}		63
Stachybotrys atra		Hg^{2+}, Cu^{2+}, Pb^{2+}, CN^-		22
Streptomyces		Mn^{2+}, Ag^+	Cu^+, Cu^{2+}, Co^{2+}	51
Trichoderma viride (T. koningi)	1.	Ag^+, Mn^{2+}, Zn^{2+}, Cu^{2+}		17
	2.	Mn^{2+}, Ag^+, Hg^{2+}, Na borate, $Na_2S_2O_5$	NaF, NH_2OHHCl, Cu^{2+}, $CaCl_2$, Na^+, Mg^{2+}, Cd^{2+}	51
Tricholoma sp.		NaF	$Ca^{2+}+ PO_4^{3-}$	49

concentration was studied. At pH 4·6 inhibition was less and zinc chloride became stimulatory. Sodium fluoride, ineffective at pH 5·6, also became stimulatory at a pH value of 4·6; various salts at low ionic strengths (sodium sulphate, sodium nitrate, and the sodium halides) which had no effect at pH 5·6 were strongly stimulatory at pH 4·6. The concentration of the salt was critical, high concentrations being very inhibitory at these low hydrogen ion concentrations. The inactivation of sucrase by silver has also been found to be dependent on hydrogen ion concentration[53], being more strongly inhibited in alkaline than in acid solution; the mechanism of this inactivation is due to the combination of silver

Table 6. Effect of Metallic Ions on Cellulase from Myrothecium verrucaria
(by courtesy, *Archives of Biochemistry and Biophysics*, 1953, **42**, p. 16)

Inhibitor	Concentration M	Mean enzyme activity %	Inhibitor	Concentration M	Mean enzyme activity %
None	—	100			
HgCl$_2$	10^{-5}	44·7	AgNO$_3$	10^{-4}	78·8
	10^{-4}	1·2		10^{-3}	15·7
	10^{-3}	0			
			Pb(NO$_3$)$_2$	10^{-4}	96·4
CuSO$_4$	10^{-4}	61·2		10^{-3}	48·8
	10^{-3}	21·6			
	10^{-2}	4·5	FeCl$_3$	10^{-3}	69·5
	2×10^{-2}	1·9			
			CdCl$_2$	10^{-4}	94·8
ZnCl$_2$	10^{-4}	97·3		10^{-3}	73·6
	10^{-3}	78·4			
	10^{-2}	34·4			

with a carboxyl group to form a feebly dissociated salt, and is reversible by hydrogen sulphide which removes the silver. Inactivation of cellulase by heavy metal salts may be affected similarly by the addition of a second compound (see *Table 7*). It can be seen that inhibition by cupric and mercuric ions is reduced by the addition of glutathione, while sodium sulphide increased the inhibition by cupric and silver ions, but decreased inhibition by mercuric ions. Inhibition by mercuric and copper ions is reversed by the addition of reduced glutathione, cysteine and cyanide. The reversal effect is explained by removal of inhibitors by preferential reaction with the added compound.

Conclusions.—There are many contradictory findings concerning the influence of metallic ions on cellulase activity, and these may be due to any one of a number of factors such as different substrates, concentration of reagents, purity of enzyme preparations or different experimental conditions. The work of Basu and Whitaker[52], mentioned above, illustrates well how critical the effect of different assay conditions can be when carrying out work of this type. Generally speaking, however, mercury, silver, copper, chromium, lead and zinc salts are inhibitory to enzymatic activity, while manganese, cobalt, magnesium and calcium with phosphate cause stimulation in certain cases; there are, of course, exceptions to this statement, as a study of *Table 5* will show.

Table 7. Effect of Additional Compounds on Heavy Metal Inactivation of Cellulase from Myrothecium verrucaria *(by courtesy,* Archives of Biochemistry *and* Biophysics, *1953,* **42***, p. 17)*

Inhibitor	Concentration M	Additional compound	Concentration M	Mean enzyme activity %
$HgCl_2$	10^{-5}	—	—	44·7
		$CuSO_4$	10^{-4}	32·1
		GSSG	2.5×10^{-3}	72·7
		PCMB	2×10^{-4}	21·7
		Iodoacetic acid	10^{-2}	48·4
		Na_2S	10^{-3}	96·8
	10^{-4}	—	—	1·3
		GSH	10^{-3}	90·0
		Cysteine.HCl	10^{-3}	97·5
		Na_2S	10^{-3}	52·9
		KCN	10^{-3}	99·3
$AgNO_3$	10^{-4}	—	—	78·8
		Na_2S	10^{-3}	71·9
$CuSO_4$	10^{-4}	—	—	63·2
		GSSG	2.5×10^{-3}	75·2
		PCMB	2×10^{-4}	34·8
		Na_2S	10^{-3}	50·9
	10^{-3}	—	—	18·1
		GSH	2×10^{-3}	77·6
		Na_2S	3×10^{-3}	13·0
		KCN	5×10^{-3}	101·0
	5×10^{-4}	—	—	30·7
		Cysteine.HCl	10^{-3}	89·9

Inactivation by heavy metals is a well known phenomenon, enzymes affected including amylases[54] and dehydrases of *Escherichia coli*[55]. Heavy metals are well known to be general protein precipitants and in high concentrations will inactivate most enzymes; it has also been suggested that they combine with thiol or carboxyl groups in the enzyme molecule. It has already been shown that the effect of metal inhibition can be reversed by the addition of metal complexing agents and the higher the concentration of any of these in a crude enzyme preparation the higher the concentration of metal required to bring about enzyme inhibition. Apparent activation of enzymes by added substances may in fact be due to the removal of some poison present which has a greater affinity for the added substance than for the enzyme. The classic example is the activation of urease preparations by the addition of blood serum, proteins, amino-acids and gum arabic, the explanation of which was due to traces of heavy

140

metals from the solder on the tin condenser being present in the distilled water used, and when glass redistilled water was used the additions had no effect[56]. Similar effects on cellulase have been noted earlier (page 137). The effect of a lower pH value reducing the degree of inhibition by metals may be explained by assuming that the metals form a complex with the enzyme more easily at a hydrogen ion concentration on the alkaline side of its isoelectric point, when it is negatively charged. This is supported by the work of Başu and Whitaker[52] who used *M. verrucaria* cellulase which has an isoelectric point at pH 4·7.

There are several possible explanations for the mechanism of activation of enzymes by metallic ions, but in few cases has the precise mechanism been definitely established:

(i) The metal may form an essential part of the active centre of the enzyme.
(ii) It may form a binding link between substrate and enzyme.
(iii) The metal may cause a change in the equilibrium constant of the enzyme reaction.
(iv) Metal ions may cause changes in the surface charge on the enzyme protein or on the substrate.
(v) Metals may remove an inhibitor by complexing with it, as mentioned earlier.

A further study of this mechanism has been presented by Dixon and Webb[57].

The influence of salts may be due to an increase of ionic strength to a value more favourable for enzymic action, although the surface potential of cellulose is known to be sensitive to salt adsorption[58] and may be altered to a more favourable value for enzymic hydrolysis.

1(b) Oxidizing, Reducing and Thiol Agents

Certain workers have studied the effects of oxidizing and reducing agents on cellulolytic activity. It was shown[47] that cysteine and glutathione inhibited the breakdown of HEC in the presence of *Helix* cellulase in phosphate buffer but not in citrate buffer. The results of Sison *et al.*[18], using an enzyme preparation from *P. vaillantii* at pH 3·2, and those of Basu and Whitaker[52], using *M. verrucaria* cellulase at pH 5·6 are shown in *Table 8*. Examination of this table shows somewhat contradictory results. Glutathione, which markedly stimulated the enzyme from *P. vaillantii*, inhibited the cellulase from *M. verrucaria*, even at a lower concentration and shorter exposure time. Potassium cyanide, which also stimulated the enzyme

Table 8. Inhibition and Activation of Cellulases from Myrothecium verrucaria *and* Poria vaillantii *by Oxidizing (O) and Reducing (R) Agents* (by courtesy, *Archives of Biochemistry and Biophysics*, 1958, **75**, p. 270 and 1953, **42**, p. 17)

Test compound	Class	*M. verrucaria*[52]		*P. vaillantii*[18]	
		Conc. M	Enzyme activity %	Conc. M	Enzyme activity %
None	—	—	100	—	100
KCN	R	5×10^{-3}	101	10^{-3}	220
		10^2	9·6	—	—
Na_2S	R	10^{-3}	106	—	—
		5×10^{-3}	80·1	—	—
Cysteine HCl	R	10^{-2}	74·0	—	—
Reduced glutathione	R	10^{-2}	86·5	—	—
Ascorbic acid	R	—	—	10^{-3}	145·5
Pyrocatechol	R	—	—	10^{-3}	273·6
Glutathione	O	5×10^{-4}	88·9	10^{-3}	161·8
		5×10^{-3}	79·8	—	—
$K_3Fe(CN)_6$	O	5×10^{-4}	88·9	8×10^{-5}	96·0
		5×10^{-3}	79·8	—	—
$K_3Fe(CN)_6 +$ $CuSO_4. 5H_2O$	O	—	—	8×10^{-5}	59·0

from *P. vaillantii* caused inhibition of *M. verrucaria* cellulase, but at a much higher concentration. Cyanide also causes inhibition of certain other preparations (see *Table 5*). Apart from acting as a reducing agent it is a metal-complexing agent, and is known to inactivate many heavy metal catalysts. It has been shown to inactivate not only enzymes which contain a metal taking an essential part in the catalytic mechanism, but also enzymes containing disulphide groups. Cyanide can act in four ways to inactivate an enzyme:

(i) It may combine with an essential metal in the enzyme.

(ii) It may remove a metal from the enzyme as an inactive complex.

(iii) It may combine with a carbonyl group in the enzyme, in a co-factor or a prosthetic group or even in the substrate itself.

(iv) It may act as a reducing agent to break essential disulphide links in the enzyme to yield thiol groups.

Other reducing and oxidizing compounds which affected the cellulase from *A. oryzae*[50] include permanganate and molybdate,

142

Table 9. Effect of Thiol Reagents on Fungal Cellulases

Thiol reagent	A. oryzae [50] Conc. M	A. oryzae [50] Enzyme activity %	P. vaillantii [18] Conc. M	P. vaillantii [18] Enzyme activity %	M. verrucaria [51,52] Conc. M	M. verrucaria [51,52] Enzyme activity %	T. viride [51] Conc. M	T. viride [51] Enzyme activity %	P. westerdijkii [51] Conc. M	P. westerdijkii [51] Enzyme activity %
None	—	100	—	100	—	100	—	100	—	100
p-chloromercuribenzoate	10^{-3}	126	5×10^{-4}	100	2×10^{-5} 5×10^{-4} $8 \cdot 7 \times 10^{-3}$	91.4 32.5 85	$8 \cdot 7 \times 10^{-3}$	75	$8 \cdot 7 \times 10^{-3}$	78
Iodoacetate	—	—	10^{-3}	91.0	$0 \cdot 6 \times 10^{-3}$ 10^{-2} $1 \cdot 6 \times 10^{-2}$	100 72.4 100	$1 \cdot 6 \times 10^{-2}$	100	$1 \cdot 6 \times 10^{-2}$	100
Iodosobenzoic acid	10^{-3}	176	—	—	—	—	—	—	—	—
Phenylmercuric chloride	—	—	Saturated solution	66.7	—	—	—	—	—	—
Phenylmercuric nitrate	—	—	Saturated solution	0.0	—	—	—	—	—	—

143

which stimulated, and bisulphite, dithionite and benzoquinone, which were inhibitory.

Thiol Reagents.—Thiol groups or potential thiol groups (i.e. those groups which on reduction yield thiol groups) are present in many amino-acids (such as cysteine and cystine) which are components of many proteins and the action of inhibitors such as cysteine, reduced glutathione or glutathione may be explained by their effect (oxidizing or reducing) on thiol groups present in the enzyme molecule. Inhibitors whose action is due to their effect on thiol groups are classified as thiol reagents; these reagents not only include compounds whose action is oxidative or reductive, but also compounds which react by alkylation (e.g. iodoacetate, which reacts with proteins to give alkylated derivatives with the liberation of hydrogen iodide[59]) and compounds forming mercaptides with thiol groups.

Table 10. Reactivation of Cellulase after Inhibition by Thiol Reagents (by courtesy, *Archives of Biochemistry and Biophysics*, 1953, **42**, p. 17 and 1958, **75**, p. 270)

Thiol reagent	Activity in presence of thiol reagent %	Reactivating agent	Activity after addition of agent %
Enzyme from P. vaillantii[18]			
Phenylmercuric chloride	66·7	Glutathione	133·4
Phenylmercuric nitrate	0	Glutathione	187·0
Enzyme from M. verrucaria[52]			
p–chloro-mercuribenzoate	56·2	Glutathione	94·6
		Cysteine.HCl	99·7
		Na₂S	94·6
		KCN	101·0

Iodoacetate, whose action is generally irreversible, has been used in studies with cellulase, while mercaptide-forming reagents, whose action is readily reversible particularly by the addition of an excess of a thiol compound with which the reagent then combines or partially combines, include p–chloromercuribenzoate and phenylmercuric salts. The effect of these reagents is shown in *Table 9* [18,50–52]. Only the phenylmercuric salts caused very effective inhibition of *P. vaillantii* cellulase and activity was restored by the addition of glutathione (see *Table 10*) which also caused reactivation after inhibition by copper sulphate and ferricyanide. Whitaker[52] observed inhibition by iodoacetate and p–chloromercuribenzoate, and interaction of the latter reagent with other inhibitors and activators (see *Table 10*) suggested the presence of essential thiol groups in both enzymes. In both cases negative results were obtained with the nitroprusside test indicating that the essential thiol groups are of the sluggish type[65] which is supported by the weak inhibition by ferricyanide. However, the crude enzymes from *A. oryzae*[50] and *S. atra*[22] were not inhibited by thiol reagents, and three crude enzymes tested by Reese and Mandels[51] were unaffected by iodoacetate, but were inhibited by p–chloromercuribenzoate, an inhibition which was completely reversed by the addition of cysteine.

2. Sugars

It is well known that the cleavage products of enzymic hydrolyses of carbohydrates frequently inhibit the enzyme concerned, e.g. maltose inhibits the activity of β–amylase while glucose and fructose inhibit the activity of invertase. Such observations led to various studies on the effects of glucose and cellobiose on the enzymic hydrolysis of cellulose, and the work has been extended to include other sugars and sugar derivatives. Early workers[66] noted inhibition of *Helix* lichenase activity by cellobiose, glucose, fructose and galactose, the retarding effect depending upon the sugar added and the hydrogen ion concentration. The influence of various sugars on the action of green malt cellulase (purified and crude) on EHEC has been studied[8]. Cellobiose and lactose (both are disaccharides containing, respectively, β–glucosidic and β–galactosidic linkages), decreased the activities of these cellulases when present at a concentration greater than one per cent; below this level cellobiose had a stimulatory effect which also occurred in the presence of xylose, mannose and, particularly, glucose (see *Figure 4*).

The inhibitory effects of cellobiose on the cellulase from *Corynebacterium fimi*[60], of glucose on the action of *Cytophaga* preparations on lichenin and cellophane[32], and of cellobiose and lactose on the action of the enzyme from *Clostridium thermocellulaseum*[31] have been noted; (arabinose, glucose, xylose, mannose, fructose, galactose, maltose and sucrose had no effect on the last-named enzyme).

Inhibition of fungal cellulases by sugars has been more widely studied, much of the work involving the use of crude enzyme extracts. Extracts from *Tricholoma nudum*[49] were inhibited in their action on a cellulose sol by the presence of cellobiose, 2·5 per cent of this disaccharide causing a 50 per cent inhibition, the effect rising to a maximum of 70 per cent inhibition at a concentration of 10 per cent of cellobiose. The action of *Aspergillus niger* cellulase on phosphoric acid swollen cellulose was inhibited by glucose[67], but a crude preparation from *S. atra*[22] was not inhibited by any of eight sugars tested. Studies, using a purified cellulase from *Irpex lacteus*[68], were made on the hydrolysis of *p*–nitrophenyl β–cellobioside, which

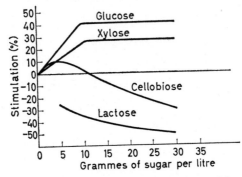

Figure 4—Effect of sugar on the cellulase activity of purified green malt cellulase (by courtesy, *Journal of the Institute of Brewing*, 1953, **59**, p. 205)

which was shown to be hydrolysed at the aglucone linkage as well as at the holosidic bond. It was shown that, while hydrolysis of the aglucone bond was hardly affected by the addition of glucose, cellobiose or phenyl β–glucoside, the presence of these compounds reduced the rate of hydrolysis of the holosidic linkage by one half to one third; phenol affected the hydrolysis of the two bonds in an exactly opposite manner. These results were interpreted in terms of a specific inhibition of cellulase by the end products of the hydrolysis reaction. The action of 'S factor' (see Chapter VI) was inhibited by the presence of cellobiose and glucose[69].

Early studies showed that cellobiose was the end product of the action of the 1: 4 β–polyglucosidase C_x which is said to hydrolyse the $(1\rightarrow4)$ β glucosidic linkages in such derivatives as CMC[70] and this observation led to an extensive study by Reese *et al.*[23] of the influence of cellobiose and other sugars on the hydrolysis of several cellulosic substrates by enzymes from various micro-organisms; most of the work was carried out using CMC, but ground de-waxed cotton and swollen cotton linters were also used. Initial results (see *Table 11*) indicated general inhibition of the reaction by cellobiose, with the exception of filtrates from two organisms whose action appeared to be stimulated by the presence of cellobiose, an effect

Table 11. *Effect of Cellobiose on Hydrolysis
of CMC by Filtrates from Various Organisms*
(by courtesy, *Physiologia Plantarum*, 1952,
5, p. 379)

Filtrate of	Cellobiose (2%)	
	pH 5·0	pH 7·0
Aspergillus flavus	I	I
Aspergillus fumigatus	I	
Aspergillus niger	I	
Memnoniella echinata	I	
Myrothecium verrucaria	S	O
Pencillium pusillum	I	I
Pestalotia palmarum	I	
Streptomyces sp.	S	I
Trichoderma viride	I	
Torula sp.	I	

I = inhibition   S = stimulation   O = no effect.

which was shown to be dependent upon the hydrogen ion concentration of the assay medium. Four organisms selected for further study were *M. verrucaria, Streptomyces* sp., *P. pusillum* and *T. viride*; the influence of hydrogen ion concentration, of cellobiose concentration and the relationship between these two factors were investigated. Results obtained varied widely for the different fungi and are represented graphically in *Figures 5* and *6*; the zone of optimum pH activity may be considerably extended by the addition of cellobiose, and as the alkalinity increased a decrease in the amount of stimulation or inhibition occurred amounting in some instances to a complete reversal of the effect; inhibition increased as cellobiose concentration was increased from 1 to 4 per cent, while the optimum concentration for stimulation was found to be one per cent for *Streptomyces* sp., and 0·5 per cent for *M. verrucaria*. The relationship between hydrogen ion concentration and cellobiose concentration is shown in *Figure 7*, from which it will be seen that at concentrations below 1·5 per cent only stimulation occurs, while at higher concentrations results similar to those in *Table 11* are obtained, that is stimulation at pH 5·0 and inhibition at pH 7·0, the concentration for maximum stimulation decreasing as the hydrogen ion concentration rises. Other sugars had little effect on CMC hydrolysis, but where stimulation by glucose did occur it had only slight dependence upon pH value and was at a maximum at about 2 per cent concentration.

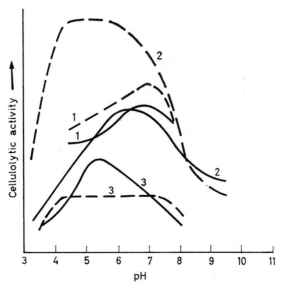

Figure 5—Effect of pH on stimulation and inhibition of fungal cellulase by cellobiose. ▬▬▬▬▬▬ with cellobiose, ▬▬▬▬ without cellobiose. 1. *Myrothecium verrucaria*; 2. *Streptomyces* sp.; 3. *Trichoderma viride* (by courtesy, *Physiologia Plantarum*, 1952, **5**, p. 382)

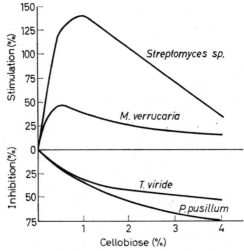

Figure 6—Effect of cellobiose concentration on stimulation and inhibition of fungal cellulases (by courtesy, *Physiologia Plantarum*, 1952, **5**, p. 384)

148

These results, using a CMC substrate, are in agreement with results obtained using other cellulosic derivatives (HEC and a cellulose acetate) indicating that the inhibition and stimulation effects reported were apparently independent of the nature of the substituents; however, hydrolyses of swollen cellulose and ground cotton fibre were both inhibited by the addition of cellobiose; no stimulation was observed under any conditions.

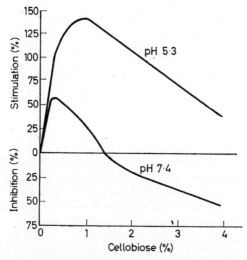

Figure 7—Relationship between hydrogen ion concentration and cellobiose concentration on stimulation of *Streptomyces* cellulase (by courtesy, *Physiologia Plantarum*, 1952, **5**, p. 383)

Various other sugar derivatives have been studied for their effect on cellulose hydrolysis. Methocel (methyl cellulose DS 1·8) was shown to inhibit the hydrolysis of soluble and insoluble substrates, by various filtrates to varying extents[23]. This work was later extended[51] and methocel was shown to cause between 40 and 50 per cent inhibition of the hydrolysis of CMC by filtrates from *T. viride*, *M. verrucaria*, and *Pestalotiopsis westerdijkii*; however cellulases from other organisms were less strongly affected. Derivatives of cellobiose and glucose, such as cellobionic acid, calcium gluconate, calcium arabonate and gluconolactone had no effect on cellulase action, but inhibited β–glucosidase activity derived from the same organisms. In general it was found that cellulase inhibitors did not inhibit β–glucosidase, and *vice versa*; methocel was the most efficient inhibitor of cellulase action and gluconolactone the best inhibitor of

β–glucosidase. In contrast gluconate caused slight inhibition of CMC hydrolysis by a preparation from *A. oryzae*[50], while it has been shown[73], in a study of the hydrolysis of CMC, cellophane, cellulose dextrin and cello-oligosaccharides by preparations from rumen micro-organisms, that gluconolactone, which completely inhibited cellobiase activity, also caused a maximum of 60 per cent inhibition of the enzyme hydrolysing CMC. As chain length of substrate increased, the degree of inhibition decreased, falling from a maximum of 100 per cent for the hydrolysis of cellobiose to 82 per cent for the hydrolysis of cellopentaose. The chief product of CMC hydrolysis was glucose and chromatographic evidence showed that gluconolactone inhibited the production of this causing only a slight accumulation of cellobiose and higher oligosaccharides; glucose production was also inhibited in the hydrolysis of cellulose dextrin and cello-oligosaccharides. It was concluded that gluconolactone caused a specific inhibition of glucose production from CMC, and as there was no marked increase in cellobiose, either glucose is split off directly from CMC, or else the production of glucose from cellopentaose and higher homologues is inhibited.

The inhibitory effect of cellobiose on the hydrolysis of cellulose and cellulose derivatives has thus been widely observed, and is in accordance with the inhibition of carbohydrases by the products of their reaction. The action may be due to cellobiose combining with the active centre of the enzyme competitively. However, lactose has also been shown to have an inhibitory effect on the action of bacterial[31], malt[8] and fungal[51] cellulases. This disaccharide and cellobiose both contain β–glycosidic bonds, similar to cellulose, and it may be that cellulase combines generally with poly- and and oligo-saccharides which have the β–configuration. This view is supported by the hydrolysis of xylan (a poly $(1\rightarrow4)$ β–xyloside) and other β–glucans[74] by many cellulolytic enzymes[75,76]. Inhibition of cellulolytic enzymes by glucose may likewise be the effect of cleavage products inhibiting enzyme action, some workers[6] stating that glucose and cellobiose are the products of cellulolytic action, not cellobiose alone.

The stimulatory effect of cellobiose is the exception rather than the rule, occurring only when soluble cellulose derivatives have been used as substrates; the reason for this effect is obscure; two possible explanations have been put forward by Reese and co-workers[23]; (i) that the sugars have a protective action on the enzyme, similar actions being reported for α–amylase by starch and its hydrolysis products, and for invertase by sucrose; (ii) that cellobiose aids the removal of undesirable products from active centres on the enzyme molecule by competing for the same areas. A third possible explanation emerges from the separation of three components from a culture filtrate obtained from *T. viride* by chromatography on a calcium phosphate gel column[77]. The action of the crude filtrate on CMC was inhibited by the addition of cellobiose, as was the action of two of the column fractions, the third fraction being unaffected. With a different batch of culture filtrate from the same organism two of the column fractions obtained were inhibited as before, while the third was highly stimulated. It is suggested that any particular crude filtrate may be inhibited or stimulated depending on the relative amounts of the three components present.

3. Proteins and Amino-acids

During the purification of *M. verrucaria* cellulase it was noted that stimulation of cellulolytic activity occurred in the presence of added proteins[20]. The activation of urease by the addition of proteins has already been mentioned, and the activation of pancreatic lipase by albumin and by peptides is well known[79]. Cellulase activation occurred in response to the addition of Dubos' medium serum, crystalline bovine plasma albumin, crystalline β–lactoglobulin, crystalline pepsin, crystalline lysozyme, gelatin and the non-dialysable fraction of a proteose-peptone, a product which contained no protein; tryptone and peptone were ineffective. The activating effect was confined to insoluble substrates. Preliminary incubation of enzyme alone for a period of twenty-four hours prior to assay caused loss in activity, while the increases in activity due to the addition of protein were not significantly different whether protein was added at the beginning or at the end of the preliminary incubation period; thus it appeared that the effect of protein was not due to the protection of the enzyme (against denaturation or inhibitors present in the assay medium). Four factors appeared to influence the extent of stimulation; it varied with hydrogen ion concentration, being more effective at low pH values, stimulation was greater at lower temperatures, stimulation was proportional to substrate concentration and inversely proportional to enzyme concentration. Similar effects have been noted by other workers, and an apparent movement of pH optimum from pH (5·7 to 6·5) to pH (5·0 to 5·7) was observed using a partially purified *M. verrucaria* preparation[72]. Stimulation of *Helix* cellulase was observed[14] if the enzyme was purified; crude enzyme was not activated by added protein, but the addition of insulin, β–lactoglobulin, crystalline bovine serum albumin and lysozyme to purified enzyme stimulated hydrolysis of soluble and insoluble substrates; pre-incubation of enzyme with protein counteracted loss of activity which occurred on pre-incubation of enzyme alone. The addition of albumin to crude enzyme caused stimulation of hydrolysis of other carbohydrates. It was concluded that the effect of protein on *Helix* cellulase activity was due to protection of the enzyme from denaturation, however, Whitaker *et al.*[20,52] concluded that the added protein was partially adsorbed on the insoluble substrate and suggested this may be responsible for the stimulation mechanism, possibly due to changes in the surface potential of the cellulose.

In contrast to these results certain other cellulolytic enzymes have been inactivated or inhibited by proteins. Thus 'S' factor was inactivated by crystalline pepsin[43] and the action of enzyme preparations from *T. viride*, *M. verrucaria* and *Pestalotiopsis westerdijkii* was inhibited by proteolytic enzymes (trypsin and ficin) under conditions favouring the action of these proteases[51]. Since these inhibitors are all proteolytic enzymes their action may be due to their proteolytic effect.

The effect of the amino-acids cystine and cysteine has been studied using filtrates of *M. verrucaria*[52] and *A. oryzae*[50]. Completely opposite effects were noted; both amino-acids caused marked stimulation of crude filtrates from *A. oryzae*, while cysteine caused slight inhibition of activity of a purified cellulase from *M. verrucaria*. These compounds are thiol reagents and the effect of these has been discussed earlier, or their action may be due to their complexing ability with other substances present in the filtrates.

4. Anionic and Cationic Compounds

Cellulases are proteins and as such are most stable and uncharged at their isoelectric point; at pH values above this point enzymes ionize as weak acids and are precipitated by cationic inhibitors, while at pH values more acid than the isoelectric point enzymes ionize as weak bases and are precipitated by anionic inhibitors. A very wide range of compounds may be included under this classification heading, of which acidic (anionic inhibitors) and basic (cationic inhibitors) dyes have been studied for their effect on *M. verrucaria* purified cellulase[52], and the effect of various surfactants on crude fungal filtrates has been observed[51].

Dyestuffs.—The influence of basic dyestuffs on bacterial dehydrogenases[80] and on fumarase, urease and sucrase[81] is well known, and it was shown that an increase in hydrogen ion concentration increased inhibition. The effect of dyestuffs on the hydrolysis of insoluble cellulose substrates by *M. verrucaria* cellulase was investigated at varying hydrogen ion concentrations[52]. Some of the results are summarized in *Table 12*.

The influence of hydrogen ion concentration is very marked, acid dyes were very inhibitory at low pH values (3·8), inhibition de-

Table 12. *Effect of Dyestuffs on* M. verrucaria *Cellulase Activity* (by courtesy, *Archives of Biochemistry and Biophysics*, 1953, **42**, pp. 18, 19)

Dye	Class	Enzyme activity %				
		pH 3·2	*pH 3·8*	*pH 4·6*	*pH 6·0*	*pH 7·0*
Disazo dyes						
Benzopurpurin*	A		4·4	64·4	93·3	
Bordeaux extra	A		5·0	40·7	93·9	
Chlorazol fast pink*	A		6·7	82·4	97·2	
Congo red*	A		2·3	2·1	89·2	80·1
Trypan blue	A		2·5	27·7	90·5	
Bismarck brown	B	217	124	95·1	92·8	90·6
Janus red	B	204	118	99·0	93·6	98·3
Monoazo dyes						
Orange G.	A		89·2	99·5	99·6	
Chrysoidine Y.	B		97·4	97·3	102	
Janus green	B	202		103	93	84·6
Xanthene dyes						
Eosin	A		4·4	71·8	87·8	
Erythrosin	A		3·5	11·8	65·0	48·1
Pyronine G.	B	172		102	91·1	80·5
Triphenyl methane dyes						
Acid fuchsin	A		61·9	90·2	93·5	89·7
Aniline blue	A		4·6	84·3	91·9	
Brilliant green	B	121		99·0	92·7	
Crystal violet	B	189	111	99·2	69·2	29·2
Victoria blue	B	151	82·7	41·7	28·5	35·7
Eurhodine dyes						
Neutral red	B	166		95·3	80·4	77·9
Thiazine dyes						
Methylene blue	B	110	104	90·9	81·6	79·6
Ketonimine dyes						
Auramine	B	106		98·1	95·1	82·3

* dye completely adsorbed by substrate.
A = acid dye. B = basic dye, substrate cotton linters.

creased as the pH value rose and on the whole these dyes had little effect at pH 6·0; basic dyes were stimulatory at low pH values (3·2 and 3·8) and inhibitory to varying extents (according to the class of dye) at the neutral point. Using a soluble substrate (CMC) the effect was similar to that obtained using cotton linters, but less pronounced. The influence of these dyes on cellulase activity is similar to their influence on sucrase activity[81] which is attributed to the formation of a sucrase-dye complex, the degree of association of which depends on the ionic charges of the components and their change with pH value, thus influencing the degree of inhibition or stimulation. It was noticed that certain dyes were adsorbed on the substrate and Basu and Whitaker suggest that if dye inhibition is due to the formation of such a complex then it is likely to be a dye-enzyme-substrate complex. The inhibition by acid dyes at low pH values and basic dyes at high pH values may be quite logically explained assuming they act as anionic and cationic inhibitors respectively. Stimulation by basic dyes at low pH values cannot be thus explained, and it was suggested that adsorption of the dye on the substrate is responsible for this phenomenon, while the effect of these substances in changing the surface potential of cellulose[58] and thus influencing enzyme action must also be taken into account.

Surfactants.—The effect of various surfactants has been investigated, using crude culture filtrates from *T. viride*, *M. verrucaria* and *Pestalotiopsis westerdijkii*. *T. viride* and *M. verrucaria* filtrates were hardly affected at all except by sodium petroleum sulphates, while the filtrate from *P. westerdijkii* was strongly inhibited by a range of compounds including some quaternary ammonium compounds and halogenated phenol derivatives. Alkyldimethylbenzylammonium chloride (Roccal), a cationic compound, and dioctyl sodium sulphosuccinate (Aerosol), an anionic compound, were selected for further study using filtrates of *T. viride* and *P. westerdijkii*. Inhibition by this type of compound was very dependent upon hydrogen ion concentration. Aerosol was inhibitory at low pH values, having only a little effect above pH 5·5, while Roccal was particularly inhibitory above pH 5·0 to 5·5, and in fact had no effect on *T. viride* filtrates below this pH value.

5. Other substances

Various other substances have been examined for their effect on cellulase activity.

(a) *Antiseptics.*—The effect of antiseptics added to assay media to prevent bacterial growth has been investigated using preparations from *Cytophaga* which were inhibited by toluene and chloroform[32], and an *Aspergillus niger* preparation, against which a whole series of antiseptics was evaluated[83], all of which inhibited cellulase activity with the exception of Dowicide D (the sodium salt of 2–chloro–4–phenylphenol). Inhibitory compounds included phenylmercuric acetate, Roccal, thymol and toluene. Toluene also inhibited the action of *M. verrucaria* cellulase[52].

(b) *Antibiotics.*—Small quantities of streptomycin and penicillin had no effect on the action of cellulase from various *Mollusca*[84]. However, certain antibiotics did affect fungal cellulases[51]; tetracycline, endomycin, polymyxin, actidione, penicillin and aureomycin had no effect; thiolutin caused from 25 to 75 per cent inhibition of the enzymes, while gliotoxin at the same concentration level (0·33 per cent), caused stimulation. Results with other antibiotics (streptomycin, griseofulvin, viridin and mycophenolic acid) were inconsistent, reacting differently with different filtrates, and varied from slight stimulation to 30 per cent inhibition. It was concluded that antibiotics were not very promising compounds for further study.

(c) *Phenols, substituted phenols, halogens and related compounds.*—An extensive investigation of these compounds has been made[51] using filtrates from the fungi *T. viride*, *M. verrucaria* and *P. westerdijkii*; the results indicated that, while phenol itself was not inhibitory, substituted phenols were very efficient inhibitors of the enzymes decomposing CMC, and in fact were more effective inhibitors of these enzymes than of β–glucosidases derived from the same organisms. Many of these compounds are insoluble in water and if assayed in citrate buffer at pH 5·3 as a suspension were relatively ineffective. However, modifications of the assay method, whereby the compounds were used in solution, increased their efficiency as inhibitors. The most active inhibitors were found to be tetra- and pentachlorophenol, and the chlorophenylphenols, all of which contain halogen molecules, but the presence of halogens in the substituent was not necessary to obtain active inhibition, thus sodium orthophenyl phenate also caused extensive inhibition. The method by which the compounds effect inhibition is unknown, but it was suggested that they may act by precipitation of enzyme protein; since phenol itself did not inhibit it was thought improbable that they complexed with the enzyme at the active centre.

Other halogen-containing compounds which were shown to affect activity included chlorine, calcium hypochlorite, and iodine which has been shown elsewhere to cause very slight stimulation of *A. oryzae* cellulose[50]. Certain organic compounds which released active halogen, were among the strongest inhibitors found in an extensive investigation; the structure R–N–X, where X represents a halogen atom, was thought to be required for activity; thus N–chloro– and N–bromo–succinimide were very active, other imides tested showed little activity with the exception of N–(trichloromethylthio) 1:2:3:6 tetrahydrophthalimide. Other inhibitors found included chloromelamine, dichloramine B and trichloro*iso*cyanuric acid. Inhibition by these compounds was strong, rapid and irreversible, but some protection was afforded by sulphydryl and amino compounds; it is possible that they react with amino groups in the enzyme.

Other iodine compounds causing inhibition included tetraglycine potassium iodide and tetraglycine hydroperiodide. Iodine may act as a weak oxidizing agent, while under mild conditions it is considered specific for the phenolic ring in tyrosine. Some protection to the enzyme may be afforded by cysteine, S–ethyl cysteine and sodium thiosulphate. These iodine compounds did not inhibit β–glucosidase to the same extent as cellulase, an observation also true for the chlorine containing compounds.

(d) *Metal complexing reagents.*—Inhibition of *A. oryzae* cellulase[50] by 8–hydroxyquinoline, nitroso–R salt, rhodizonic acid and cupferron has been recorded, the action of the latter being completely reversed by ferric compounds. Dithiocarbamates (disodium ethylenebis– and zinc ethylenebis–) were reported to inhibit fungal cellulases derived from *T. viride* and *M. verrucaria*, but were ineffective against *P. westerdijkii* cellulase and against β–glucosidases derived from these three organisms[51].

(e) *Miscellaneous.*—Sodium naphthenate and sodium stearate (both representative of classes of compounds used as rot-proofing agents for cellulosic textiles) had a slightly inhibitory effect on the action of *M. verrucaria* purified cellulase[52]. Caffeine, adenine, quinine, betaine and certain simple amines (methylamine– and dimethylamine hydrochlorides) inhibited *A. oryzae* enzymes, while trimethylamine hydrochloride caused marked stimulation of these enzymes[50]. Phenylmercuric acetate, mercury dibutyl and octyl gallate, salicylanilide and nitrosopyrazoles all caused some inactivation of enzymes from *T. viride*, *M. verrucaria* and *P. westerdijkii* which decomposed CMC. These compounds were relatively ineffective in inhibiting β–glucosidases derived from the same organisms[51].

(f) *Choice of buffer.*—In assessing compounds used in activation and inhibition studies, the choice of buffer used in assay may have an influence on the effect of the reagent. Thus Ziese[12], using a preparation of *Helix* cellulase, found that glutathione and cysteine in phosphate buffer caused inhibition of this enzyme, but not in citrate buffer of the same pH value. Crude extracts from *Fusarium moniliforme* were shown to be nearly twice as active in acetate buffer compared with phosphate buffer of the same molarity and hydrogen ion concentration[75]. Results obtained by Jermyn[50] testing various inhibitors using acetate buffer and McIlvaine buffer (a phosphate-citrate buffer) of approximately the same pH value (iodine consumption using CMC was practically identical in both cases) are shown in *Table 13*. Thus in assessing results of activation and

Table 13. *Effect of Buffer on Inhibition of* A. oryzae *Cellulase by Various Compounds* (by courtesy, *Australian Journal of Scientific Research*, 1952, **B5**, pp. 424, 426)

Inhibitor	Enzyme activity %	
	Acetate buffer	McIlvaine buffer
None	100	100
Cyanide	46	0
Dithionite	0	0
Cupferron	0	54
Nitroso R salt	66	108
Caffeine	56	39
Betaine	30	17

Concentrations of individual compounds were identical in each case.

inhibition studies the components of the buffer used, as well as the hydrogen ion concentration, is yet another variable which has to be taken into consideration.

Conclusions

From the above account it can be seen that the action of cellulases is influenced by a large number of substances including metallic ions, sugars, dyes, proteins and halogen-containing compounds. It has been shown that the action of any one substance on cellulase can be changed from inhibition to stimulation or *vice versa* by even a slight alteration of external conditions. This factor probably accounts for many of the divergent results which have been obtained, and emphasizes the need for very strict control and careful consideration of the influence of other factors in work of this type. The extensive use, which has been made in the majority of these studies, of impure enzymes may be desirable because tests have thus been carried out in the presence of proteins, polysaccharides and other foreign matter which may exert a protective influence on the enzyme, and as such a closer emulation of natural conditions, which fungicides might meet in practical use, will have been obtained than in studies using pure enzymes; however the use of these latter enable the mechanism of inhibition or activation by any particular compound to be studied.

COMPOSITION AND STRUCTURE OF CELLULASES

All enzymes are believed to be proteins, and may be simple proteins, containing a special structure—the active centre—or they may be bound to an additional prosthetic group such as the enzymes concerned in oxidation, which are conjugated proteins where the apoenzyme (protein part) is attached to a prosthetic group such as haematin, riboflavin phosphate or pyridoxal phosphate. In most cases the activity of the prosthetic group alone is nil and the activity arises from the active centre of the protein or its combination with the apoenzyme. Enzyme structure therefore includes consideration of the structure of the protein part (size, amino-acids present and their sequence, arrangement of peptide chains), nature of the active centre (including number of active centres per enzyme molecule and chemical nature of the substrate binding and activating groups in the active centre) and the structure of the prosthetic group, if any, and its mode of attachment to the protein portion. Certain parts of the protein molecule of some enzymes appear to be inessential for activity, thus certain parts of the protein molecule of chymotrypsin can be removed without impairing activity. However certain parts of the enzyme molecule cannot be removed or changed without loss of the activity and these groups are the essential groups of the enzyme, some of which are essential because they are involved in the binding of the substrate molecule, others have nothing to do with the formation of the enzyme-substrate compound, but are essential to its decomposition. Essential groups in some cases may be demonstrated by ordinary chemical methods, in other cases by inactivation or inhibition of the enzyme by specific reagents, as in the case of sulphydryl groups.

Little work has been done on the structure of cellulases. Evidence for the existence of essential thiol groups by inhibition and activation studies has already been presented in enzymes from *M. verrucaria*[52] and *P. vaillantii*[18], while failure to prove their presence by similar means in the case of *S. atra*[22] and preparations from *M. verrucaria*, *T. viride* and *P. westerdijkii*[51] has been seen. No cysteine or cystine was found in these four enzyme preparations on analysis; however, fourteen amino-acids found in crude cellulase from *S. atra* were aspartic and glutamic acids, serine, glycine, histidine, lysine, arginine, threonine, alanine, proline, tyrosine, valine, phenylalanine and leucine[22]. Characterisation of purified *M. verrucaria* cellulase has given evidence of only one N–terminal amino-acid, while work is in progress characterizing the S–linkages[85].

Little else is known concerning cellulase structure, apart from the work of Whitaker *et al.*[25] on some of the physical properties of cellulase isolated from *M. verrucaria*. A summary of the properties determined is given as follows:—

Diffusion coefficient, $D_{w,20}$ $= (5.6 \pm 0.1) \times 10^{-7}$
Sedimentation constant, $S_{w,20}$ $= (3.7 \pm 0.05) \times 10^{-3}$
Intrinsic viscosity, $[\eta]$ $= 0.087 \pm 0.002$
(assuming a nitrogen content of 16 per cent).

From these figures, and making various assumptions, it was possible to deduce the molecular weight to be $63,000 \pm 1,500$, and the frictional coefficient to be 1.44 ± 0.02. The hydrodynamically equivalent ellipsoid is said to be prolate with an axial ratio estimated between 5 and 10.

These calculations enabled these workers to say that the enzyme molecule was cigar shaped, roughly 200Å long and 33Å broad at its widest point, and if oriented lengthwise along a fully extended cellulose chain, it would cover nearly 20 cellobiose repeating units.

The presence of several protein components in crude cellulolytic preparations and their separation has been discussed elsewhere (Chapter IV). The close association of protein with carbohydrate in some of these has been noted[22,86], although it has been shown that the purified preparation from *M. verrucaria* has no such carbohydrate moiety[71]. It has been shown that a β–glucosidase preparation from *S. atra*[3] contained such a carbohydrate component, which was essential for the stability of the enzyme, but not for its activity. The carbohydrate found in association with *S. atra* cellulase[22] yielded galactose, mannose, glucose and small quantities of xylose on acid hydrolysis.

The close association of cellulase proteins with such polysaccharides or, possibly, other metabolic products may provide an additional explanation of the confusion of properties reported in the literature.

SYNTHESIS OF CELLULASES

Two distinct types of enzymes have been recognized, those which are 'constitutive' and are produced by an organism independently of the presence of the substrate in the external medium, and those which appear only in the presence of the substrate or a structurally related analogue, known as 'adaptive'. These latter enzymes may arise by two distinct processes; a few cells present in any culture may possess the enzyme, it having arisen by mutation, and in the presence of the substrate these may multiply preferentially; this is true adaptation in an evolutionary sense. In the second case it has been shown that enzymes may be produced when washed cells are placed in a medium containing substrate plus an assimilable nitrogen source, under conditions when no appreciable increase in cell numbers occurs. It has been shown that the enzyme is directly induced in the cells by the presence of substrate and does not arise by the growth of mutants. These enzymes are said to be 'inducible' rather than 'adaptive'. The distinction between inducible and constitutive enzymes appears to be one of amount rather than of type, for it is established that most inducible enzymes are present in traces, even without the presence of an inducer, and the amount of many constitutive enzymes increases in the presence of their substrates.

When attempting to classify enzymes the question arises as to which compounds can be said to act as inducers; in most cases only substances closely related to the substrate of a particular enzyme can act as inducers. An extensive survey was carried out by Monod et al.[47] on the ability of a series of galactosides, sugars and other glycosides to act as inducers for the β–galactosidase of *Escherichia coli*. It was shown that the enzyme was not produced in response to galactose-free sugars, deoxygalactosides, galacturonates, β–L–arabinosides or 2–, 3–, 4– or 6– substituted β–galactosides; however, effective inducers included galactose, various β–D–galactosides and α–D–galactosides (but not raffinose). It was observed that all inducers possessed the galactose ring, and a compound might be an inducer but not a substrate and *vice versa*, and the efficiency of different compounds to act as inducers varied considerably.

Few such detailed studies have been made on the constitutive or inducible nature of cellulases. It has been shown that certain bacteria (*Clostridium thermocellum* and *Cellulomonas* sp.) produced cellulases when grown on media containing cellulose, cellobiose, glucose, starch, hemicellulose, xylose, mannitol and glycerol as carbon sources[64]. Other workers obtained cellulase from cultures of *Clostridium thermocellulaseum* grown on xylose[31]. If the work of Monod et al. can be regarded as supplying a definition of inducible character then, clearly, these bacterial cellulases must be regarded as constitutive. The position is less clearly defined for fungal cellulases, but generally they are regarded as being inducible. The production of cellulases by 33 fungi grown on various carbon sources has been studied[78]. It was found that, by the majority of cellulolytic fungi, cellulase was produced in varying amounts during growth on a variety of cellulosic substrates ranging from wood and cotton to hydroxyethylcellulose, alkali cellulose and dextrin; in only one case, *Aspergillus luchuensis*, was the enzyme produced in appreciable quantities during growth on glucose. Clearly, then, these enzymes must be regarded as inducible. A detailed study[82] of cellulase production by *Trichoderma viride* has been made and it was found that the enzyme was produced during growth on cellulose, cellobiose, glucose and lactose, all of which contain D–glucose; no enzyme was detected during growth on a wide variety of other substrates including pentoses, hexoses, di- and tri-saccharides, alcohols including glycerol and mannitol, sugar acids, glucosides, substituted sugars and polymeric carbohydrates including starch and xylan. Various forms of cellulose used for growth all acted as inducers, but with varying degrees of efficiency. This enzyme can probably be regarded as inducible, as can the enzyme from *Stachybotrys atra*[22] which was produced in very minute amounts during growth on glucose, and in much larger amounts in response to cellulose. In contrast to these results, appreciable amounts of cellulase were produced from cultures of *Fusarium roseum* grown on xylan. In analogy to the results quoted above this enzyme must, then, be regarded as constitutive[75]; if the specificity of substrate required by the β–galactosidase of *E. coli* be regarded as a criterion to be applied generally, then the difference in structure between β–D–galactosides (substrates) and β–L–arabinosides (non-substrates) is similar to that between cellulose and xylan, then the synthesis of cellulases by the growth of microorganisms on non-cellulosic substrates or the hydrolytic products therefrom (e.g. xylan, lactose, starch, mannitol or glycerol) must lead to a query on the inducible character of the enzyme. Indeed if spatial configuration is considered, a crystalline cellulose may exhibit even greater differences from a branched-chain xylan than do the compounds mentioned above. However, if a pure cellulase from *F. roseum* hydrolysed xylan (*cf.* purified cellulase from *M. verrucaria*[76]) then the production of this enzyme on xylan may not be indicative of its constitutive nature at all. Clearly the position regarding the nature of fungal cellulases requires much more detailed study and until this is done no definite answer can be given to the question whether these enzymes are inducible or constitutive.

KINETICS OF CELLULASE ACTION

Although the specific function of cellulases is the catalysis of cellulose hydrolysis, the heterogeneous nature of this substrate has prompted many workers to study the mechanism of enzymic hydrolysis of soluble substrates ranging from carboxymethylcellulose to cellobiose.

Many older accounts of the kinetics of cellulose hydrolysis by crude enzyme mixtures have demonstrated that the reaction follows the monomolecular law[12,87,88]. It is difficult to assess the reaction kinetics of such crude enzymes, especially when it is realized that some of the major impurities may be proteins, many of which have a stimulatory action on the hydrolysis; other impurities, such as heavy metals and some carbohydrates, may act as inhibitors. On insoluble and crystalline substrates, it must be borne in mind that the primary action of crude enzymes and particularly of micro-organisms may not be simple hydrolysis; an account of the swelling action on cellulose is given in Chapter VI.

Certain general relationships have emerged in spite of these strictures; for example, a crude snail cellulase acting on Bemberg rayon gave a logarithmic relation between enzyme concentration and extent of hydrolysis[89]:

$$\text{Reducing sugar yield } (A\%) = -k \log V$$

where V is the dilution of the enzyme extract; these hydrolyses were carried out for incubation periods from 72 to 288 hours at 36°. For short periods of hydrolysis, Karrer[88] showed that the monomolecular law was followed, although later the *Aspergillus niger* cellulase of Walseth[83] did not follow either this law or the Schutz rule (i.e. the extent of the hydrolysis is proportional to the square root of the reaction time); on the other hand, the cellulase of *Puccinia graminis* followed the Schutz rule[63].

Considering only the effect of the concentration of the enzyme, no direct relationship between this quantity and the extent of hydrolysis has been found. Many workers have determined the increase in rate of substrate decomposition when enzyme concentration was doubled; typical values for the increase in rate generally lie in the range 1·2 to 1·8 times. Pringsheim and Baur[90] noted that such proportionality depended on the type of cellulosic substrate. Levinson and Reese[91] found direct proportionality between cellulase concentration and rate of hydrolysis for the enzyme from *Myrothecium verrucaria*, but not for other fungal enzymes, and then only if the reaction was followed by viscometry using a soluble substrate. A direct relationship could not be demonstrated with the cellulase of *Clostridium thermocellulaseum*; if an interval for the rate of change of specific fluidity $\left(\dfrac{d\phi_{sp}}{dt}\right)$ of 0·006 to 0·015 was chosen using an ethyl hydroxyethylcellulose substrate, the extent of hydrolysis was increased by only 1·75 times when the enzyme concentration was doubled[31]. Whitaker has studied the effect of enzyme concentration on the rate of hydrolysis of cellobiose and various precipitated and swollen celluloses; typical values are given below:

	Precipitated cellulose			Swollen linters		
Enzyme concentration	2	4	6	2	4	6
Reducing sugar produced	1	1·63	2·08	1	1·73	2·33

Even for cellobiose, the extent of hydrolysis increased 1·73 times on doubling the enzyme concentration[6]. These results may be fitted to the equation:

$$\text{Extent of hydrolysis} \propto \log [E]$$

where $[E]$ is the enzyme concentration. By using his modification of the Hultin equation for the viscometric assay of enzyme activity (see Chapter IV), Thomas[22] investigated the influence of enzyme concentration on the activity of *Stachybotrys atra* extracts. Using the equation:

$$\text{Enzyme activity} = \left(\eta_{sp}\right)_{t=0}^{1\cdot25} \left(\frac{d\phi_{sp}}{dt}\right)^{1\cdot1}$$

it was shown that an almost linear relationship existed between $[E]$ and activity. In the same paper, Thomas has also considered the effect of enzyme concentrations on activity at various substrate concentrations $[S]$, and showed that the above equation was obeyed at three values of $[S]$, whereas the linear relationship between $[E]$ and the rate of change of fluidity forecast by the Hultin equation

$$[E] = [S]^2 \left(\frac{d\phi_{sp}}{dt}\right)$$

did not apply in the range of $[S]$ values used.

In considering the effect of substrate concentration on activity, it is possible to arrange either to maintain a constant value for $[E]$ or to keep the ratio of $[E]:[S]$ the same while varying $[S]$. Walseth[83] studied both these conditions; for an increase in $[S]$ at constant $[E]$ the extent of hydrolysis fell, whilst for constant ratio of $[E]:[S]$ of 0·298:1 the extent of hydrolysis increased with increasing $[S]$. These results confirm a statement made by Karrer[88] that to obtain maximum hydrolysis of cellulose, solutions of the highest possible concentrations should be used. However, Walseth points out that, for a given value of $[E]$, the enzymic hydrolysis of a high total fraction of a given cellulosic substrate is promoted by a low ratio of substrate to the volume of the solution. Most other workers[22,91] have concentrated on relationships between specific fluidity changes and $[E]$ at various values of $[S]$, as discussed above.

Whitaker has investigated the action of his purified cellulase on a wide range of substrates under different conditions; whilst his consideration of steric factors in the hydrolysis of cello-oligosaccharides does not belong to the field of kinetics, his careful analysis of rate constants and activation energies deserves attention here. Using oligosaccharides containing two to five β–glucose units, Whitaker[44] showed that while the rate constant for the enzymic hydrolysis was increased by a factor of approximately 450 as the series was ascended (from DP 2 to DP 5), the activation energy for the reactions remained at about 12,000 calories. In a rare application of the classical collision theory, the results are taken to indicate that this increase in rate constant with DP is determined by an increase in a steric factor with DP. Thus, the partial reduction of the oligoglucosides in the presence of Raney nickel[92] gave a range from sorbityl–β–glucoside to sorbityl–β–cellotetraoside, and this addition of the β–sorbityl group increased the rate constant; but this increase was less than that attributable to the addition of the anhydroglucose unit, and, relative to the latter, these rate constants decreased as the DP of the oligosaccharide chain (undergoing addition) was increased. The differential effects recorded were interpreted as implying that the enzyme, like the substrate, can undergo structural changes, the effect of which on enzymic action vary with the DP of the substrate; it was suggested that the lower the DP, the less is activity toward it favoured by the properties of the enzyme. This effect is supplemented by the conclusion, arrived at from considerations of the differential effects of enzyme denaturation, that the lower the DP of the substrate, the less is activity toward it favoured by certain changes in enzyme properties. Whitaker considered the effects of surface and thermal enzyme denaturation to account, at least in part, for the multiple components found by Gilligan and Reese[77] in their *Myrothecium* cellulase.

REFERENCES

1. FRENCH, KNAPP AND PAZUR, *J. Amer. chem. Soc.* 1950, **72**, p. 1866.
2. SÖRENSEN, *Biochem. Z.* 1909, **21**, p. 131.
3. JERMYN, *Aust. J. biol. Sci.* 1955, **8**, p. 541.
4. MASSEY AND ALBERTY, *Biochim. Biophys. Acta*, 1954, **13**, p. 354.
5. HASE, *J. Biochem. Japan*, 1952, **39**, p. 257.
6. WHITAKER, *Arch. Biochem. Biophys.* 1953, **43**, p. 253.
7. MICHAELIS AND DAVIDSON, *Biochem. Z.* 1911, **35**, p. 386.
8. ENEBO, SANDEGREN AND LJUNGDAHL, *J. Inst. Brewing*, 1953, **59**, p. 205.
9. TRACEY, *Biochem. J.* 1950, **47**, p. 431.
10. KARRER AND ILLING, *Kolloidzschr.*, Special No., 91 (April 1925).
11. FREUDENBERG AND PLOETZ, *Hoppe-Seyl. Z.* 1939, **259**, p. 19.

12. ZIESE, *Hoppe-Seyl. Z.* 1931, **203**, p. 87.
13. HOLDEN AND TRACEY, *Biochem. J.* 1950, **47**, p. 407.
14. MYERS AND NORTHCOTE, *Biochem. J.* 1959, **71**, p. 749.
15. GREENFIELD AND LANE, *J. biol. Chem.* 1953, **204**, p. 669.
16. HUNGATE, *Biol. Bull.* 1942, **83**, p. 303.
17. TOYAMA, *J. Ferment. Technol. Japan*, 1956, **34**, p. 281.
18. SISON, SCHUBERT AND NORD, *Arch. Biochem. Biophys.* 1958, **75**, p. 260.
19. WHISTLER AND SMART, *J. Amer. chem. Soc.* 1953, **75**, p. 1916.
20. WHITAKER, *Science*, 1952, **116**, p. 90.
21. STONE, Ph.D. Thesis, University of London, 1954.
22. THOMAS, *Aust. J. biol. Sci.* 1956, **9**, p. 159.
23. REESE, GILLIGAN AND NORKRANS, *Physiol. Plant.* 1952, **5**, p. 379.
24. MANSOUR AND MANSOUR-BEK, *Enzymologia*, 1937, **4**, p. 1.
25. WHITAKER, COLVIN AND COOK, *Arch. Biochem. Biophys.* 1954, **49**, p. 257.
26. REESE AND GILLIGAN. *Arch. Biochem. Biophys.* 1953, **45**, p. 74.
27. HIRSCH, *Experientia*, 1954, **10**, p. 80.
28. SAUNDERS, SIU AND GENEST, *J. biol. Chem.* 1948, **174**, p. 697.
29. SCHUBERT AND NORD, *J. Amer. chem. Soc.* 1950, **72**, p. 978.
30. TOYAMA, *J. Ferment. Technol. Japan*, 1952, **30**, p. 409; 1953, **31**, p. 315.
31. ENEBO, *Studies in Cellulose Decomposition*, 1954, Stockholm.
32. FÅHRAEUS, *Symbolae botan. Upsalienses*, 1947, **9**, p. 1.
33. NORTHROP, *Ergebn. Enzymforsch.* 1932, **1**, p. 302.
34. NORTHROP AND KUNITZ, *Ergebn. Enzymforsch.* 1933, **2**, 104.
35. COLOWICK AND KALCKAR, *J. biol. Chem.* 1943, **148**, p. 117.
36. MEYER AND RAPPORT, *Advances in Enzymology*, 1952, **13**, p. 199.
37. McCOLLOCH AND KERTESZ, *Arch. Biochem.* 1948, **17**, p. 197.
38. SANDEGREN AND ENEBO, *J. Inst. Brewing*, 1952, **58**, p. 198.
39. KOOIMAN, ROELOFSEN AND SWEERIS, *Enzymologia*, 1953, **16**, p. 237.
40. PRINGSHEIM, *Hoppe-Seyl. Z.* 1912, **78**, p. 266.
41. AITKEN, EDDY, INGRAM AND WEURMAN, *Biochem. J.* 1956, **64**, p. 63.
42. SISON AND SCHUBERT, *Arch. Biochem. Biophys.* 1958, **78**, p. 563.
43. MARSH, BOLLENBACHER, BUTLER AND GUTHRIE, *Text. Res. J.* 1953, **23**, p. 878.
44. WHITAKER, *Canad. J. biochem. Physiol.* 1956, **34**, p. 102.
45. PUTNAM, *The Proteins*, ed. Neurath and Bailey, Vol. I, p. 807, 1953, Academic Press, New York.
46. VEIBEL, *The Enzymes, Chemistry and Mechanism of Action*, Vol. I, part 1, p. 583, 1950, ed. Pigman and Myrbäck, Academic Press Inc., New York.
47. MONOD, COHEN-BAZIRE AND COHN, *Biochim. Biophys. Acta*, 1951, **7**, p. 585.
48. MISRA AND RANGANATHAN, *Proc. Indian Acad. Sci.* 1954, **39B**, p. 100.
49. NORKRANS, *Symbolae botan. Upsalienses*, 1950, **11**, p. 5.
50. JERMYN, *Aust. J. Sci. Res.* 1952, **B5**, p. 409.
51. REESE AND MANDELS, Research Report from Pioneering Research Division, Quartermaster Research and Development Centre, Microbiology Series No. 17, February, 1957.

52. BASU AND WHITAKER, *Arch. Biochem. Biophys.* 1953, **42**, p. 12.
53. MYRBÄCK, *Hoppe-Seyl. Z.* 1926, **158**, p. 4.
54. MYRBÄCK, *Hoppe-Seyl. Z.* 1926, **159**, p. 1.
55. YUDKIN, *Enzymologia*, 1937, **2**, p. 161.
56. SUMNER AND HAND, *J. biol. Chem.* 1928, **76**, p. 149.
57. DIXON AND WEBB, *Enzymes*, p. 447, 1958, Longmans, Green and Co., London.
58. MASON, *Tech. Ass. Pulp Pap. Ind.* 1950, **33**, p. 413.
59. MIRSKY AND ANSON, *J. gen. Physiol.* 1935, **18**, p. 307.
60. MATTHIJSSEN, *Diss. Abstracts* 1957, **17**, p. 2141.
61. GRASSMANN, ZECHMEISTER, TOTH AND STADLER, *Annalen*, 1933, **503**, p. 167.
62. FUKOMOTO AND KISHI, *Sci. Ind.* 1952, **26**, p. 295.
63. VAN SUMÈRE, VAN SUMÈRE-DE PRETER AND LEDINGHAM, *Canad. J. Microbiol.* 1957, **3**, p. 761.
64. HAMMERSTROM, CLAUS, COGHLAN AND MCBEE, *Arch. Biochem. Biophys.* 1955, **56**, p. 123.
65. BARRON, *Advances in Enzymology*, 1951, **11**, p. 201.
66. KARRER AND STAUB, *Helv. chim. Acta*, 1924, **7**, p. 918.
67. WALSETH, *Tech. Ass. Pulp Pap. Ind.* 1952, **35**, p. 233.
68. NISIZAWA, *J. Biochem. Japan*, 1955, **42**, p. 855.
69. REESE AND GILLIGAN, *Text. Res. J.* 1954, **24**, p. 663.
70. LEVINSON, MANDELS AND REESE, *Arch. Biochem. Biophys.* 1951, **31**, p. 351.
71. THOMAS AND WHITAKER, *Nature, Lond.* 1958, **181**, p. 715.
72. ROTH, *Diss. Abstracts* 1956, **16**, p. 1591.
73. FESTENSTEIN, *Biochem. J.* 1958, **69**, p. 562; 1959, **72**, p. 75.
74. KOOIMAN, *Enzymologia*, 1957, **18**, p. 22.
75. GASCOIGNE, M. M., unpublished results.
76. BISHOP AND WHITAKER, *Chem. and Ind.* 1955, p. 119.
77. GILLIGAN AND REESE, *Canad. J. Microbiol.* 1954, **1**, p. 90.
78. REESE AND LEVINSON, *Physiol. Plant.* 1952, **5**, p. 345.
79. GERTLER, *Fermentforschung.* 1936–1938, **15**, p. 171.
80. QUASTEL, *Biochem. J.* 1931, **25**, pp. 629, 898, 1121; 1932, **26**, p. 1685.
81. QUASTEL AND YATES, *Enzymologia*, 1936, **1**, p. 60.
82. MANDELS AND REESE, *J. Bact.* 1957, **73**, p. 269.
83. WALSETH, *Tech. Ass. Pulp Pap. Ind.* 1952, **35**, p. 228.
84. FISH, *Nature, Lond.* 1955, **175**, p. 733.
85. WHITAKER, Review of the National Research Council, p. 41, 1958, Ottawa, Canada.
86. MILLER AND BLUM, *J. biol. Chem.* 1956, **218**, p. 131.
87. TRAGER, *Biochem. J.* 1932, **26**, p. 1762.
88. KARRER, *Kolloidzschr.* 1930, **52**, p. 304.
89. KARRER, SCHUBERT AND WEHRLI, *Helv. chim. Acta*, 1925, **8**, p. 797.
90. PRINGSHEIM AND BAUR, *Hoppe-Seyl. Z.* 1928, **173**, p. 188.
91. LEVINSON AND REESE, *J. gen. Physiol.* 1950, **33**, p. 601.
92. LEVENE AND KUNA, *J. biol. Chem.* 1939, **127**, p. 49.

VI

MODE OF ACTION OF CELLULOLYTIC ENZYMES

ENZYME extracts from some organisms degrade only reprecipitated cellulose or soluble derivatives, whilst other preparations are capable of catalysing the breakdown of highly crystalline native celluloses; the ratio of these two types of activity varies widely between extracts from different sources. The ability to hydrolyse modified celluloses is widespread, whereas the catabolism of native cotton is more restricted[1]. In view of these facts, it was suggested that at least two enzymes were involved in the production of low-molecular weight compounds from native celluloses; the first enzyme (C_1) is said to produce linear anhydroglucose chains from cotton cellulose, which are then hydrolysed to soluble products (cellobiose or glucose) in in the presence of the second enzyme (C_x). This second C_x enzyme is also active in the case of the linear chains produced during modification by reprecipitation or substitution. The entire process may be represented as:

Cotton cellulose $\xrightarrow{C_1}$ linear chains $\searrow C_x$

cellobiose

Modified celluloses $\nearrow C_x$

β–glucosidase

glucose

For the cell metabolism it may be unnecessary to bring about the hydrolysis of cellobiose to glucose, as it has been shown that the cell can also adsorb the disaccharide[2]. Much evidence has been presented to support this multienzymatic hypothesis, including the isolation of numerous components from certain sources which differed in their action on celluloses. However, other workers claim that only a single enzyme is involved in cellulose hydrolysis. Apart from this controversy, the mode of cellulose hydrolysis remains a subject of debate; it may be either a random attack on any linkage in the chain, or a specific action in which cellobiose (or other units) are removed from the ends of the chains. With these possibilities in mind, consideration must now be given to the action of cellulases in the hydrolysis of all types of cellulose, and to the influence of substrate structure upon enzymatic hydrolysis; upon such factors rests the present state of knowledge concerning the number of cellulolytic enzymes and their action pattern.

ENZYMIC ACTION ON CELLULOSE

EFFECT OF MOLECULAR STRUCTURE

The complexity of cellulose structure has already been discussed (Chapter I); the heterogeneous nature of the cellulose/cellulase system makes it necessary to consider some of the peculiarities of insoluble substrates. The surface area of the substrate exposed to attack will affect the rate of reaction, and in turn, the effective surface may depend upon the size and ability of the enzyme molecule to penetrate between adjacent chains; loosely-packed chains permit easy entry and the surface area of the substrate is greatly increased, whereas tightly-packed chains (as in native celluloses) will not accommodate the enzyme molecule and will be less susceptible to enzymic action. Obviously, the amorphous character, linked as it is with greater chemical reactivity, must play a part in the enzymic action, and it has long been known that swelling and regeneration of cotton render such substrates more susceptible to enzymic hydrolysis[3]. Similar observations have been made more recently[4,5], while Karrer and Schubert[6] have drawn attention to the variables in the nature of the substrate affecting the rate of reaction; these included substrate area, and degree of crystallinity, although no relationship could be established between the molecular size (DP) of the substrate and the enzymic reaction. Orientation of the cellulose micelles has been shown to influence the reaction from experiments involving the hydrolysis of viscose threads stretched during precipitation to different extensions[7], and also of cotton mercerized under and without tension[8]. Although the degree of crystallinity is a useful property to consider, it must be borne in mind that a comparison of the enzymic hydrolysis of a range of substrates (e.g. cotton, swollen linters, filter paper, viscose, saponified acetate rayon) must involve a consideration of many factors other than crystalline content.

Taking the moisture regain values of a series of celluloses as a measure of their crystallinities, Walseth[9] showed that substrates with higher regain values (i.e. higher amorphous contents) were more susceptible to enzymic hydrolysis. The relative rates of hydrolysis of a series of specially prepared celluloses of known crystalline content in the presence of an enzyme preparation from *Trichoderma viride*[10] are shown in *Table 1*, while the amount of hydrolysis of

Table 1. *Effect of Crystallinity on Enzymic Hydrolysis* (by courtesy, *Textile Research Journal*, 1957, **27**, p. 626)

Cellulose sample	Treatment	Crystalline content %	Relative hydrolysis rate
A	Kiered cotton	90	1·7
B	Kiered cotton, mercerized without tension	70	2·6
C	Kiered cotton, amine–decrystallized (laboratory)	40–50	3·5
D	Kiered cotton, amine–decrystallized (pilot plant)	0	7·4

various substrates with various cellulase preparations is given in *Table 2*; it must be pointed out that different methods and conditions of hydrolysis have been used by the different workers, and comparisons between groups of substrates cannot be made. However, the results reported are consistent with a decreasing amount of crystallinity of the substrate making for ease of enzymic hydrolysis.

Table 2. *Degree of Hydrolysis of Cellulosic Substrates by Different Enzyme Preparations*

Enzyme source	Cellulosic substrates (in order of decreasing crystallinity)	Hydrolysis %	Ref.
Clostridium thermocellulaseum	Cotton	3·6	11
	Cellulose wadding	12·8	
	Cellodextrin	51·0	
Myrothecium verrucaria 1.	Filter paper powder	1·6	12
	Cotton wool	6·4	
	Regenerated cellulose	42	
2.	Cotton linters	1·2	13
	Swollen linters	5·2	
	Precipitated cellulose	12·0	
3.	Dewaxed cotton fibre	9·4	14
	Ball milled cotton	16·8	
	Ball milled cellophane	27·0	

This conclusion is supported further by the results for both enzyme preparations[15-18] and for micro-organisms[19,20]. It follows that any process disrupting the crystalline regions, such as mechanical disintegration, swelling, solubilization and reprecipitation or solubilization by chemical substitution, renders the substrate more liable to enzymic attack. As with acid hydrolysis[21], the extent of enzymic hydrolysis may be used for comparative measurement of the amount of crystallinity in a previously unexamined sample. A particular example of this is shown in the work of Sison, Schubert and Nord[16] in which the following amounts of hydrolysis were recorded for animal, fungal and bacterial celluloses respectively:

Phallusia mammilata cellulose	4·5%
Saprolegnia sp. cellulose	47·3%
Acetobacter xylinum cellulose	5·4%

These values enable a high degree of crystallinity to be attributed to both bacterial and animal celluloses; such results are more in accordance with the work of Mann and Marrinan[22] than with the values of Hermans and Weidinger[23].

INFLUENCE OF THE DEGREE OF POLYMERIZATION (DP)

The length of cellulose molecules varies considerably and this variation would be expected to affect hydrolysis, especially if the attack commences at the ends of molecules; however, this hydrolysis pattern was not borne out by work with micro-organisms[14,20,24,25]. Other workers[18,26] were unable to demonstrate a correlation between DP and enzymatic cleavage in the range DP 100 to 700. In contrast to this, Gilligan and Reese[27] separated chromatographically three components (A, B and CD, see Chapter IV, *Figure 9* (b)) from a crude filtrate of *Trichoderma viride* which differed in their activities towards two regenerated cellulose samples with DP 500 and DP 50 respectively. Thus, the activity of Fraction B on the long chains was 1·6–times that on the short chains, while the activity of Fraction CD on the long chains was 0·66–times that on the short chains; fraction A had nearly equal activity on both substrates. It was suggested that the components of a cellulolytic enzyme system may differ in their preference or affinity for chains of a particular length.

The importance of this influence of DP on cellulolytic action is twofold. Firstly, material of low molecular weight has many chain ends, and if enzymic attack is *endwise* it will be more susceptible to hydrolysis. Secondly, there is an upper limit of substrate molecular weight for the action of β–glucosidases and a lower limit for the action of cellulase[28]; if the components of a cellulolytic enzyme system differ in their preference for chains of a particular length, there may be components bridging the gap between β–glucosidases and cellulases[29].

CHANGES PRODUCED IN CELLULOSE BY ENZYMIC ACTION

EARLY CHANGES

Certain changes in cellulose undergoing enzymic attack have been detected before the production of reducing sugar, weight loss, loss in tensile strength or change in degree of polymerization became evident. Marsh, Guthrie and Butler[30] studied such early changes occurring in the growing cotton boll due to the action of micro-organisms and weather; the changes included a rapid increase in pH value and an increased swelling of the cotton in alkali. This alkali swelling increase could also be brought about by other deteriorative agents such as hydrochloric acid, sodium hypochlorite and culture filtrates from some micro-organisms; the effect is probably due to a weakening or rupture of the outer (primary) wall of the fibre[31], and the factor responsible for such effects has been termed 'S–factor'. After only one hour's exposure to S–factor sources cotton fibres showed the increased swelling in alkali, and the factor is thought to be an enzyme, although this point is by no means settled. Marsh[32] suggested a procedure for estimating S–factor, which consisted of swelling a known weight of cotton fibre (or other cellulose) in a solution of sodium hydroxide (18% w/v), centrifuging off the interfibrillar liquid, and determining (without further drying) the percentage weight increase of the fibre, which was termed 'alkali centrifuge value'; it is essential to maintain a standard procedure for this test, with particular care to the dry weight of the sample, the time of swelling, and the speed of centrifugation. The difference in the alkali centrifuge values of the original substrate and that of the same substrate after exposure to an active culture filtrate was used as an index of S–factor activity.

The S–factor activity of *Myrothecium verrucaria* could be precipitated with acetone, and activity was exhibited over a wide pH value range with a maximum between 4·0 and 4·5. It had considerable thermal stability, not being inactivated by heating at 100° for 30 minutes. Heavy metal salts (Hg^{2+}, Ag^+ and Cu^{2+}) and pepsin inhibited the activity, while certain neutral salts (0·1M solutions of KCl, NaCl, $CaCl_2$ and $MgSO_4$) also depressed activity. Five micro-organisms, not normally considered cellulolytic, produced S–factor in their culture filtrates, as also did preparations from two bacteria which *in vivo* cause soft rot in vegetables; in addition, these latter preparations contained cellulase and protopectinase activities[33]. The existence of S–factor does not rest solely on the evidence of Marsh and his colleagues, for Reese and Gilligan[34] have measured both S–factor and C_x activities from several micro-organisms; both enzymes were shown to be inducible. Other similar properties were toleration of dialysis and solvent precipitation, stability at pH 5·5 and 55° and inactivation at pH values of 3·0 and 9·6; the two enzymes were inhibited by urea, cellobiose and a methyl cellulose, and had similar temperature-activity relationships. However, differences were established in the relationships between the activity and the pH value of the test solutions in some of the organisms examined; for example, the S–factor/pH value curve showed double maximum activities at pH 3·0 and 5·2. Separation of the two enzymes was not possible, but the ratio of activities (S/C_x) varied with the micro-organism producing them, the conditions of growth and method of purification; it is evident, therefore, that at least two enzymic components are active in the breakdown of cellulose.

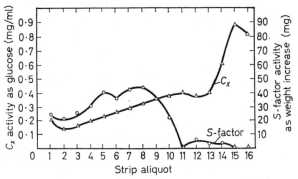

Figure 1—Location of various types of activity factors on paper chromatograms. Filtrate of *Pestalotia palmarum* (by courtesy, *Textile Research Journal*, 1954, **24**, p. 666)

Further evidence for the separate characters of S–factor and the C_x enzyme has been provided by chromatographic studies. While several C_x components have been demonstrated in *Myrothecium verrucaria* filtrates[35], the rate of migration of S–factor was low and was associated with only the slowest moving C_x component. In filtrates from *Pestalotia palmarum*, containing three C_x components, S–factor has been separated into two fractions, neither of which

172

corresponded in mobility to any of the C_x components; *Figure 1* shows the non-identity of S–factor with the major C_x component[34]; similar findings resulted from later work[27]. The action of S–factor was directed to the cellulose and not to other substances, such as waxes, protein or pectin, present in the primary wall of the cotton fibre[34]; further, it was suggested that S–factor is active on some common linkage in the cellulose fibril and is not restricted to primary wall cellulose, this latter action being that detected in the alkali swelling test. The place of S–factor in the action pattern of the enzymic hydrolysis of cellulose will be discussed later.

Certain other physical changes occurring without corresponding increases in reducing sugar values or losses in weight have been noticed in the early stages of enzymic action; rapid losses in the tensile strength of cellophane[36] and of cotton and viscose[37] have been noted. In some cases a rapid fall in the degree of polymerization has been recorded[38-40]. Microscopic examination of attacked cotton fibres showed that the initial degradation was confined to the fibre surface and to spiral planes of susceptibility within the fibre mass; the rapid fall in tensile properties was thought to be the primary result of attack along these planes[37]. Such physical changes may indicate an initial random disintegration of the molecular chains into molecules retaining a high molecular weight and without any large increase in reducing groups.

FURTHER EFFECTS OF ENZYMIC ACTION

As hydrolysis proceeds many other effects become evident, including production of reducing sugars, loss in weight, changes both in crystallinity and degree of polymerization, changes in alkali solubility and the viscosity of solutions of soluble derivatives. Reducing sugar is produced rapidly after the initial period mentioned above, then later production is slowed down; a similar pattern is obtained when weight loss is used as a measure of enzymic activity. As has been noted previously, the rate and extent of hydrolysis are influenced to a large extent by the type of cellulose used as substrate, as shown in *Figure 2*[16], and modification of the cellulose brings about increased weight loss and reducing sugar production. The levelling-off of the rate of enzymic hydrolysis has been discussed frequently[9,37] and an explanation for the phenomenon was advanced by Walseth[9], who analysed the effect of three variables on the reaction: (i) the thermal denaturation of the enzyme, (ii) the inhibition of hydrolysis by the accumulated products, and (iii) the increase of crystallinity during the reaction, as measured by moisture regain values of the residue. While the first two variables influenced the rate of hydrolysis to a small extent, the principal cause of the levelling-off in rate could be attributed to the decreased reactivity of the residue. Treatment of the residue to render it more amorphous by swelling in phosphoric acid (producing an increase in the moisture regain value) made it possible for further rapid enzymic hydrolysis to

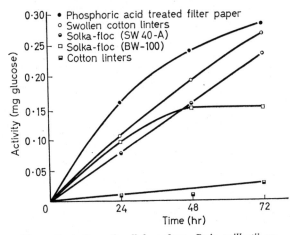

Figure 2—Action of cellulase from *Poria vaillantii* on different types of cellulosic substrate (by courtesy, *Archives of Biochemistry and Biophysics*, 1958, **75,** p. 268)

occur. Complete hydrolysis can be achieved by successive swelling, or other modification, of the resistant residues, but in general with partly crystalline celluloses the rate of hydrolysis decreases until a limit is reached beyond which no further hydrolysis can be detected; typical results for different substrates and the nature of the resistant residues are shown in *Table 3*. It will be noticed that the amount of decomposition at the limit of hydrolysis is lower for native celluloses than for cellulose samples which have been modified to give increased 'hydratability'. The greater accessibility of modified celluloses is reflected in the longer time taken to reach the limit of hydrolysis. The optimum conditions for enzymic hydrolysis, with particular attention to temperature of incubation, concentration of buffer, substrate and enzyme, the nature of the buffer solution and the pH value, must be arranged in order to achieve maximum hydrolysis; the influence of these variables has been discussed in Chapter V.

Alongside the production of reducing sugar and the loss in weight of the substrate, the rate at which the degree of polymerization (DP)

Table 3. Enzymic Hydrolysis Limits and Nature of Residues

Description of cellulose	Enzyme source	Decomposition at limit of reaction (%)	Description of residue	Ref.
Cellulose sol — repptd. from wood cellulose D.P. 338	*Collybia* sp. *Streptomyces* sp. *Polyporus annosus*	65	D.P. *c.* 50, a homogenous mass of particles 300Å × 150Å	39
A. Purified cotton linters Moisture regain (M. R.) 5·58%, D.P. 1140		6·68 in 144 hr	D.P. 1105, M.R. 5·35%	
B. Sample A swollen 10 min. in cold H_3PO_4 M.R. 6·30%, D.P. 1120	*Aspergillus niger*	37·6 in 144 hr	D.P. 1080, M.R. 5·43%	9
C. Sample A swollen 2 hr. in cold H_3PO_4 M.R.9·37%, D.P. 740		79·3 in 144 hr	D.P. 295, M.R. 5·25%	
A. Kiered cotton, Crystallinity 90%, D.P. 4970		25	D.P. 4200 after 20% weight loss	
B. Sample A mercerized without tension in 24% NaOH soln. Crystallinity 70%, D.P. 5040	*Trichoderma viride*	35	D.P. 3040 after 31% weight loss	10
C. Sample A decrystallized with ethylamine. Crystallinity 40–50%, D.P. 4670		35	D.P. 3100 after 25% weight loss	
D. As C, but in pilot-scale plant, D.P. 3920		65	D.P. 1630 after 69% weight loss	
Hydrocelluloses were prepared by acid hydrolysis of the above samples A, B, C under conditions producing level-off D.P. (2·5 N.HCl, 80°, 4 hr.)				
A. Hydrocellulose, D.P. 225 Particles 1000–1500Å × 150Å		*c.* 20	D.P. 227, no observable change in particle size	
B Hydrocellulose, D.P. 138, 500–800Å, but slightly narrower than AH	*Trichoderma viride*	*c.* 20	D.P. 145, no observable change in particle size	10
C Hydrocellulose, D.P. 133		*c.* 20	D.P. 128	
D Hydrocellulose produced by severe acid hydrolysis of D (4N. HCl, 97°, 30 min.) D.P. 112, 500–800Å, slightly narrower than AH (Cellulose III)		over 40	D.P. 104, no observable change in particle size, at 27·4% weight loss	

changes has also been studied. Thus, enzymes from *Tricholoma nudum* caused an initial fall, during the first eight hours' hydrolysis, amounting to one-third of the original DP; the reducing sugar production can be seen in *Table 4*[38]. Similar effects were noted by Whitaker[40], who determined the weight loss and changes in both weight average and number average DP of a phosphoric acid swollen cellulose at several intervals of time. A rapid fall in DP occurred initially with

Table 4. Changes Brought About by Tricholoma nudum *Enzymes* (by courtesy, *Symbolae Botanicae Upsalienses*, 1950, **11**, p. 5)

Time of Incubation (hr)	D.P. (by light scattering)	Reducing Sugar as Glucose (mg)
0	178	0
8	110	2·6
15	105	3·9
36	91	6·5
45	79	20·8

no loss in weight (see *Figure 3*), to be followed by decreases in the rate of change of DP and in the rate of hydrolysis, until finally a level-off DP was almost achieved. This rapid fall in DP without other changes indicates a random attack on the cellulose molecule rather than the removal of glucose or cellobiose units from the chain ends; the latter process would result in gradual and related changes in DP and reducing sugar production. Norkrans and Rånby[39] showed the residue after hydrolysis of a cellulose sol to consist of particles 300Å long and 150Å wide with a DP of 50. The molecular size of the cellulase molecule from *Myrothecium verrucaria* (see *Chapter V*) is only slightly shorter than such residues and covers almost twenty cellobiose repeating units (i.e. a DP of 40). During the enzymic hydrolysis of a series of hydrocelluloses no changes in particle size of the residues were noticed (see *Table 3*)[10]. As mentioned above, Walseth[9] showed that the moisture regain values of residues from hydrolysis were smaller than those of the original substrate; in fact, the regains for the residues from widely different substrates all reached values between 5·0 and 5·4 per cent, indicating residues of similar crystallinities. Whilst it can be stated with certainty that the hydrolysis residues are more highly crystalline than the unhydrolysed cellulose, the crystalline nature of enzymically hydro-

176

lysed celluloses requires attention. If some recrystallization occurs it might be expected to occur in the Cellulose II form, although there is some evidence[41] for an amorphous ball-milled wood pulp recrystallizing as Cellulose I.

Other evidence for recrystallization has been provided by Walseth[9], who noticed that, after the initial rapid fall in DP from 1290 to 830, there followed a rise in DP to a final value of over 1000.

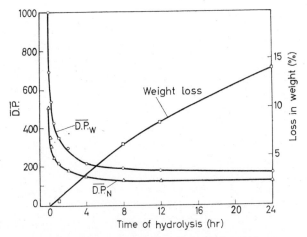

Figure 3—Effect of enzymatic hydrolysis on weight loss and D.P. of swollen cellulose (by courtesy, *Canadian Journal of Biochemistry and Physiology* 1957, **35**, p. 739)

If an initial random attack occurred in the most accessible regions producing enough shortened chains to reduce the DP significantly, then these chains would be hydrolysed rapidly, leaving only the longer chains in the less accessible regions in the final residue. The alternative explanation of recrystallization of some of the amorphous regions during prolonged periods of enzymic action may also be advanced. Storage of swollen cotton linters in a buffer solution for 16 hours at 47° did not alter the rate of subsequent enzymic attack. However, more prolonged incubation in the acetate buffer solution at pH 4·5 (in the absence of enzymes) brought about a fall in DP from 1300 to 1180 in 48 hours, but after a further 72 hours' storage the value had risen to 1290, indicating that some recrystallization had occurred. A similar phenomenon was observed by Reese[42], who found that the residue left after alkali extraction of enzyme-hydrolysed cotton had a higher DP than the original cellulose, as also had the residue left after unhydrolysed cotton was subjected to alkali treatment, as shown below:

$$\text{Cellulose} \quad 10\% \text{ aq. NaOH}$$
$$\text{DP } 519 \longrightarrow \text{DP } 752$$

Enzyme | treatment

$$\downarrow \quad 10\% \text{ aq. NaOH}$$
$$\text{DP } 407 \longrightarrow \text{DP } 850$$

It was suggested that, as cotton cellulose has a distribution of chain lengths, the shorter chains are appreciably soluble in alkali, leaving a residue of higher average DP after treatment; after enzymic hydrolysis, during which cellulase may act preferentially on the shorter chains, the alkali soluble fraction is increased leaving behind a residue with even higher DP.

While discussing the action of alkali, attention must be drawn to the increase in the alkali solubility of fungally degraded cotton[15], which has been further studied[10] with the results shown in *Table 5*.

Table 5. Changes in Alkali Solubility and Degree of Polymerization

Cellulose substrate	Crystalline form	Crystallinity %	D.P. of substrate	Solubility in alkali before hydrolysis %	Relative rate of attack	D.P. of residue after hydrolysis	Solubility in alkali after hydrolysis %
A	I	90	4970	4·9	1·7	4200	7·6
B	II	70	5040	6·8	2·6	3040	12·3
C	I	40–50	4670	7·9	3·5	3100	15·7
D	I + III	—	3920	11·2	7·4	1630	35·8

Cellulose substrates prepared as described in *Table 3*, ref. 10.

It will be noticed that the order of susceptibility to enzymic attack corresponds to the orders of increasing alkali solubility and of decreasing crystallinity. Correlation between DP and alkali solubility is not so apparent, although it can be discerned within one crystalline form, but in general the enzymic hydrolysis brings about a decrease in DP, as well as an increase in alkali solubility. Reese, Segal and Tripp[10] emphasized the fact that although the enzyme-hydrolysed products had greater alkali solubility than the starting materials, the former were less susceptible to further enzyme hydrolysis. This

178

anomaly may be the result of the accessibility of such materials, in which the enzymic attack is largely confined to the available surfaces.

COMPARISON OF ENZYMIC HYDROLYSIS WITH
ACID HYDROLYSIS

The effects of enzyme-catalysed hydrolysis of cellulose may be listed as:

(i) decrease in degree of polymerization, which on exhaustive hydrolysis reaches a limiting value, after which only negligible changes take place,

(ii) increase in degree of crystallinity,

(iii) initial rapid weight loss and production of reducing sugar, followed by only minor changes,

(vi) rapid loss of tensile strength,

(v) increase in alkali solubility.

In comparing acid- and enzyme-catalysed reactions, the differences in the nature of the catalysts must be considered. Acid molecules have a much smaller molecular size than protein molecules (e.g. HCl 36·5, cellulase 63,000 in molecular weight[43]), and consequently greater penetration by acid molecules into the more resistant regions of cellulose is to be expected. Despite this it has been shown that, while hydrolysis may be more complete using acids particularly with the aid of heat, enzymes are more efficient hydrolysing agents. At 50°, 10^5 times as much acid as enzyme is required to bring about the same degree of hydrolysis; at the molecular level this difference is even more pronounced, 10^8 molecules of acid being required to catalyse the same amount of hydrolysis as one enzyme molecule[42], and catalysis occurs at a much lower energy level. Enzymic hydrolysis is much more specific than acid hydrolysis; acids attack all types of glycosidic and acetal linkages indiscriminately whereas some idea of the specificity of enzymic action has been given in Chapter II. The purest cellulase yet produced brings about the hydrolysis of $(1\rightarrow4)$ β–glucosidic and $(1\rightarrow4)$ β–pentosidic linkages, but it is possible that the specificity of cellulases may be as complex as the action patterns of the amylolytic enzymes. If cellulases can be as clearly defined in their specificities and action patterns as the amylases and phosphorylases, a very sensitive tool for the elucidation of β–linked carbohydrate structure will be available.

Despite the efficiency of cellulases, their conversion of native celluloses to soluble products is very incomplete, and modifications of structure to render the substrate more accessible do not cause complete solubilization such as can be achieved with only one hour's exposure to a combination of the action of cold concentrated sulphuric acid and hot dilute acid[44]. Much greater degradation is achieved using the cellulolytic organism itself rather than the isolated enzyme system. Heterogeneous acid hydrolysis of cellulose proceeds rapidly at first, becomes slower and eventually appears to come to a standstill. The type of X-ray diffraction of the residue remained unaltered[45] but a greater intensity in the pattern[46,47] revealed that hydrolysis occurs preferentially in the amorphous or para-crystalline regions and this attack is continued rapidly as long as the amorphous areas persist, after which hydrolysis is

Table 6. Comparison of Acid and Enzyme Catalysis

Sample[10]	Type of cellulose and D.P.	Acid hydrolysis		Enzyme hydrolysis	
		Weight loss at level-off %	D.P. after reaction	Weight loss at level-off %	D.P. after reaction as given in Table 3
A	Kiered cotton 4970	4	225	25	4200
B	Mercerized 5040	6·5	138	35	3040
C	Decrystallized 4670	7	133	35	3100
D	Decrystallized 3920	8·9	112	65	1630

Sample	Type of cellulose	Acid hydrolysis			Enzyme hydrolysis		
		Time of reaction hr	Weight loss %	D.P. of residue	Time of reaction hr	Weight loss %	D.P. of residue
W	Cotton linters 1140	48	6·34	105	48	5·35	—
					144	6·68	1105
X	H_3PO_4–swollen cotton linters 1120	48	8·3	80	144	37·6	1080
Y	H_3PO_4–swollen cotton linters 740	48	13·9	40	48	62·7	270
					82	70·5	295
					144	79·3	—

continued at a lower rate with the diffusion of the acid into the crystalline regions. The residue is predominantly crystalline ('crystallites') with chain lengths of 200 to 300 anhydroglucose units for native celluloses and 100 units for some regenerated celluloses. Rånby and Ribi[45] have shown that such crystallites are 500 to 600Å long and 50 to 100Å wide, whilst for cotton, ramie and wood pulp the crystallite length has been estimated as 1300 to 1500Å[48]. The work of Reese, Segal and Tripp[10], reported in *Table 3*, has been extended to compare the weight losses and size of crystallites obtained by both acid and enzyme hydrolyses, and these results are presented in *Table 6*. From these values and those of Walseth[9] quoted in the same table it will be observed that acid hydrolysis effected a much larger decrease in DP than did enzymic hydrolysis, although the weight losses were in the reverse order. Although Walseth's value of DP for cotton linters was unusually low, the weight loss after enzymic hydrolysis for 144 hours was approximately the same as that brought about by acid in only 48 hours. The crystallites produced on prolonged acid hydrolysis are resistant to further hydrolysis with the aid of enzymes[5,10]. The sharpening of definition in the X-ray diffraction patterns during acid hydrolysis has been attributed, in part, to the recrystallization of cellulose, chain rupture in the amorphous regions increasing the mobility of the chain ends and permitting re-orientation into crystalline order; a similar sharpening of patterns has been observed during enzymic hydrolysis[39].

The large enzyme molecules, unable to diffuse into the cellulose readily, catalyse the hydrolysis of the regions accessible to them to soluble products rapidly and completely; the reaction then proceeds slowly only at the surfaces of crystalline areas with the rapid dissolution of each chain as it becomes exposed to the surface. In this way hydrolysis would continue with only a transient existence of dextrins of intermediate chain length. The much smaller acid molecules are able to penetrate deeply into the structure, hydrolysing many more glucosidic bonds, giving rise to shorter chains before extensive solubilization occurs, and without completing their rapid hydrolysis to glucose. Acid hydrolysis is further characterized by an increase in the fluidity of a solution of the fibre due to the fall in chain length and this is accompanied by a loss in fibre tensile strength. There is a linear relationship between fluidity and strength changes, indicating relatively uniform attack by acid, as opposed to the enzymic or microbial degradation where loss of strength is not accompanied by a large change in fluidity; the latter attack is therefore regarded as localized.

WATER SOLUBLE PRODUCTS AND INTERMEDIATES IN
ENZYMIC HYDROLYSIS

Few reports have presented evidence for the presence of cellodextrin and higher cello-oligosaccharide intermediates between cellulose and cellobiose or glucose. During the hydrolysis of a cellodextrin, with a cellulase from *Myrothecium verrucaria* in the presence of radioactive cellobiose, cello-triose, -tetraose, and -pentaose were detected by paper chromatography[50]. The assay of radioactivity demonstrated that the quantities of these oligosaccharides arising by transglucosylation from cellobiose were negligible. Paper chromatographic evidence for the existence of the same oligosaccharides among the products of hydrolysis of cellodextrins, acid and alkali swollen celluloses, and cellulose precipitated from cuprammonium hydroxide solution has been presented[51]; this enzyme mixture had been heated to destroy the activities of thermolabile cellobiase and transglycosylase. The heated enzyme also brought about the hydrolysis of cello-triose, -tetraose, and -hexaose to give cellobiose and glucose, but hydrolysis of cellobiose itself was very slow. The oligosaccharides arising during the hydrolysis of the various forms of cellulose were considered to be produced by the random splitting of bonds and the enzymic action was unienzymatic. Cellotetraose has been reported in the hydrolysate of a phosphoric acid swollen cellulose[52], while cellotriose in addition to glucose and cellobiose, all in equal amounts, were probably produced during the early stages of enzymic hydrolysis[53]. Stone[54] has also detected such intermediates in the hydrolysis of cellodextrins. During the hydrolysis of cellophane and carboxymethylcellulose by a preparation from rumen micro-organisms it was probable that both cello-triose and -tetraose were produced[55], while other intermediates in the hydrolysis of CMC have the structure of substituted sugars[2].

The end products of cellulose hydrolysis have been recorded as cellobiose or glucose, or a mixture of the two sugars. If a cellobiase is present in the enzyme solution, the presence of glucose may well originate from the action of this enzyme or of any relatively unspecific β–glucosidase. However, glucose may arise directly from the hydrolysis of cellulose; for example, the purified *M. verrucaria* enzyme of Whitaker[57] produced both glucose and cellobiose from cellulose, although the enzyme had very low activity towards cellobiose, and it was concluded that both compounds were produced directly by random cleavage. This view was supported by Reese[42], who had shown earlier[2] that cellobiose occurred as the end product in the early stages of hydrolysis, while glucose appeared much later; in the latter case it is possible that very low concentrations of a β–glucosidase produced glucose from cellobiose on prolonged incubation. Relatively few workers[1,50,58,61] have isolated the end products as crystalline derivatives, but have relied on paper chromatography.

Cellobiose alone has been noted as the end product by various workers, some of whom[58,59] claim that the action of the enzyme was a cleavage of the disaccharide from the ends of cellulose chains, but other workers[2] prefer the random cleavage mechanism. It may well be that both types of action exist, and the analogy with amylose hydrolysis must be emphasized where both random and endwise attack are known. It will be recalled (Chapter V) that D–glucono–1:4–lactone can act as a specific inhibitor for the hydrolysis of cellobiose, so that glucose was not produced from cellulose in its presence[55].

ACTION ON CELLULOSE DERIVATIVES

The heterogenous nature of the hydrolysis of native and other insoluble celluloses and the difficulties in the investigation of the mechanism can be overcome to some extent by the use of water soluble derivatives of cellulose, such as the various ethers and esters discussed in Chapter I. Although water soluble dextrins of low molecular weight and containing only $(1 \rightarrow 4)$ β–glucosidic linkages can be used as substrates, in spite of their chain length being much shorter than that of cellulose, it has been found[27] that components of a cellulolytic filtrate act at different rates on compounds of different chain lengths. Certain organisms produce enzymes catalysing the hydrolysis of cellulose ethers and esters, but without action on native celluloses; in such cases the activity measured has been called 'C_x activity' and this enzyme has been discussed earlier. However, this type of enzyme is probably produced in response to the $(1 \rightarrow 4)$ β–glucosidic linkage and is not specific for the substituted chain of the derivative.

With the substituted celluloses as substrates, both reducing sugar production and reduction of solution viscosity can be taken as indices of cellulolytic activity (see Chapter IV). The viscosity method is a very sensitive means for determining either small amounts of enzyme or enzymes of low activity; the cleavage of only a few bonds brings about a large decrease in viscosity, but it is difficult to define a cellulase unit in terms of such measurements. If all the chains of the sodium salt of a carboxymethylcellulose (CMC) were reduced to half their length by enzymic cleavage, the increase in reducing sugar value was only 0·3 per cent, but a large fall in viscosity was recorded[60].

Effect of Molecular Structure

Degree of substitution (DS) and Degree of polymerization (DP).—While the viscosities of solutions of cellulose derivatives may be regarded as functions of the degrees of polymerization, the solubility of a derivative depends to some extent on its degree of substitution; thus some derivatives, such as CMC, are soluble at a DS of 0·4 to 0·5, while others (e.g. methyl cellulose) require a DS of 2·0 or over before they become water-soluble. No difference in the enzymic hydrolysis rates of three samples of CMC having average values of DP of 125, 150 and 200 was noted, and thus C_x activity appeared to be independent of the DP of the substrate[1]. On the other hand, the initial DS of a substrate greatly influences enzymic attack; the hydrolysis rate was found to be inversely proportional to the DS from measurements on reducing sugar production[1], and confirmation has been obtained from fluidity data[62]. The latter results suggested that one substituent per anhydroglucose unit rendered the derivative refractory to attack; however it should not be taken that a DS of 1·0 is necessarily adequate for protection from enzymic or microbial attack, as this value merely implies an average DS and fractions of lower DS will be present in the sample. Some cases of enzymic hydrolysis of substrates with DS above 1·0 have been reported, and here it can be considered that the side chains are more than one substituent in length (as in hydroxyethylcellulose built up from polyethylene oxide units), or that there is an uneven distribution of substituents, either cause leading to some unsubstituted anhydroglucose units in the cellulose chain. While distribution of substituents is frequently regarded as random in cellulose ethers of high DS, the ethers of lower DS cannot be so regarded and the 'degree of unsubstitution' (i.e. 3—DS) only gives an average picture without consideration of crystalline character or of steric effects within the cellobiose unit cell. A better measure of susceptibility to enzymic attack is this number of unsubstituted anhydroglucose units and only bonds joining two such units can be hydrolysed. However, even this generalisation cannot be fully maintained, as it has been found that certain derivatives having only one of a pair of adjacent anhydroglucose units unsubstituted were attacked[60]. The influence of the chemical nature of the substituent has not been studied in detail, although Thomas[17] has noted that ethylhydroxyethylcellulose was less sensitive to attack than CMC. In general, Reese[64] found that more glucose was produced by the enzymic hydrolysis of cellulose esters than from ethers of the same DS.

Changes in substrates.—During the early stages of the enzymic hydrolysis of soluble derivatives the solution viscosity falls rapidly, although the production of reducing sugar is a much slower process. The rate of change in DP can be followed from changes in the intrinsic viscosity, although the determination of average molecular weight by this method has not been attempted frequently with the degraded derivatives; during such early stages the specific fluidity increases at a constant rate for a given enzyme system. The extent of hydrolysis is limited by the DS of the substrate. Exhaustive hydrolysis (310 hr) of the sodium salt of carboxymethylcellulose (CMC) gave an increase in reducing sugar production equivalent to a 40 per cent scission of the substrate, while a similar value for ethyl methylcellulose was 17 per cent[60]. According to Spurlin[65] in such a sample of CMC of DS 0·45 about 36 per cent of the anhydroglucose units would be unsubstituted and would lie adjacent to other unsubstituted units. If it is assumed that only bonds between unsubstituted units can be hydrolysed, this value of 36 per cent lies close to the experimental value of 40 per cent. In the ethyl methylcellulose substrate (DS 1·3) approximately 18 per cent of the anhydroglucose units would be unsubstituted and some 3·3 per cent of unsubstituted units would be contiguous. These values led to the suggestion, mentioned previously, that the linkages adjacent to only one unsubstituted unit could be attacked.

The products of enzymic hydrolysis are principally glucose and cellobiose, although some higher saccharides have been detected from CMC[16,55]. However, analysis by paper chromatography is frequently complicated by the appearance of substituted glucose compounds, and care must be taken in assigning chromatographic mobilities unless reference compounds can be analysed at the same time; some possibly erroneous conclusions from this source have been commented upon by Festenstein[55]. While no enzymes capable of removing the substituents from such derivatives have been found, it has been reported[64] than an esterase occurring widely in fungi brought about the deacetylation of cellobiose octa-acetate. Many cellulolytic organisms were found to grow on this latter compound as a carbon source, but the esterase could only be detected in the culture filtrates of a few species, which included *Pestalotiopsis westerdijkii*, *Chaetomium elatum*, *Humicola fuscoatra*, *Aspergillus flavus*, and *A. sydowi*. The enzyme was also produced when the organisms were grown on cellulose, a holocellulose, sucrose octa-acetate, or on a water-soluble cellulose acetate; however, cellulose triacetate was not hydrolysed and in view of the action on cellobiose octa-acetate (also water-insoluble), the longer chains appear to be protected from attack by this esterase. Other esters capable of hydrolysis include *o*–nitrophenylacetate, and it was possible to convert

80 per cent of a soluble cellulose acetate (DS 0·76) to water-soluble products. The enzyme exhibited optimum activity at pH 5·0.

ACTION ON CELLODEXTRINS

The enzymic hydrolysis of a cellodextrin of DP 24 has already been considered, and it will be recalled that hydrolysis in the presence of ^{14}C–labelled cellobiose resulted in little radioactivity being found in the cello-oligosaccharides produced[50]. This result largely eliminated transglycosylation as a mode of formation, and simple hydrolysis was found to be the only process operative from a study of concentration changes in glucose and oligosaccharides as the reaction proceeded. After a period of one hour, the DP of the dextrin had been reduced to 21. This evidence of random attack was confirmed by the production of a mixture of glucose and oligosaccharides by the action of a heated enzyme, which had lost its transglucosylase and cellobiase activities[51].

The degradation of cello-oligosaccharides has been studied systematically by Whitaker[63,66] using his purified cellulase from *Myrothecium verrucaria*. During hydrolysis of cellotriose, the glucosidic linkage adjacent to the non-reducing end of the chain was broken preferentially, the rate of hydrolysis of this linkage being five times greater than that of the other linkage (adjacent to the reducing end). A study of the breakdown of a series of oligoglucosides from cellotriose to cellohexaose revealed that the increase in molecular weight was accompanied by an increase in the rate of hydrolysis, this effect being particularly marked as the DP increased from 2 to 4. The net effect of an increase in DP from 2 to 5 was to multiply the hydrolysis rate constant by 400 to 450. The addition of a β–linked sorbityl group to any one sugar caused an increase in the hydrolysis rate, but the addition of a β–linked glucosyl unit caused an even greater increase in reaction velocity. Thus, sorbityl–β–cellobioside had a velocity constant (K) for hydrolysis of $1·3 \times 10^{-2}$ min^{-1}, which was 9·3 times greater than that for cellobiose, whilst the value of K for cellotriose was higher still. Whitaker[63] pursued this study and interpreted his results on the steric factors in such hydrolyses in terms of the classical collision theory[67]. As chain length increased hydrolysis became more random. The central ether linkage of cellotetraose was broken preferentially to the two terminal linkages; a similar preference was shown in cellopentaose, but at least one of its terminal linkages was cleaved at a higher rate than that for either of the terminal linkages of cellotetraose. On reaching cellohexaose, very little evidence was obtained for any preferential cleavage.

The products from the action of the various amylases on amylose undergo mutarotation, and this effect was not observed in the cellulase field until Whitaker[66] investigated the hydrolysis of cellopentaose. Upward mutarotation was found after addition of ammonia to the hydrolysates to bring them to pH 10, thus providing evidence that the cellulase catalysed the hydrolysis of a β–glucosidic linkage to give a reducing end group in the β–configuration. This retention of configuration during hydrolysis parallels the action of α–amylase (see *Chapter I*); in view of this and the other evidence presented it was suggested that this resemblance may be extended to the mechanism of enzymic degradation of the two polymers. The hydrolysis of cellodextrins by the enzymes of *Aspergillus niger* was studied by Grassmann *et al.*[28], and more recently by Stone[54], but the mechanism of hydrolysis has only been studied in detail by Whitaker.

ACTION ON OTHER GLYCOSIDES

Little work has been done on the action of purified cellulases on glycosides other than those mentioned above. Nisizawa and his co-workers have examined the action of their purified *Irpex lacteus* enzymes on a number of glycosides. The purified cellulase catalysed the hydrolysis of p–nitrophenyl–β–D–cellobioside as much as the hydrolysis of carboxymethylcellulose; in the former case cleavage occurred at both aglucone and holosidic bonds, giving rise to a mixture of p–nitrophenol, cellobiose, p–nitrophenyl–β–D–glucoside, and glucose. This cellulase preparation was free from cellobiase, amylase and aryl–β–glucosidase, and the finding that units were split from a β–cellobioside in pairs was put forward as evidence for the hypothesis that hydrolysis with this enzyme occurred by the cleavage of cellobiose units from the end of the cellulose chain[68]. The *Irpex* β–glucosidase also brought about the hydrolysis of this cellobioside[69], and a study of the specificities of both cellulase and β–glucosidase from this Basidiomycete was undertaken[70]. While the cellulase catalysed the rapid hydrolysis of aryl–β–D–cellobiosides, substrates not attacked included alkyl–β–D–cellobiosides, cellobiose, and aryl–β–D–cellobiosides in which the aglucone was large in size, such as naphthyl or the hydroquinone bis–β:β'–D–glucoside; all four classes of substrate were broken down in the presence of the β–glucosidase. It was suggested that for a cellobioside to be amenable to the action of *Irpex* cellulase it must have a molecular structure resembling that of cellotriose. This later work revealed that the aglucone linkage of the aryl–β–D–cellobiosides was preferentially hydrolysed by the cellulase. This enzyme also had transferase activity, as shown by its ability to catalyse the transfer of the cellobiosyl unit from p–nitrophenyl–β–D–cellobioside to methanol.

Many other reports have been made of the catalysis of glycoside hydrolysis (non-cellulosic substrates), but many of these cases involve enzyme mixtures[12,38] and the few cases where pure or partially purified cellulases attack other polysaccharides are listed in *Table 7*. The enzyme from *Stachybotrys atra* and the heated enzyme

Table 7. *Polysaccharides Attacked in Presence of Cellulases*

Enzyme	Polysaccharide	Ref.
Purified *M. verrucaria* cellulase	Wheat straw xylan	49
Stachybotrys atra cellulase–extensively dialysed	Xylan	17
Heated cellulase of *M. verrucaria*	Crown gall $(1{\rightarrow}2)\beta$–glucan	74
	Lutean, $(1{\rightarrow}6)\beta$–glucosidic link	
	Laminarin, $(1{\rightarrow}3)\beta$– glucosidic link	
	Konjak flour glucomannan, $(1{\rightarrow}4)$ and $(1{\rightarrow}6)$ bonds	
	Lichenin	
	Xylan	
Helix pomatia partially purified cellulase	Laminarin	56
	Yeast glucan	
	Ivory nut mannan	

from *Myrothecium verrucaria* are comparatively impure, but the finding that the pure *M. verrucaria* cellulase brought about the hydrolysis of linear chains of $(1{\rightarrow}4)$ β–xylopyranoside chains raises the question of the identity of cellulase and xylanase[49]. In general, crude cellulase preparations have xylanase activity, and it is not difficult to free xylanase from cellulase activity, by ethanol precipitation methods for example. However, until recently the converse separation proved more difficult, but Myers and Northcote[56] have now achieved this end, and their snail cellulase was free from action on xylan. Jermyn[53,71] has worked extensively on the specificities of cellulases, intra- and extra-cellular β–glucosidases from *Aspergillus oryzae* and *Stachybotrys atra* in an attempt to fit the facts of carbohydrate hydrolysis into a unified picture of the mechanism[72]. It appears that cellulases of different specificities exist and that no cellulase with an absolute specificity for the macromolecular cellulose has yet been prepared (see also Chapter V).

ADSORPTION OF CELLULASE ON CELLULOSE

The adsorption of cellulolytic enzymes on cellulose and the different rates of elution of enzyme components from cellulose have formed the basis for chromatographic and electrophoretic separations of such enzymes, as described in Chapter IV. Better recovery of cellulase activity was obtained when paper coated with protein was used for this separation[35], thus implying the strong affinity of cellulose for the enzyme, a fact which had been recognized earlier[73], and it was shown that the extent of adsorption of the C_x enzyme on cotton varied with the organism from which it was derived, and also with the pre-treatment of the cotton; adsorption increased on raising the pH value of the solution. Considerable adsorption (40 to 60 per cent) of cellulase on Whatman filter paper powder and on acid swollen cellulose has been recorded[17], while the adsorption of enzyme activity on a pulped filter paper was as high as 80 per cent[11]; however, the recovery of activity after adsorption was not measured. Differences in the degree of adsorption of cellulase and cellobiase have been used to confirm the individuality of a cellobiase which disappeared on heating the impure *Myrothecium verrucaria* enzymes. Thus, the cellobiase existed before heating and heating did in fact destroy an individual enzyme, and not merely alter the specificity of a cellulase[74].

SUMMARY OF THE MODE OF ACTION
OF CELLULASES

Two important questions concerned with the enzymic hydrolysis of cellulose still require conclusive answers; these are the mode of attack (i.e. whether the cleavage of the cellulose chain is random, or whether cellobiose or other units are removed from reducing or non-reducing ends of the chains), and the number of enzymes involved in the hydrolysis of cellulosic polymers. The belief that enzymic action proceeded 'endwise' was held by Clayson[75] and this was supported more recently by Nisizawa and Kobayashi[58]. The latter workers found that cellobiose was formed from a hydrocellulose by the action of an *Irpex* cellulase which was free from cellobiase activity. The copper value of the hydrocellulose recovered after enzymic attack had increased almost proportionally to the decrease in weight of the substrate. This evidence was supported by the mode of cleavage of *p*–nitrophenyl–*β*–cellobioside by the same enzyme. An endwise cleavage of cellulose was also noted in the presence of the cellulase from *Corynebacterium fimi*[59].

However, much evidence has accumulated for a purely random attack, notably from the careful work of Whitaker cited earlier, but other more indirect evidence has been obtained such as:

(a) the reduction in viscosity of soluble cellulose derivatives before appreciable increase in the reducing sugar concentration,

(b) the formation of oligosaccharides during hydrolysis, where this cannot be accounted for by transglycosylation,

(c) the formation of mixtures of glucose and cellobiose using a pure cellulase free from cellobiase activity,

(d) the apparent independence of the rate of hydrolysis on the initial degree of polymerization of the substrate,

(e) the high degree of substitution necessary to protect certain cellulosic derivatives from attack,

(f) the rapid loss in tensile strength of cellophane strips and rapid fall in DP of regenerated celluloses with no corresponding increase in reducing sugars produced.

The number of enzymes involved in the hydrolysis of $(1\rightarrow4)$ *β*–linked glucans has long been a point of controversy. Whitaker obtained an electrophoretically homogeneous enzyme and the enrichment in activity during its preparation towards five different substrates ranging from cotton to cellobiose was approximately the same; the end products were cellobiose and glucose. The unienzymatic hypothesis is supported by Kooiman, except that a cellobiase is invoked for the conversion of cellobiose to glucose. However, extensive chromatographic and electrophoretic studies of cellulases (see Chapter IV) show the presence of many cellulolytic components in crude culture filtrates, although it is interesting to note that here Whitaker again differed, in that he found only one active cellulolytic component in a protein mixture from his crude filtrate separated by electrophoresis, this being the component observed in his purified enzyme. On the other hand, the enzyme fractions obtained by Reese *et al.* had differing reactivities towards different substrates, as well as different mobilities, and when the components were recombined they displayed a definite synergistic interaction.

If the reaction is multienzymatic in character, the question of the number of enzymes involved and how their actions differ arises. Early work[28] suggested that a cellulase was able to hydrolyse cellulose and polysaccharides down to cellohexaose, and a cellobiase acted in the hydrolysis of cellobiose and oligosaccharides up to cellohexaose. The findings of Reese and his co-workers were explained by the enzymic components differing largely in their preference for substrates of different chain lengths, but an alternative explanation may be found in differences in the mode of action of the components; the components appearing to have a preference for short chains may, in fact, act by endwise hydrolysis. The nature of the enzyme (C_1) responsible for the ability of some filtrates to catalyse the hydrolysis of native cellulose, which is lacking from other filtrates, still remains unresolved. The opening up of native cellulose structure need not be an enzymic process although Siu[76] has mentioned a 'hydrogenbondase', and the exact place of 'S-factor', which causes swelling with no changes in DP, tensile strength or reducing value, in the pattern of cellulose breakdown is also undetermined. The enzyme C_1 may merely be a C_x component acting only on the longest chains, or its action may be to open up the physical structure of cellulose, or it may even act upon a rare or anomalous linkage in native cellulose.

REFERENCES

1. REESE, SIU AND LEVINSON, *J. Bact.* 1950, **59**, p. 485.
2. LEVINSON, MANDELS AND REESE, *Arch. Biochem. Biophys.* 1951, **31**, p. 351.
3. SEILLÈRE, *C. R. soc. biol. Paris*, 1906, **61**, p. 205; 1907, **63**, p. 515; 1910, **68**, p. 107.
4. KARRER AND ILLING, *Kolloidzschr.* 1925, **36**, p. 91.
5. HUSEMANN AND LÖTTERLE, *Makromol. Chem.* 1950, **4**, p. 278.
6. KARRER AND SCHUBERT, *Helv. chim. Acta*, 1926, **9**, p. 893; 1928, **11**, p. 229.
7. FAUST, KARRER AND SCHUBERT, *Helv. chim. Acta*, 1928, **11**, p. 231.
8. FAUST AND KARRER, *Helv. chim. Acta*, 1929, **12**, p. 414.
9. WALSETH, *Tech. Ass. Pulp Pap. Ind.* 1952, **35**, p. T.233.
10. REESE, SEGAL AND TRIPP, *Text. Res. J.* 1957, **27**, p. 626.
11. ENEBO, *Studies in Cellulose Decomposition*, 1954, Stockholm.
12. AITKEN, EDDY, INGRAM AND WEURMAN, *Biochem. J.* 1956, **64**, p. 63.
13. WHITAKER, *Nature, Lond.* 1951, **168**, p. 1070.
14. GREATHOUSE, *Text. Res. J.* 1950, **20**, p. 227.
15. ABRAMS, *Text. Res. J.* 1950, **20**, p. 71.
16. SISON, SCHUBERT AND NORD, *Arch. Biochem. Biophys.* 1958, **75**, p. 260.
17. THOMAS, *Aust. J. biol. Sci.* 1956, **9**, p. 159.
18. NISIZAWA, MATSUZAKI AND HIGUCHI, Res. Reports, Faculty of Textiles and Sericulture, Shinshu Univ. (Japan), 1953, **3**, p. 69.
19. PERLIN, MICHAELIS AND MACFARLANE, *Canad. J. Res.* 1947, **25C**, p. 246.
20. BASU AND GHOSE, *J. Text. Inst.* 1952, **43**, p. T278.
21. SHARPLES, *J. Polym. Sci.* 1954, **13**, p. 393.

22. MANN AND MARRINAN, *Trans. Faraday Soc.* 1956, **52**, p. 492.
23. HERMANS AND WEIDINGER, *J. Polym. Sci.* 1949, **4**, p. 135.
24. FULLER AND NORMAN. *Proc. Soil. Sci. Soc. America*, 1942, **7**, p. 243.
24. BURKHOLDER AND SIU, *Prevention of Deterioration Abst.* 1948, **4**, p. 72.
26. WALSETH, *Enzymatic Hydrolysis of Cellulose*, 1948, Institute of Paper Chemistry, Appleton, Wisconsin, U.S.A.
27. GILLIGAN AND REESE, *Canad. J. Microbiol.* 1954, **1**, p. 90.
28. GRASSMANN, ZECHMEISTER, TOTH AND STADLER, *Annalen*, 1933, **503**, p. 167.
29. JERMYN, *Aust. J. Sci. Res.* 1952, **B5**, p. 433.
30. MARSH, GUTHRIE AND BUTLER, *Text. Res. J.* 1951, **21**, p. 565.
31. MARSH, MEROLA AND SIMPSON, *Text. Res. J.* 1953, **23**, p. 833.
32. MARSH, *Plant Disease Reporter*, 1953, **37**, p. 71.
33. MARSH, BOLLENBACHER, BUTLER AND GUTHRIE, *Text. Res. J.* 1953, **23**, p. 878.
34. REESE AND GILLIGAN, *Text. Res. J.* 1954, **24**, p. 663.
35. REESE AND GILLIGAN, *Arch. Biochem. Biophys.* 1953, **45**, p. 74.
36. FÅHRAEUS, *Experientia*, 1946, **2**, p. 413.
37. BLUM AND STAHL, *Text. Res. J.* 1952, **22**, p. 178.
38. NORKRANS, *Symbolae Botan. Upsalienses*, 1950, **11**, p. 5.
39. NORKRANS AND RÅNBY, *Physiol. Plant.* 1956, **9**, p. 198.
40. WHITAKER, *Canad. J. Biochem. Physiol.* 1957, **35**, p. 733.
41. HOWSMON AND MARCHESSAULT, *J. Appl. Polym. Sci.* 1959, **1**, p. 313.
42. REESE, *Appl. Microbiol.* 1956, **4**, p. 39.
43. WHITAKER, COLVIN AND COOK, *Arch. Biochem. Biophys.* 1954, **49**, p. 257.
44. SAEMAN, BUBL AND HARRIS, U.S. Dept. of Agriculture, Forest Service, Bulletin R1458 (1944), Madison, Wisconsin, U.S.A.
45. RÅNBY AND RIBI, *Experientia*, 1950, **6**, p. 12.
46. INGERSOLL, *J. Appl. Phys.* 1946, **17**, p. 924.
47. HOWSMON, *Text. Res. J.* 1949, **19**, p. 152.
48. MOREHEAD, *Text. Res. J.* 1950, **20**, p. 549.
49. BISHOP AND WHITAKER, *Chem. and Ind.* 1955, p. 119.
50. WHITAKER, *Canad. J. Biochem. Physiol.* 1956, **34**, p. 488.
51. KOOIMAN, ROELOFSEN AND SWEERIS, *Enzymologia*, 1953, **16**, p. 237.
52. HASH AND KING, *Science*, 1954, **120**, p. 1033.
53. JERMYN, *Aust. J. biol. Sci.* 1952, **B5**, p. 409.
54. STONE, Ph.D. Thesis, University of London, 1954.
55. FESTENSTEIN, *Biochem. J.* 1959, **72**, p. 75.
56. MYERS AND NORTHCOTE, *Biochem. J.* 1959, **71**, p. 749.
57. WHITAKER, *Arch. Biochem. Biophys.* 1953, **43**, p. 253.
58. NISIZAWA AND KOBAYASHI, *J. Agric. chem. Soc. Japan*, 1953, **27**, p. 239.
59. MATTHIJSEN, *Diss. Abstracts*, 1957, **17**, p. 2141.
60. HOLDEN AND TRACEY, *Biochem. J.* 1950, **47**, p. 407.
61. HIRSCH, *Experientia*, 1954, **10**, p. 180.
62. LEVINSON AND REESE, *J. gen. Physiol.* 1950, **33**, p. 601.
63. WHITAKER, *Canad. J. Biochem. Physiol.* 1956, **34**, pp. 83, 102.
64. REESE, *Ind. Eng. Chem.* 1957, **49**, p. 89.

65. SPURLIN, *J. Amer. chem. Soc.* 1950, **61**, p. 2222.
66. WHITAKER, *Arch. Biochem. Biophys.* 1954, **53**, pp. 436, 439.
67. MOELWYN-HUGHES, *The Kinetics of Reactions in Solution*, 2nd ed., The Clarendon Press, Oxford, 1947.
68. NISIZAWA, *J. Biochem. Japan*, 1955, **42**, p. 825.
69. NISIZAWA AND KOBAYASHI, *J. Agric. chem. Soc. Japan*, 1953, **27**, p. 242.
70. NISIZAWA AND HASHIMOTO, *Arch. Biochem. Biophys.* 1959, **81**, p. 211.
71. JERMYN, *Aust. J. biol. Sci.* 1959, **12**, p. 213.
72. JERMYN, *Science*, 1957, **125**, p. 12.
73. REESE AND LEVINSON, *Physiol. Plant.* 1952, **5**, p. 345.
74. KOOIMAN, *Enzymologia*, 1957, **18**, p. 371.
75. CLAYSON, *J. Soc. chem. Ind. London*, 1943, **62**, p. 49.
76. SIU in *Cellulose and Cellulose Derivatives*, Part I, p. 189, ed. Ott, Spurlin and Grafflin, Interscience Publishers Inc., New York, U.S.A. 1954.

VII

HEMICELLULASES

It will be recalled that the hemicelluloses may be divided broadly into two classes, the polyuronide type and the cellulosans. The hydrolysis of these compounds is catalysed by enzymes from animals, plants and micro-organisms; these enzymes have not been given the detailed attention that the cellulases have and are receiving, but in view of the close association of hemicelluloses and cellulose in Nature some consideration must be given to the hemicellulases. In plants the hemicelluloses consist of mixtures of hexosans, pentosans and polyuronides, and relatively few hemicelluloses have been isolated as pure compounds. Hence, with this complexity of substrates the enzymes catalysing their hydrolyses are numerous. However, very few enzymes with a specificity limited only to one class of hemicellulose have been prepared; probably the pentosanases have received most attention and these will be discussed together with a brief account of mannanases and mannogalactanases.

PENTOSANASES

In the majority of cellulase-producing organisms pentosanases also occur. The similarity between xylan and cellulose is often emphasized too much, for the highly crystalline native celluloses do not bear a great resemblance to the amorphous, often branched chain xylans, except in the occurrence of the $(1\rightarrow4)$ β–glycosidic linkage. The large majority of cellulases recorded in this book also act in the hydrolysis of xylans, so that expected sources of pentosanases are the snail[1], barley malt[2] and the fungi[2]. It is not intended to give a detailed survey of the extracellular enzymes, as the methods of production and purification closely follow the lines of cellulase separation outlined in previous chapters and have also been reviewed by Pigman[3] and Weidenhagen[4]. However, some of the more recent papers on this subject are listed in *Table 1*.

PURIFICATION

Inaoka and Soda[13] claim to have crystallized a xylanase from a *Bacillus* sp. grown on a xylan, meat extract, peptone and mineral salts medium for seven days. After concentration of the culture

Table 1. Some Sources of Pentosanases

Source of enzyme	Substrate(s)	Comments	Ref.
FUNGI			
Aspergillus niger	aspen hemicellulose	Rohm and Haas E19 enzyme	5
Myrothecium verrucaria	wheat straw xylan	Hydrolysed to L–arabinosyl–D–xylobiose + D–xylose	6, 7
Aspergillus batatae	xylan	Crystalline: random attack	8
Aspergillus foetidus	corn cob xylan	Mixture of enzymes separated	9
Fusarium roseum	esparto xylan	Xylanase separated from cellulase	10
Chaetomium globosum	wheat straw xylan	Random hydrolysis	11
Trichoderma viride	—	Influence of growth	
Aspergillus niger	—	medium on pentosanase production	12
BACTERIA			
Bacillus sp.	xylan	Crystalline, no xylose produced	13
Sporocytophaga myxococcoides	wheat straw xylan	Principally growth experiments. Suggested that cellulase could cleave xylan	14
Bacillus subtilis, Bacillus pumites Other bacteria and fungi	wheat flour pentosan and pentosan in starch slurries	Study of conditions for optimum production of enzymes	15–17
RUMEN			
Cattle rumen contents	rice straw xylan	Acetone precipitate from	18
Sheep rumen contents	wheat flour and algal pentosans	Enzymes in toluene treated suspension of rumen bacteria	19
ANIMAL			
Helix pomatia	wheat straw and walnut xylan	Digestive tract extracts	20
PLANT			
Barley	rye araboxylan	Four enzyme systems described	21, 22
Marine algae	esparto and algal xylan		23
SOIL	wheat straw xylan	Amount enzyme depends on amount xylan in soil	24

filtrate, lead acetate solution was added, the precipitate rejected and ammonium sulphate was added to the supernatant liquid to give 70 per cent saturation. The resultant precipitate, dissolved in phosphate buffer (0·067M, pH 6·0), was dialysed against distilled water. To the dialysate was added a solution of rivanol (6:9–diamino–2–ethoxyacridine lactate) and the precipitate formed was discarded. From this supernatant liquid the enzyme was precipitated by the addition of acetone; after drying *in vacuo*, the precipitate was dissolved in water (10 vol.) and a precipitate obtained by adding acetone (3 vol.) was removed and discarded. To the supernatant solution further acetone (2 vol.) was added and after holding the solution at 5° for a day crystals appeared; from 5 litres of culture medium 30 mg of crystals were obtained. Other crystalline xylanases have been obtained from the culture medium of *Aspergillus batatae*[8].

Earlier workers have demonstrated the separation of xylanase from some of the enzymes of *Aspergillus oryzae* by selective adsorption methods[25], while a considerable concentration of xylanase was obtained from malt extract by adsorption on aluminium hydroxide followed by elution with a phosphate buffer solution at pH 8·33 [26]. Two enzyme preparations were obtained by Sørensen[11] from *Chaetomium globosum* growing on a mineral salts medium containing various carbon sources; in the case of wheat straw xylan, the polysaccharide was dissolved in sodium hydroxide solution (N) and the solution was neutralized with acetic acid. After 2 to 3 days' growth at 25° the mycelium was harvested, washed with water, ground in acetone and ether, and finally dried *in vacuo*. Cell-free enzyme solutions were obtained by water extraction of the acetone mycelium powder, followed by ultrafiltration (a sintered glass filter of porosity 5 on 3); no further purification was attempted. Another interesting fractionation was carried out by Whistler and Masak[9] from the fungus *Aspergillus foetidus* grown on a glucose, peptone and mineral salts medium; after 4 days' growth at 25°, the culture was filtered and the enzymes from both the filtrate and a sodium chloride extract of the ground mycelium were fractionated by precipitation with ammonium sulphate at 80 per cent saturation. The precipitate from the filtrate was dialysed over a collodion membrane and freeze-dried (Fraction A). Apart from the precipitate (Fraction B) from the mycelium, the cell-free mycelium extract was fractionated by adsorption on a cation exchange resin column (Amberlite IRC 50) in the hydrogen form, followed by elution with McIlvaine's citrate-phosphate buffer at pH 6·5 (see Chapter IV); assay of the fractions collected showed two principal components (Fractions C and D) having different actions on xylan. Fraction C was then passed down a column of carboxymethylcellulose (degree of substitution 0·563) which had been previously washed with a phosphate buffer at pH 5·1. The column was rapidly eluted, to minimise C_x enzyme action on the packing, with a phosphate buffer at pH 6·5; two major components (Fractions E and F) resulted, again with different actions on xylan. The mode of actions of these fractions is discussed later.

Thirteen fungi were tested for hydrolysing action on esparto xylan by the present authors[10] and *Fusarium roseum* was selected for further study. The extracellular enzyme systems of this fungus, grown on an esparto xylan and mineral salts medium in shaken culture, were fractionated by ethanol precipitation, and the properties of one of the fractions obtained were investigated. Extensive purification was not carried out, but the selected fraction had no action on cellulose. The enzymes concerned with the degradation of cereal hemicelluloses are discussed in Chapter VIII.

MODE OF ACTION OF PENTOSANASES

One of the crystalline enzymes of Fukui and Sato[8] catalysed the random hydrolysis of polyxylosides to give a limit polyxylosan, xylotriose, an arabinosylxyloside, xylobiose together with small amounts of xylotetraose and arabinose, but no xylose was produced. The other crystalline enzyme gave xylose from the hydrolysis of both oligo- and poly-xylosides, presumably due to attack from the end of chains; however, this enzyme also had transpentosylase action since xylobiose and xylotriose were converted to higher saccharides. The crystalline xylanase from a *Bacillus* species[13] catalysed the hydrolysis of xylan in two stages, initially producing a rapid decrease in the viscosity of a xylan solution, and followed by the much slower second stage. Again, the enzyme appeared to act in a random manner producing xylo-oligosaccharides with no xylose being detected by paper chromatography. In all such accounts the action of trans-pentosylases, frequently not recorded, must be borne in mind. Such enzymes were noted in the culture medium of *Fusarium roseum*[10] where one fraction catalysed the hydrolysis of esparto xylan to xylose, arabinose, a trace of glucose and xylo-oligosaccharides and the enzyme action on xylobiose and xylotriose gave rise to higher oligosaccharides. Similar random cleavage of a rye flour araboxylan and a spruce γ–cellulose was found; the rate constant for a first order reaction on xylan was calculated as $7·3 \times 10^{-7}$ sec^{-1}. No transpentosylase action has been noticed in the cellulase enzyme system from *Myrothecium verrucaria*, although hydrolysis of xylan resulted in the isolation of a trisaccharide containing xylose and arabinose[6].

The xylanases of *Chaetomium globosum* mycelium[11] brought about the hydrolysis of 55 to 60 per cent of a wheat straw xylan on prolonged action, xylose being the principal product together with some arabinose; the ratio of xylose to arabinose obtained depended upon the method of extracting and drying the mycelium. The dried mycelium itself tended to autolyse leading to the appearance of glucose on paper chromatograms, and it was not possible to decide if the glucose had been cleaved from the xylan enzymatically. The cell-free mycelium extract brought about the hydrolysis of xylan to xylose, arabinose and a range of oligosaccharides. After removal of undecomposed xylan from a dried mycelium-xylan digest, the addition of baryta and ethanol precipitated a barium salt; the filtrate from this precipitation contained xylose, a little arabinose and a component of higher molecular weight, apart from glucose produced by autolysis. The barium salt on acid hydrolysis gave xylose, arabinose, glucose and a uronic acid; thus, the wheat straw xylan contained an enzyme-resistant, water soluble polysaccharide having these components. A similar result was obtained by O'Dwyer[27] from the hydrolysis of an oak hemicellulose with the aid of the crude enzyme taka-diastase.

Jermyn and Tomkins[28], studying the enzymic hydrolysis of pectin, suggested three ways in which a polysaccharide could be broken down:

(a) by random cleavage of the chain,
(b) by removing single sugar units from the end of the chain,
(c) by removing oligosaccharide groups from the end of the chain, followed by the hydrolysis of these groups possibly by a second enzyme.

Sørensen's work, as indicated above, supported a random scission of xylan chains. Storage of these enzymes or thermal denaturation resulted in the loss of xylose-producing power, and this could be interpreted as due to the thermolability of xylobiase (acting in the mechanism (a) or (c) above), in line with the findings on cellobiase and cellulase[29,30]. Similar observations have been made by Kooiman[31].

The enzymes fractionated from *Aspergillus foetidus*[9] have different actions on various substrates as shown in *Table 2*. The hemicellulose B was prepared[43] from corn cob holocellulose by solution in alkali, removing the precipitate on acidification, and collecting hemicellulose B obtained by precipitating from the supernatant liquid with

198

Table 2. Hydrolysis Products from Action of A. foetidus Enzymes

Enzyme fraction	Substrate	Hydrolysis products
A (extracellular)	corn cob xylan	oligosaccharides only
	Walseth cellulose	no action
	xylobiose	no action
	xylotriose	no action
	xylotetraose	xylobiose
B ($(NH_4)_2SO_4$ ppt. from mycelium extracted with NaCl)	corn cob xylan	xylose + xylo-oligosaccharides
C (from cell free mycelium extract)	corn cob xylan	xylose only
D (from cell free mycelium extract)	corn cob xylan	xylose + xylo-oligosaccharides
	cellulose	glucose + cellobiose
E (fractionated from C)	corn cob xylan	xylose
	hemicellulose B	xylose + oligosaccharides
	xylobiose	xylose
	xylotriose	xylose + xylobiose in 4 hr.
		xylose in 8 hr.
	xylotetraose	xylose + xylobiose + xylotriose in 4 hr.
		xylose + xylobiose in 7 hr.
		xylose in 8 hr.
F (fractionated from C)	corn cob xylan	no action
	hemicellulose B	oligsoaccharides only

ethanol. The enzymes responsible for the cleavage of xylan chains were separated from those catalysing the hydrolysis of hemicellulose B by further fractionation with ammonium sulphate on a Celite column[32], as well as by adsorption of the mycelium extract on a column of carboxymethylcellulose, followed by elution at pH 6·5 with a buffer solution. A search for phosphorylated sugars by paper chromatography in xylan hydrolysates was not successful[33]. Whilst paper chromatography is so often relied upon in the examination of enzymic hydrolysates, Whistler and Masak[9] point out that this method only constitutes a useful indication of components produced from polysaccharides whose constituent sugars have been determined by acid hydrolysis and subsequent isolation of crystalline compounds. The action of the crude enzymes emulsin and taka-diastase on β–xylosides has been studied by Morita[34]. The latter enzyme source contained an arabanase which hydrolysed arabans from sugar beet and orange peel to L–arabinose[41]; the 'cup-plate' diffusion method has been applied to the assay of this enzyme[42].

PROPERTIES OF PENTOSANASES

The xylanase of *Fusarium roseum*[10] was active at 30° over the pH range 4·2 to 8·5 with optimum action on esparto xylan at pH 6·3 using a phosphate buffer (0·099M). Similar optima were found for the enzymes of *Chaetomium globosum* (pH 6·5)[11], and of cattle rumen fluid (pH 6·2)[18]. These values all lie outside the region reported by Whistler and Masak[9], who found the optimum activities for their various fractions to be much lower; these and other properties are recorded in *Table 3*, and it will be noted that the activities were only

Table 3. Properties of Xylanases from Aspergillus foetidus

Fraction	Active over pH range	Optimum pH value	Temperature optimum
A (extracellular)	2·8–5·0	3·4	37°
B (mycelium extract)	3·0–5·5	4·5	37°
C (mycelium extract)	3·0–5·0	3·8	45°

tested over the range pH 2·8 to 5·0. It would be advisable to extend this range in view of the findings for other fungi, and also the report of double pH value optima of cellulases, especially when their actions were inhibited by the presence of a disaccharide[35]. The optimum pH value for a malt pentosanase was 5·0, and inactivation was complete at pH 9·0 [26].

The temperature for optimum activity of xylanases generally lies between 30° and 37°, although *Table 3* shows an intracellular enzyme from a fungus to have maximum activity at 45°, which latter value has also been recorded for the malt enzyme[26]. Xylanases are inactivated by heating; the activity of the enzyme from *C. globosum*[11] decreased sharply after the enzyme had been held at 60° for 10 minutes in a phosphate buffer solution at pH 6·5, although some activity was retained even after heating at 100°; the xylanase of *F. roseum*[10] was progressively inactivated on heating above 30° with complete denaturation by 75°. The activity of certain fractions from *Aspergillus foetidus* was destroyed on heating at 65°; this procedure allowed the 'xylose-producing' Fraction C, which was stable at 65° for 30 minutes, to be separated from the thermolabile Fraction D, which latter produced xylose and xylo-oligosaccharides from xylan[9].

Little information exists on the activation of pentosanases; a bacillary xylanase was activated by calcium and magnesium ions[13], whilst another xylanase was not stimulated by albumin, although in such a crude preparation containing 14 per cent of protein this was hardly to be expected[10]. Studies on the inhibition of xylanase activity are principally confined to Sørensen's enzyme[11], where complete suppression was found in the presence of $0 \cdot 01 M$ solutions of lead, mercuric and silver ions, some inhibition by copper and cobalt ions, and weak inhibition by azide, fluoride and iodoacetate ions; no inhibition occurred in the presence of $0 \cdot 01 M$ solutions of sodium cyanide, sodium molybdate, or urethane. The weak inhibition by a thiol reagent (iodoacetate) is interesting in view of the report that a crude fungal xylanase[10] was not inhibited by p–chloromercuribenzoate at concentrations from $0 \cdot 0009 M$ to $0 \cdot 005 M$; the presence of thiol (sulphydryl) groups near to the active centres of a pure cellulase has been noticed, and it may be that further research will enable this property to be used to assess differences between cellulases and xylanases.

The inducible and constitutive natures of cellulases have been discussed in Chapter V, and a similar state of affairs exists in the pentosanase field. Simpson[15] claimed that bacterial pentosanases are constitutive and the fungal enzymes inducible. Support for this view has come from Sørensen[11] who grew *Chaetomium globosum* on glucose, starch, a cellodextrin, mannan and xylose, and examined an extract of the fungal mycelium for xylanase activity. A small but definite amount of xylanase was produced by growth on the last three named carbon sources, although considerably more of the enzyme was produced by growth on xylan. Many cellulases, synthesized by fungi growing on various forms of cellulose, have been found to catalyse the hydrolysis of xylan. The enzymes xylanase and cellulase are different, as shown by their separation[10,36], but the production of each enzyme on alternate carbon sources does not permit an application of the strict criterion of inducible character suggested by Monod *et al.*[37].

OTHER HEMICELLULASES

Few studies have been made of the enzymes catalysing the hydrolysis of hemicelluloses other than the pentosans; the hydrolysis of polyuronides is outside the scope of this book, but an excellent review on pectic enzymes has been given by Deuel[38]. *Chaetomium globosum* produced an enzyme which brought about the hydrolysis of tuber salep mannan, when the mycelium was grown on this mannan, or to a lesser extent when grown on glucose or starch[11]. Extracts from sprouted barley catalysed the hydrolysis of a carob bean mannogalactan[32], whilst a partial separation of this enzyme from cellulase by ammonium sulphate solution elution from Celite has been achieved[39]. The cell wall splitting enzymes of rust uredospores (*Puccinia graminis*), which have been shown to contain the cellulase C_x, had various hemicellulase activities[40]. The spores were extracted with sodium chloride solution (0·6%) in a ball mill, débris was removed by centrifugation, and the proteins in the supernatant liquid were precipitated by addition of ammonium sulphate; attempts to fractionate the enzymes by ethanol or acetone precipitation resulted in a loss of 50 to 80 per cent of the activity. Hemicellulose substrates used were prepared from carob (*Ceratonia siliqua* L.) [a main chain of D–mannose units (80%) linked $(1{\rightarrow}4)\beta$, to which were attached by $(1{\rightarrow}6)$ β linkages D–galactose side chains (20%)], from barley, from tuber salep (a mannan), and from rust-resistant and rust-sensitive strains of wheat. It was found that the hemicellulase activity, followed viscosimetrically, was greatest in spores stored for one year, while germinated fresh spores had higher activity than fresh resting spores. The mannogalactanase activity reached an optimum value at pH 5·5 and 40°. The extract from aged spores produced galactose and only a small amount of mannose from the carob substrate, while from the wheat hemicellulose xylose and a range of xylo-oligosaccharides resulted. Inhibitors of these hemicellulase activities included copper, mercuric and silver ions, while sodium sulphide stimulated activity. Iodoacetate only depressed activity slightly at a concentration of 0·01M at pH 5·5; addition of cysteine did not reverse the inhibition caused by mercuric acetate, and the proposal that these hemicellulases contained thiol groups close to their active centres cannot be upheld on this evidence alone.

REFERENCES

1. EHRENSTEIN, *Helv. chim. Acta*, 1926, **9**, p. 332.
2. VOSS AND BUTLER, *Annalen*, 1938, **534**, pp. 161, 185.
3. PIGMAN, *The Enzymes*, ed. Sumner and Myrbäck, 1951, Vol. I, Part 2, p. 739, Academic Press, New York.
4. WEIDENHAGEN, *Die Methoden der Fermentforschung*, ed. Bamann and Myrbäck, 1940, p. 1910, G. Thieme, Liepzig.
5. JONES, MERLER AND WISE, *Amer. Chem. Soc.*, 128th meeting, 1955, **5E**.
6. BISHOP, *J. Amer. chem. Soc.* 1956, **78**, p. 2840.
7. BISHOP AND WHITAKER, *Chem. and Ind.* 1955, p. 119.
8. FUKUI AND SATO, *Bull. agric. Chem. Soc. Japan*, 1957, **21**, p. 392.
9. WHISTLER AND MASAK, *J. Amer. chem. Soc.* 1955, **77**, p. 1241.
10. GASCOIGNE AND GASCOIGNE, *J. gen. Microbiol.* 1960, **22**, p. 242.
11. SØRENSEN, *Physiol. Plant.* 1952, **5**, p. 183.

12. SIMPSO N, *Canad. J. Microbiol.* 1959, **5**, p. 99.
13. INAOKA AND SODA, *Nature, Lond.* 1956, **178**, p. 202.
14. SØRENSEN, *Nature, Lond.* 1956, **177**, p. 845.
15. SIMPSON, *Canad. J. Microbiol.* 1954, **1**, p. 131.
16. SIMPSON, *Canad. J. Microbiol.* 1956, **2**, p. 28.
17. SIMPSON, *Canad. J. Technol.* 1955, **33**, p. 33.
18. INAOKA AND SODA, *Mem. Ehime Univ.*, Sect. VI, 1955, **1**, p. 1.
19. HOWARD, *Biochem. J.* 1957, **67**, p. 643.
20. MYERS AND NORTHCOTE, *J. Exp. Biol.* 1958, **35**, p. 639.
21. PREECE, AITKEN AND DICK, *J. Inst. Brewing*, 1954, **60**, p. 497.
22. PREECE AND MACDOUGALL, *J. Inst. Brewing*, 1958, **64**, p. 489.
23. DUNCAN, MANNERS AND ROSS, *Biochem. J.* 1956, **63**, p. 44.
24. SØRENSEN, *Nature, Lond.* 1955, **176**, p. 74.
25. GRASSMANN *et al.*, *Annalen*, 1933, **502**, p. 20; 1933, **503**, p. 167.
26. LÜERS AND VOLKAMER, *Wochenschr. Brau*, 1928, **45**, pp. 83, 95.
27. O'DWYER, *Biochem. J.* 1939, **33**, p. 713.
28. JERMYN AND TOMKINS, *Biochem. J.* 1950, **47**, p. 437.
29. PRINGSHEIM AND KUSENACK, *Z. physiol. Chem.* 1924, **137**, p. 265.
30. LEVINSON, MANDELS AND REESE, *Arch. Biochem. Biophys.* 1951, **31**, p. 351.
31. KOOIMAN, *Enzymologia*, 1957, **18**, p. 371.
32. VAN SUMÈRE, *Naturwiss.* 1953, **40**, p. 582.
33. WHISTLER AND SMART, *J. Amer. chem. Soc.* 1953, **75**, p. 1916.
34. MORITA, *J. Biochem. Japan*, 1956, **43**, p. 7.
35. REESE, GILLIGAN AND NORKRANS, *Physiol. Plant.* 1952, **5**, p. 379.
36. MYERS AND NORTHCOTE, *Biochem. J.* 1959, **71**, p. 749.
37. MONOD, COHEN-BAZIRE AND COHN, *Biochim. Biophys. Acta*, 1951, **7**, p. 585.
38. DEUEL AND STUTZ, *Adv. in Enzymology*, 1958, **20**, p. 341.
39. VAN SUMÈRE, *Intern. Tijdschr. Brouw. en Mout.* 1955, **15**, p. 9.
40. VAN SUMÈRE, VAN SUMÈRE-DE PRETER AND LEDINGHAM, *Canad. J. Microbiol.* 1957, **3**, p. 761.
41. EHRLICH AND KOSMAHLY, *Biochem. Z.* 1929, **212**, p. 162.
42. DINGLE, REID AND SOLOMONS, *J. Sci. Food Agric.* 1953, **4**, p. 149.
43. WHISTLER, BACHRACH AND BOWMAN, *Arch. Biochem.* 1948, **19**, p. 25.

VIII

INDUSTRIAL SIGNIFICANCE OF CELLULASES

THE previous chapters have been concerned with the ways in which biological catalysts bring about the breakdown of cellulose and hemicelluloses. In many industries cellulose and its derivatives play important rôles and the studies already recorded have outlined the mechanism of decay for these compounds, but peculiar conditions within an industry (e.g. the water supplies in a paper mill or the sizes in textile fabrics) may have an important bearing on the presence and growth of cellulolytic micro-organisms and of the enzymes associated with them. The occurrence, noted previously, in germinating grains of cellulases and hemicellulases makes it necessary to review the activity of these enzymes in fermentation processes and animal nutrition. In order to understand the various processes of cellulose breakdown, consideration must first be given to the energy changes occurring during the complex sequence of chemical reactions.

ENERGETICS

As it is necessary here to deal with micro-organisms and plants, as well as with the enzymes they contain or secrete, the living cell of such organisms needs to be regarded as a storehouse dealing in energy; a tightly regulated stock control and intricate accountancy is needed before potential energy can be liberated. As in any efficient economy, special devices within the cell release only as much energy in a usable form as can be utilized by other parts of the cell. The biological breakdown of cellulose may therefore be regarded as a process of energy liberation and transfer. The overall energy changes may be divided into the liberations and transfers needed in three processes[1]:

(i) the germination of spores (or other reproductive processes) on the cellulosic fibre,
(ii) the conversion of cellulose into water-soluble products,
(iii) the utilization of these water-soluble compounds within the cells.

As glucose and disaccharides occur in most living tissues it is not surprising that most attention has been given to the process (iii) above. The energetics of carbohydrate metabolism have been reviewed recently by Elsden and Peel[2] and it is not intended to discuss the breakdown of hexoses further. Whilst the metabolism of glucose by cellulolytic micro-organisms had not been studied widely, the oxidative enzymes (oxidases) required by many organisms for the formation of ethanol, fatty acids and carbon dioxide from glucose have been detected in cellulose decomposing fungi[3,4] and in a cellulolytic bacterium *Vibrio perimastix*[5]. An invertase has been found in the spores of the strongly cellulolytic fungus *Myrothecium verrucaria*, although Mandels[6] has shown that, in spite of the invertase being present in excess of metabolic requirements, sucrose was utilized in a non-hydrolytic reaction. It was suggested that the breakdown of sucrose was catalysed by a sucrose phosphorylase, although this enzyme could not be detected in the fungal spores. Whatever the intermediate steps in the breakdown of soluble sugars, ethanol and compounds of low molecular weight are frequently found in fungal cultures growing on cellulosic materials. Wood rotting fungi, for example, produce ethanol from glucose, but utilize the acetic acid formed in their further metabolic pathways[7]. Whitaker[8] has shown that forty species of wood rotting fungi from twenty-one genera under conditions of aerated culture on a glucose-urea medium produced carbon dioxide and mycelium as their principal end-products. The widespread presence of transglycosylases in bacterial and fungal cultures leads to a complication in the picture of cellulose breakdown. It has been shown that *Clostridium thermocellulaseum* fermented cellobiose at a rate several times higher than that for glucose; it was suggested that this bacterium may prefer to split only every second glucosidic linkage and then consume the disaccharide oxidatively[9]. However, the build-up of higher oligosaccharides of the cellulose series has been observed (see Chapter II) from cellobiose and even from glucose[10], and the catabolism of these products may proceed by hydrolysis, phosphorolysis and oxidation.

CONVERSION OF CELLULOSE TO WATER-SOLUBLE PRODUCTS

At first sight, it appears that the only reaction concerned in this conversion is hydrolysis. However, two major stages in this process must be recognized:

   (a) the separation of the cellulose molecules of the micelles into individual molecules,
and (b) the hydrolytic cleavage of glucosidic bonds.

A third process, postulated by Siu[1], is the breakdown of cross linkages between molecules to give linear chains. At the present time the evidence for the existence of such links is scanty (see Chapter I) and the energy associated with such links in cellulose has not been studied. A very small number of anomalous linkages occur in native celluloses and probably a slightly larger number in regenerated celluloses[11,17], but such bonds are more sensitive to acid hydrolysis than the $(1\rightarrow4)$ β-glucosidic bonds. However, if *strong* cross linkages do exist and their breakdown involves oxidation, the liberated energy would be of the order of 676 kilocalories per mole of glucose; if such energy could be utilized, it could set in motion the whole chain of reactions necessary for the breakdown of cellulose. The energy required for the process (a) depends on the physical arrangement of the molecular chains with respect to one another. Mark[12] considered 'amorphous areas as highly distorted crystalline lattices in which the single atoms are shifted to a considerable degree out of their normal equilibrium position', and these areas to have a higher energy content than the crystalline regions. Stone[13] draws the conclusion that the activation energy contribution for the amorphous region will be lower than that for the crystalline regions, and therefore the amorphous regions will be more easily disrupted. The energy involved in hydrogen bonding is about 5 kilocalories per mole, which is quite small compared with that involved in a covalent bond, but it is certainly larger than the energy associated with the weak van der Waal's forces operative in the amorphous regions.

In the process (b), Jermyn[14] has calculated the activation energy required for this cleavage to be about 10 kilocalories per gram mole from experiments with *Aspergillus oryzae* enzymes acting on carboxy-methylcellulose, cellodextrin and salicin. The rate constants for the hydrolysis of cellobiose, cellotriose, cellotetraose and cellopentaose by the purified cellulase from *Myrothecium verrucaria* gradually increased as the series was ascended, but the activation energy for the hydrolysis of all four compounds remained at about 12 kilocalories per gram mole[15]. It will be recalled that the activation energy for the acid catalysed cleavage of the bonds in cellulose is of the order of 28 kilocalories per gram mole[16].

THE GERMINATION OF SPORES

Energy is required in any reproductive process, and in the case of fungi the bursting of the outer layer (often at thin places, the 'germ pores') occurs through the absorption of water and an increase in size. The protoplasm of the spore and sometimes the inner layer of the spore wall are extruded to form a germ tube. Not all spores are able to germinate and an enormous wastage of the rich stores of foodstuffs and vitamins in spores takes place; for example, although the wood rotting fungus *Polyporus squamosus* produces 11×10^9 spores in each bracket-shaped fruit body, only one in every 10^{12} spores is successfully established on a suitable substrate[18]. The energy required for expanding the spore volume is of the order of 10^{-4} μ cals. per spore, but a greater quantity of energy (c. 10^{-2} μ cals.) is available to the spore from respiration (Mandels, quoted by Siu[1]). Without some source of carbon, spores do not swell or germinate rapidly to any significant extent[19], but at least a few spores can germinate by calling on their food reserves in the complete absence of external organic matter (Mandels G.R. personal communication). Apart from these energy considerations, it has been shown that the nature of the medium upon which sporulation takes place has a pronounced effect on the viability, respiration and physiology of the spores of the cellulose-decomposing fungi *Myrothecium verrucaria*, *Aspergillus luchuensis* and *Memnoniella echinata*[20]. The spores from *M. verrucaria* grown on filter paper lost no viability up to forty days, whereas spores grown on non-cellulosic substrates (e.g. peptone, potato-glucose agar) were very short-lived. However, no cellulolytic activity has been detected in fungal spores. It is evident that this point of commencement of fungal and bacterial attack needs much further study; to kill spores high temperatures or spore-penetrating chemicals are required, and further research into spore germination and its prevention may yield rich rewards when the widespread damage brought about by fungi on cellulosic materials is considered. Probably the largest field for the use of cellulosic materials is the textile industry, and microbial and enzymic attack of these fibres and fabrics must be considered.

DEGRADATION OF CELLULOSIC TEXTILES

Although much knowledge has accumulated on the deterioration of textiles due to micro-organisms, little enzymic work has appeared which has not been mentioned in previous chapters. The whole subject has been excellently reviewed up to 1951[1], while the microbial attack on the cellulosic part of jute, flax and other native bast fibres has been studied to some extent[22-24]; the degradation of viscose has not received much attention[21], although it has been shown that both viscose and highly oriented yarns (e.g. *durafil*, *tenasco*, *fortisan*) are susceptible to attack by a large number of micro-organisms[25].

Opportunities for the occurrence of cellulolytic micro-organisms on cellulosic fibres are found at various stages before or during processing, and on the finished yarn or fabric. For cotton and bast fibres, contamination may occur while the fibre is still part of the plant standing in the field before harvesting; damage is more likely to occur if the plants are exposed to damp conditions, and especially if the temperature is high as in the tropics, where cotton is often left for several weeks after the opening of the boll before harvesting. Damp storage and transit conditions before, during and after processing afford ideal conditions for the growth of microbes; organisms which have actually contaminated the fibres before harvesting may persist through such mechanical processes as ginning, picking and carding, and then develop rapidly during storage of sliver or yarn under suitable (and frequently occurring) conditions of humidity and temperature. Generally, cotton needs a moisture content of at least 9 per cent for the development of micro-organisms[26]. Cellulosic materials are frequently used in exposed locations, thus marine cordage and fish nets are subject to the action of specialized marine organisms (see Chapter III), and can be completely rotted within weeks. Jute is widely used as a packaging material and often comes into contact with soil and water, while the cellulosic materials used for tents and tarpaulins need to withstand outdoor conditions of all kinds, in addition to damp storage.

TYPES OF MICRO-ORGANISMS

Micro-organisms found on damaged textiles include both cellulolytic and non-cellulolytic types of fungi and bacteria, and the environment plays a large part in determining the contaminating microflora; thus, fabric exposed to soil contact is likely to be infected with many forms not found on similar fabric exposed to air-borne organisms only. Comprehensive surveys of textile microflora have been given by Siu[1], and only a short summary need be given here. Native fibres are known to be contaminated with large numbers of micro-organisms; thus, one million bacteria and half that number of fungi have been counted in a single gram of raw field cotton[26], and these values appear to be low when compared with other reports[1]. Cellulolytic bacteria isolated from exposed cotton fabrics include *Sporocytophoga, Cellulomonas* and *Cellvibrio* species, while other cellulolytic Myxobacteria have been found on raw cotton[27]. Fungi occurring on field cotton before harvesting include representatives of the genera *Alternaria, Fusarium* and *Cladosporium*, while plants affected by tight-lock disease also contain *Diplodia* spp. In damp storage members of many other genera of fungi have been found on cotton including *Aspergillus, Penicillium, Chaetomium* and *Stachybotrys*. Cellulolytic activity has been found in isolates from all these genera, and cellulolytic filtrates have been obtained from some (see Chapter

III). It is interesting to note that the highly cellulolytic *Myrothecium verrucaria* is rarely reported as occurring on growing cotton or on exposed fabrics[1], although it has been isolated occasionally[28].

A study of micro-organisms occurring on jute, and their ability to degrade filter paper cellulose has been made by Basu[29]; the following species classified by Siu[1] as very strong or strong cellulose decomposers were detected: *Aspergillus fumigatus, Chaetomium indicum, C. globosum, Fusarium* sp., *Memnoniella echinata*, and *Trichoderma viride*. Micro-organisms isolated during the retting process of some fibres belong to several genera (bacterial, as well as fungal) which contain cellulolytic members. Thus, *Corynebacterium, Clostridium* and *Pseudomonas* species were found in water in which esparto grass had been retted[30]. The pectin was rapidly attacked by *Clostridium* spp., as well as by members of the genera *Bacillus* and *Escherichia*. Fungi found to be true dew-retting agents of flax included *Alternaria* spp., *Cladosporium herbarum* and *Dematium pullulans*, but certain members of the genera *Alternaria* and *Stachybotrys* also present caused tendering of the fibres themselves[31]. Other fungi isolated from retting fibres include *Aspergillus niger* and *Penicillium glaucum*[32]; all the fungal species mentioned above, with the exception of *Dematium pullulans* (= *Pullularia pullulans*), contain strains which possess cellulolytic activity[1,13].

INFLUENCE OF FIBRE CONSTITUENTS ON ATTACK

The effects of the chemical and physical properties of cellulose itself on enzymic attack have been considered in Chapter VI, but the effect of the presence of other substances in textile materials must now be discussed. Associated natural polymers frequently affect the process of degradation; lignin occurs in fibres such as coir and jute, and coir with a lignin content of 40 per cent[33] is one of the most resistant of natural fibres[34]. Early workers[35-37] showed that a decrease in lignin content resulted in increased susceptibility to microbial attack, and this has been confirmed by the extensive work of Basu *et al.*[38,39]. Lignin was shown to be the most resistant component of the jute fibre, although some organisms are able to utilize it to some extent[29]. The lignin layers may afford physical protection to the rest of the fibre, but a chemical linkage between lignin and other fibre constituents has frequently been postulated. As hemicelluloses were progressively removed from jute holocellulose (i.e. delignified jute), the residue became more resistant to microbial degradation, and conversely, jute α–cellulose was more liable to attack in the presence of added hemicellulose. Certain fungal species, unable to decompose jute α–cellulose alone, strongly attacked the holocellulose; however, a hemicellulose residue (c. 25 per cent of total jute hemicelluloses) was found which was no more susceptible to attack than the α–cellulose associated with it. Flax fibre, which also has a high hemicellulose content[40], is known to be very susceptible to microbial attack; the alkali boil process for the yarn helps to remove some of the more sensitive substances. Fargher[41] showed that cotton from which pectins and hemicelluloses had been removed was less liable to support mould growth than unprocessed cotton. After removal of pectin alone by water extraction at 110° the residue was more liable to mould growth and greater strength loss than the residue remaining after extraction of both pectin and hemicellulose by alkali (1% NaOH) at 125° in the absence of air. Thus, in this case, the hemicellulose was preferentially attacked by fungi and appeared to shield the α–cellulose from attack. The importance of symbiosis in mixed microbial cultures and particularly in the soil must not be overlooked, and the subject is discussed further when considering the paper industry.

Attention has already been drawn to the fact that micro-organisms cause greater strength loss in an unbleached cotton fabric than in a similar bleached fabric when incubated under identical conditions[1]; the addition of growth factors, in the form of yeast extract, to the bleached fabric overcame this difference, and similar growth factors are present in unprocessed cotton. The presence of trace elements in raw cotton, which are capable of stimulating microbial growth, has also been shown[42]. Confirmation of the effect of growth factors and trace elements on growth and attack has been obtained from experiments on jute in which marked stimulation of cellulose decomposition was noticed when a concentrated aqueous extract of jute was used as a nitrogen source[43]. Growth factors actually present in jute include biotin and thiamin, which are necessary for the growth of *Memnoniella echinata*[44] and *Chaetomium brasiliensis*[45] respectively; both of these fungi decompose cellulose in the presence of the appropriate vitamin. Although the extraction of jute with hot water produced a more resistant residue and this has been ascribed to the extraction of micro-nutrients[39], the removal of pectin by the same procedure must also be considered.

While many substances stimulating microbial growth on textiles may be removed during processing, other stimulants may be applied during finishing processes; growth can then either occur exclusively on the finishing agent, causing no damage to the cellulose, or the presence of the finishing agent may encourage the growth of organisms which subsequently cause tendering of cellulose. Sizing and stiffening agents include starches, starch ethers and esters, locust bean gum, flour, carboxymethylcellulose and proteins like gelatine; fabrics and warps sized with flour, starches and carbohydrate gums are particularly susceptible to mildew, and it is common practice to include an antiseptic compound in the mixing. A study of the growth of a range of fungi on unsized jute and jute sized with maize starch showed that the sized fabric in every case supported more profuse growth, and in some cases growth occurred only on the sized fabric[29]. Some fungi, which grew strongly on both sized and unsized jute, grew only sparsely on maize starch; however, most of the fungi tested showed good growth on this starch and produced measurable quantities of acid from it. The increase in the use of soluble cellulose derivatives, particularly carboxymethylcellulose, as textile sizes must be guarded in a similar way to the starch finishes. It has been shown many times in the previous chapters that fungi which attack cellulose also attack these soluble derivatives, sometimes with greater rapidity. Although these sizes are readily removed before bleaching and dyeing, the stimulation of the growth of cellulolytic fungi by the size may well lead to the rapid breakdown of the yarn itself where warps are stored under humid conditions. Micro-organisms occurring on sizes containing gelatin are less likely to be able to damage continuous filament viscose yarns, than are those occurring on carbohydrate sizes. It must be borne in mind that organisms growing on gelatin or other protein sizes produce proteolytic enzymes, and the effect of these enzymes on fibre blends or wool-viscose fabrics may damage the protein type fibre. The majority of the synthetic resins used in textile finishing are relatively resistant to microbial attack, and their use in rot proofing is discussed later.

Exposure of jute to heat, light, acids and alkalis renders it more resistant to bacterial attack, but more susceptible to fungal attack[46,47]. The physical agents may have decomposed the non-cellulosic part of the jute fibre giving rise to products toxic to bacteria, while the chemical agents probably removed some nutrient compounds required by the bacteria for their growth. Cellulolytic enzymes from fungi and bacteria acted in a similar manner on modified jute, and the difference in behaviour of fungi and bacteria has been attributed to a factor influencing enzyme action rather than to a fundamental difference in their enzymic action; however, it is likely that the toxic substances produced from the lignin and hemicelluloses would inhibit bacterial growth more than fungal growth, and the fungi are more adaptable to growth on the modified cellulose than are bacteria. Treatment of cotton with dilute mineral acid or weak organic acid reduces the susceptibility of the residue to

211

enzymic hydrolysis. In view of the differences between the effects of different micro-organisms discussed above careful control of processes such as acid chlorite or alkaline peroxide bleaching must be exercised to ensure that the finished product is not rendered more liable to microbial attack. Exposure of fibres to ultra-violet light increased their resistance to subsequent attack by *Myrothecium verrucaria* (= *Metarrhizium glutinosum*)[48]. In line with this finding, it has been shown that fabrics exposed to weathering are more resistant to subsequent attack by *Chaetomium globosum* than unweathered fabrics, and this difference was attributed to photochemical modification of the amorphous regions of the cellulose molecules[49]. More recently, Reese[50] has reported that irradiation of cellulose by cathode rays in doses up to 30 megareps decreases the susceptibility to attack. Above 30 megareps the susceptibility increased, and at a radiation dose of 60 megareps the resultant cellulose was as susceptible as the untreated sample. (A megarep is the radiation dose, obtained in this instance from a van der Graaf accelerator, which produces energy absorption of 93×10^6 ergs per gram of sample irradiated.) It has been suggested[51] that cathode ray irradiation of cellulose leads to random depolymerization of both the amorphous and crystalline regions, and such a breakdown may increase the susceptibility of cellulose to cellulases. However, the work quoted above shows the dependence of susceptibility on radiation dose, and the two effects need further research. Mechanical disintegration of both cotton and jute[50,39] made them more liable to microbial attack, due to increased surface area, decrystallization, and possibly depolymerization.

CHANGES BROUGHT ABOUT BY BIOLOGICAL AGENTS

Although the degradation of textiles by micro-organisms is stressed here, it must be remembered that many insects (e.g. silverfish, termites) contain cellulases in their guts, and widespread damage occurs where care is lacking in the exclusion of such pests (see Chapter III)[52]. Fungal and bacterial damage to cellulosic textiles may be purely superficial and be detected by discoloration, a musty odour, and in the case of fungi the spores and mycelium of the causative organism may be visible to the naked eye. Microscopic examination will almost certainly reveal the micro-organism responsible, and perhaps early damage to the fibres. Where the latter occurs it is likely that some other property (e.g. tensile strength, fluidity) of the fibre will be affected, and these changes will be considered later. Discoloration of dyed fabrics may be due to the chemical reaction of a by-product of metabolism with the dyestuff, but in some cases the change in colour arises from the fungal or bacterial growth itself; thus, the Myxobacterium *Angiococcus cellulosum* causes a tan-pink coloration[27]. Discoloration caused by highly pigmented fungi may require treatment by special bleaching processes[26]. Fluorescent spots on raw cotton were associated with the prior growth of micro-organisms on the fibres; thus a characteristic bright greenish-yellow spot arises from *Aspergillus flavus*[53]. If there is no visible evidence of microbial growth, the microscopic examination of stained or unstained fibres either in the swollen or original state may reveal the presence of organisms and of structural damage to the fibre. The staining techniques include processes in which the organism is stained and the fibres remain uncoloured or are stained a contrasting colour, or in which the damaged fibres stain to a deeper shade than the undegraded fibres. Such staining processes have been compared in a recent review[54].

In studies on degraded cotton fibres it was shown that the cuticular layer was digested in the first stages of attack. Bacterial attack then proceeds from the surface inwards; members of the Myxobacteria orient themselves parallel with the spiral planes of the fibre structure[27,55]. After removal of the cuticle by fungi, the hyphae may penetrate the secondary cell wall to the lumen where profuse growth then occurs[56]; alternatively it has been suggested that fungal attack also occurs from the outside inwards, the fungal hyphae surrounding the secondary wall[57]. In the case of both fungal and bacterial attack the digestion of cellulose with the aid of enzymes is highly localized, only occurring very close to or at the point of contact of the fibre with the organism. Microscopic observations on cotton, using enzyme-containing filtrates from *Myrothecium verrucaria*, showed loss of the usual spiral appearance and the occurrence of deep fissures during attack[58]. Extensive fragmentation and the appearance of a a large number of transverse cracks have also been observed in the damaged fibre[59]. Degraded samples of viscose rayon could be stained heavily and the filaments were split into fibrils[58].

The properties of cotton fibres which have been attacked prior to or immediately after harvesting undergo changes during subsequent storage resulting in deterioration of quality of the cotton. Such material has been termed *cavitomic cotton*; these fibres have a high pH value, a high alkali centrifuge value (described in Chapter VI), and contain an abnormally small amount of soluble reducing matter[60]. Microscopic observation revealed many fibres damaged by fungal growth, and cavitomic cotton has a shorter fibre length, lower fibre crimp and lower flat bundle strength (measured using a 5 mm wide clamp spacing). These effects were thought to be consistent with a localized weakening of the fibres due to direct microbial

213

or enzyme action during storage; the net result is that the fibres break more easily during processing, and the fibre length distribution curve is displaced revealing the greater number of shorter fibres, these changes probably being responsible for the deterioration in quality characteristics. Other workers[61] noted similar increases in the pH values of fibres exposed to wet weathering in the field during and after the opening of the boll; under such conditions there was a very high incidence of tight lock disease resulting from the growth of certain fungi found to give rise to high pH values in cotton[62]. Both cellulolytic and non-cellulolytic fungi and certain bacteria growing on raw cotton and a cotton fabric in the laboratory in a humid atmosphere gave rise to high pH values; it was suggested that the decreased acidity arose from the decomposition of malic and other organic acids in the fibre[61]. Thus, while the pH value change may give a rapid indication of the growth of micro-organisms on cotton, other tests are essential to ascertain if the fibre is being destroyed. These changes in properties have been confirmed by laboratory studies of fungal growth on uninfected cotton fibres and fabrics[63]. The use of cavitomic cotton in the manufacture of yarn results in the reduction of processing efficiency[60], over twice as much waste being produced compared with a normal sample; less even slivers, rovings and yarns are obtained, there are 45 per cent more end breakages, and the yarn is up to 10 per cent weaker than normal yarn, but only minor differences are noticeable in the finished fabric.

Many of the effects of microbial or enzymic attack are similar (e.g. loss in tensile strength and weight), but there is a major difference in that no enzyme preparation can bring about the degradation of native cellulose as rapidly and as completely as the organism can; this difference applies in a lesser degree to the action on modified celluloses. Thus, Reese[50] has stated that the consumption of cellulose by highly cellulolytic micro-organisms in shake culture is over 50 per cent in three days, but the cell-free filtrate from these cultures achieve only a fraction of this breakdown. Possible explanations for this difference were advanced:

(a) accumulation of end products in the enzyme solution which inhibited further enzyme action,
(b) all cellulolytic enzymes are not found in the culture filtrate.

However, the greater degradation achieved by fungi was attributed largely to the close association of fungal hyphae with the cellulose fibres.

The rate at which such physical changes as weight and strength losses of textiles occur is influenced by the numerous factors discussed earlier (e.g. environmental conditions, type of organism, structure of cellulose); other textile properties affecting this rate include type of fibre, weight of fabric and closeness of weave. Thus, viscose yarn incubated for three weeks with *Chaetomium globosum* lost all its tensile strength, while cotton yarn under similar conditions retained 50 per cent of its strength[25]. Heavy and closely woven fabrics tend to be degraded less rapidly than light and open-weave fabrics. The influence of microbial attack on the fluidity of the residual celluloses is not clear; most workers record no change in the fluidity of attacked cotton fibres, but further work is required to establish this effect in all cellulosic materials.

BIOLOGICAL DECAY OF WOOD

Wood contains a wide range of chemical compounds amongst which cellulose, hemicelluloses, lignin, water soluble carbohydrates and terpenes all have bearings on the type of attack to be expected from biological agents. Although wood is thought of as a very durable material, it is prone to attack and subsequent decay both as felled prepared timber and as standing trees. An account of the effects of weathering, moisture and drying has been given by Wise *et al.*[65], and this review will be restricted to the attack of wood by biological agents which degrade the cellulose, hemicellulose and lignin components; of these the principal predators are fungi.

FUNGAL INVASION OF PLANT TISSUES

Three main types of fungal attack on plant tissues have been described[66,67]:

(i) the decomposition of soluble sugars and starch by members of the Uredineae and Ustilaginaceae (rusts and smuts respectively).

(ii) the breakdown of sugars, starch, hemicellulose and cellulose by saprophytic fungi (e.g. *Penicillia, Aspergilli*).

(iii) attack by cellulose-, hemicellulose-, and lignin-degrading Basidiomycetes and Ascomycetes.

As long ago as 1886, de Bary[68] observed fungal attack on plant cell walls, and many higher fungi have been shown to secrete the enzyme cellulase. The soluble sugars are in turn used for the intracellular metabolic processes of the fungi. *Table 1* gives examples of wood-inhabiting fungi which produce cellulases, while *Table 2* lists the

Table 1. Cellulase Producing Fungi

Type of rot	Fungus	Ref.
white	Collybia velutipes	70
white	Daedalea flavida	71
brown	D. quercina	70
white	Fomes annosus	70
brown	Hydnum henningsii	72
brown	Lenzites trabea	70
white	Pholiota adiposa	70
white	Pleurotus ostreatus	70
	Polyporus ostreiformis	71
brown	P. palustris	73
white	P. rugulosus	72
white	P. zonalis	74
white	Polystictus hirsutus	71
white	P. leoninus	71
white	P. sanguineus	71, 75
white	P. versicolor	70, 76
brown	Poria monticola	70
brown	P. vaillantii	77
white	Stereum purpureum	70, 78
	Trametes cingulata	71
white	T. lactinea	71

occurrence of cellulase and other enzymes concerned in wood decay, compiled largely from the work of Garren[69]. The synthesis of cellulases by micro-fungi of the Ascomycetes and Fungi Imperfecti ('soft rots') has been noted in Chapter III, and also by Reese and Levinson[70], whilst the production of hemicellulases by soft rots has been mentioned in Chapter VII.

CHEMISTRY OF WOOD DECAY

In the early years of the present century two types of wood decaying fungi were distinguished, brown rots and white rots. The former type was reported as attacking cellulose but not lignin, while the white rots were said to attack lignin but not cellulose. Much of the evidence for this classification came from experiments with mixtures of fungi[82]. Another type of decay has also been described[83,84], in which the fungal hyphae tunnel in the cell walls of the timber. Such decay occurs in timber immersed in sea water[85] or in contact with soil[86], and is generally termed 'soft rot'.

Table 2. *Enzymes of Wood Rotting Fungi*

Fungus	Enzymes present					Type of rot
	Cellulase	Hemi-cellulase	Ligninase	Emulsin	Amylase	
Armillaria mellea	p[79]	p[79]		p[79]	p[79]	white
Daedala confragosa	p[79]	p[79]		p[79]	p[79]	white
Echinodontium tinctorium	p				p	brown
Fomes fraxinius	a			p	p	white
F. igniarius	p			p	p	white
F. pinicola	p[70]				p	brown
Lenzites saepiaria	p		p	p	p	brown
Merulius lacrymans	p[80]			p[80]	p[80] maltase	brown
Paxillus panuoides	p[81]			p[81]	p[81]	brown
Polyporus abietinus	p		p	p	p	white
P. betulinus				p	p	brown
P. hispidus	p	p[183]	p	p		white
P. lucidus	p[79]	p[79]		p[79]	p[79]	white
P. squamosus	a			p	p	white
P. sulphureus	p[70]			p	a	brown
P. versicolor	p[76]		p[76]	a[76]	p[76]	white
P. volvatus	p			p	p	white
Schizophyllum commune	p[70]		a	p	p	white

Where no reference number is given the presence (p) or absence (a) of the enzyme is recorded by Garren[69].

ACTION OF BROWN ROT FUNGI

The similarity between the action of brown rot fungi (e.g. *Trametes serialis*) on spruce wood and the acid hydrolysis of this wood was shown by Campbell and Booth[87], and Wehmer[88] concluded that the essential enzymic action was hydrolytic. Brown rot attack brings about an increase in the alkali solubility of the residual wood and the cellulose content is reduced; for example, the attack by *Paxillus panuoides* on silver fir wood gave an increase in alkali solubility (1% NaOH) of 15 per cent, while cellulose content fell from 57 to 7 per cent[81]. The early stages of attack on pine wood by *Merulius lacrymans* were shown to be hydrolytic and the final product was probably a trisaccharide[89]. It was suggested that this product of hydrolysis was oxidized within the cells of the fungi, confirming Findlay's earlier observation[81] that the only extracellular enzymes produced by these fungi growing on wood were hydrolases. The carbohydrate metabolisms of *M. lacrymans* and *Marasmius chordalis* have been studied, and the end products of the attack on cellulose and cellobiose are oxalate, acetate and ethanol[90]. Although cellulases have been detected in many brown rot fungi, it is only recently that the purification and the determination of the properties of the cellulase of *Poria vaillantii* have been carried out[77]; this work has been described in Chapters IV and V. Little is known of the hemicellulase activities of brown rot fungi, although it would be expected that the cellulases of such fungi would catalyse the hydrolysis of some hemicelluloses, as do most extracellular cellulases from the lower fungi. The cellulose in spruce wood was almost completely hydrolysed by four brown rot fungi, but the pentosans proved more resistant to attack[91]. It is difficult to be categorical about the fate of lignin in prolonged attack by brown rots, although it has been shown that some changes occur in the lignin of rotted pine wood[92]. From such observations, it is thought that the hydrolases of brown rot fungi alter lignin or the lignin-cellulose complex in such a way as to release the wood polysaccharides for enzymic hydrolysis without producing further catabolism of the lignin itself. Recently, a crude enzyme system (Rohm and Haas no. 19) has been shown to decompose powdered wood[93]; the residual lignin, after 95 per cent of the carbohydrate of the wood had been removed, still contained some 13 per cent of carbohydrate material. This carbohydrate was quite firmly attached to the lignin and was polymeric. Linkages between lignin and carbohydrate may be of the acetal, ether or hydrogen bonding types, or even a sort of mechanical entanglement.

ACTION OF WHITE ROT FUNGI

The chemistry of white rot decay is complicated by the fact that lignin, pentosans and cellulose are all attacked. Two important differences between the actions of brown and white rots exist; in the former case the decayed wood is more soluble in alkali than the original wood, whereas with white rots the alkali solubility does not show such striking increases as decay progresses. The carbon contents of wood decayed by the two types also show differences; for example, when spruce wood was rotted by a brown rot (*Merulius lacrymans*) the carbon content rose on decay by 5 per cent, whereas attack by a white rot (*Fomes annosus*) caused a fall in carbon content of 3·1 per cent[94]. The lignin content of wood attacked by white rot decreased at all stages of decay, but both cellulose and hemicelluloses were not degraded appreciably unless the decay was greatly prolonged. Campbell[95] has shown that white rot fungi vary in the order and extent of their degradation of the three principal wood components. Some white rots utilized both polysaccharides and lignin in the proportions in which they occurred in sound wood[96],

218

whilst others (e.g. *Armillaria mellea*) attacked the cellulose and hemi-celluloses before proceeding to the degradation of the lignin[97]. The type of wood attacked is also a major factor and care must be taken in interpreting the results of various workers (e.g. Campbell[98] reported that *Polyporus versicolor* attacked lignin and hemicelluloses first, whereas Scheffer[96] noted that this fungus attacked all three components of sound wood).

The possibility of the formation of a carbohydrate-lignin complex in wood has been frequently discussed, but its existence has not yet been proved[99]. Hemicelluloses separated from linden wood were readily hydrolysed by the digestive juices of the snail *Helix pomatia*, but these hemicelluloses *in situ* as part of the cell wall were very resistant to enzymic hydrolysis[100]. Wood substance regenerated from cupriethylene diamine solution and the insoluble residue from this dissolution were both hydrolysed in the presence of snail enzymes, but the rate of attack fell and finally stopped when the carbohydrate: lignin ratio was 1:1; it was suggested that pentosans were not present in such a complex. However, many workers[101,102] have advanced indirect experimental evidence for the existence of a lignin-hemicellulose association. The white rots have been further sub-divided, according to the appearance of the decay in wood, into white mottled, white stringy, white flaky and white spongy rots[103].

No account of the enzymatic breakdown of wood is complete without some reference to another important class of enzymes—those catalysing the oxidation of wood components, especially lignin. It has been seen that the function of brown rots is principally hydrolytic, whereas the white rots combine the two processes, hydrolysis and oxidation. The extracellular enzymes, polyphenoloxidases, are present in most white rot fungal cultures, and this fact forms the basis of a useful test for differentiating the two large classes of fungi[104]. These enzymes are of the laccase type[105] and some properties of them are discussed below.

EXTRACELLULAR OXIDIZING ENZYMES

These oxidases bear certain resemblances to the tyrosinase found intracellularly in potatoes and mushrooms[106]. The nature and amount of these enzymes formed by various fungi vary with the type of culture medium[107], the presence or absence of ammonium salts[108], and the presence of certain phenols or amines capable of acting as substrates[109]. From the last mentioned studies it was concluded that laccase was not strictly an inducible enzyme, but the formation of the enzyme could be stimulated by the presence of

P 219

substituted phenols and amines. The amounts of laccase formed by *Polystictus versicolor* and by *P. zonatus* were increased by increasing the pH value of the medium or by adding very small amounts of potassium iodide[110].

The enzyme laccase has been known since 1883[111], but laccase of mushrooms and other fungi have been studied only recently[112]; the oxidations of various polyhydric phenols, hydroquinone and *p*–phenylene diamine are catalysed. The two last-named compounds have been used as substrates for the determination of laccase activity[112,113]. Laccase may be distinguished from tyrosinase, as the latter enzyme has no action on hydroquinone; the oxidation of monohydric phenols is not catalysed by laccase. For many years it was thought that laccase contained both copper and manganese, especially as the highly purified enzyme has a blue colour[114]. In spite of this hypothesis and the suggestion that the enzyme was not necessarily a protein, it has been established[115] that laccase is a copper protein, and that manganese is not present; copper can be extracted from the enzyme by alkaline cyanide treatment[116]. Laccase has been purified recently[117], and the catalytic activity has been ascribed to the change from Cu^{2+} to Cu^+ from electron spin resonance studies of the enzyme from *Polyporus versicolor*[118]. More extensive experiments with a study of the kinetics of oxidation are needed to be certain of the rôle of the copper atom. The relationship between activity and the change from the cupric to the cuprous state does not exist in the case of tyrosinase[119].

Undoubtedly, such enzymes play a part in the degradation of lignin, but it is difficult (probably impossible) to ensure that lignin isolated by any procedure has the same physical and chemical composition as it had in the timber. However, many white rot fungi grow on media containing such isolated lignins as the sole or a limiting source of carbon[120,121]. The filtered culture medium from *P. versicolor* had tyrosinase activity, and was able to oxidise both Braun's lignin and alcohol lignin[121]. The products of laccase action consist of oxidized fragments of the phenylpropane building blocks of the lignin molecule. In the resulting complex mixture vanillin[92,122], vanillic acid[126], syringic acid[123], anisic acids[124], and esters of cinnamic acid[125] have been detected. The literature on the biological decomposition of lignin has been surveyed recently[184]. Whitaker[8] has made a detailed carbon balance study of forty species of wood rotting fungi growing in surface culture on a glucose-urea medium, and has concluded that carbon dioxide and mycelium are the only major end products from the majority of species examined; however, when aeration was restricted D–mannitol and ethanol were also found in some cases[127]. The breakdown of wood substance is more complex, and the action of the lower fungi must also be discussed to complete the picture of fungal degradation. It is interesting to note that Reese and Levinson[70] have tested culture filtrates from wood rotting fungi grown on strips of cotton duck for polyphenoloxidase activity, and all species that gave a positive reaction were white rots; brown rots and the borderline fungus *Schizophyllum commune*[104] did not produce the enzyme. However, it was concluded that, as the presence of the enzyme extracellularly was infrequent among cellulolytic fungi, the enzyme probably played no part in the degradation of cotton cellulose.

ACTION OF SOFT ROT FUNGI

The rapid decay of timber by micro-fungi of the classes Ascomycetes and Fungi Imperfecti is termed 'soft rot', and often the decay is not as visible in the cell lumens as are the effects of brown or white rots. From the culture medium of isolated species of such micro-fungi many cellulolytic enzymes have been separated as shown in Chapter III. It has been shown that the micro-fungus *Chaetomium globosum* in pure culture on beech wood principally attacked the cell wall carbohydrates[128]. However, a difference between soft rots and brown rots is evident from the alkali solubility of the residue after attack; in the former case, a slow, steady decrease occurs in the alkali solubility, whereas brown rots bring about an increase. In soft rot attack both α–cellulose and pentosans are removed almost completely, without much reduction on lignin content. During prolonged attack by *C. globosum* degradation of lignin increased, but as polyphenoloxidase is not present in this fungus, another enzyme system must be responsible for this attack on the lignin of the secondary cell wall. Thus, soft rots only attack lignin when the associated carbohydrates have been appreciably degraded. The heavily lignified middle lamella is little attacked. As a result of this work, Savory and Pinion[128] felt that there are such differences in the three types (brown, white and soft rots) of attack as to justify the separate classification of the soft rots on chemical as well as biological grounds. Recently, other micro-fungi (*Pencillia* and *Aspergilli*) have been shown to utilize lignin sulphonates for growth in mixed cultures[129]. However, in pure cultures the individual fungi showed limited growth on this carbohydrate-free substrate. The only product identified from the growth on lignin sulphonates was oxalic acid. Similar findings have been recorded with other micro-fungi, including *Chaetomium indicum*[130] and *Stachybotrys atra*[43].

As would be expected from its enzyme production, *Chaetomium*

221

globosum attacks the hemicelluloses in wood[128]. In particular, the pentosans included in the Cross and Bevan cellulose determination appear to be attacked to a greater extent than other pentosans. This effect has analogies in the attack on soft woods by *Paxillus panuoides*[81] and by some white rots[95], but is contrary to the effects observed during acid hydrolysis of wood.

It has been suggested that soft rot is important economically in fallen timber or in hardwoods in contact with wet soil. Under such conditions the growth of Basidiomycetes would be inhibited by excessive moisture or by poisons which soft rots can withstand. Woods from broad-leaved trees are generally less resistant to soft rots than are coniferous woods. Conditions of high humidity and relatively high temperature, such as exist in water cooling towers, bring about severe attack on softwoods; under such conditions the decay is mainly confined to the surface layers, so that thin laminates such as plywood were found to be particularly susceptible to soft rots[131]. In the ultimate breakdown of preserved wood the rôle of these soft rots must not be overlooked, and a number of species of such micro-fungi, in pure and mixed cultures, should be included in tests for assessing the efficiency of wood preservation processes[132]. These micro-fungi, some species of which have pigmented hyphae, sometimes give rise to the blue stain of pine sapwoods. but such staining does not significantly affect the durability of the sapwood[133]. However, it has been shown that heavily stained sapwood is 30 per cent less tough than uninfected wood[134]. Blue stain has also been noticed in heartwood[135].

ATTACK OF WOOD BY BACTERIA

As far back as 1919 it had been noted[136] that, although cellulose-degrading bacteria did not decompose wood under natural conditions, the presence of saprophytic bacteria enhanced the action of the higher fungi. This lack of bacterial attack may be due to toxic substances in wood or to the natural acidity of wood[137], although each of the major components of wood can be attacked in an isolated condition. The physical state of the wood also influences attack; for example Virtanen and Hukki[138] claimed that thermophilic bacteria readily ferment both cellulose and hemicelluloses in very finely ground wood. In aspen dust, some 73 per cent of the cellulose and 88 per cent of the pentosans were fermented in thirty days, during which time 11 per cent of the lignin present had also been attacked. The reduction in crystallinity of cellulose during grinding may well render the wood more susceptible to bacterial attack, but the possible cleavage of a carbohydrate-lignin linkage may also play some part. The highest concentration of extracellular cellulases occurs on the outer surface of the bacteria (not necessarily thermophilic types), and only those cellulose molecules very close to the bacterial cell wall would be attacked. It has been reported that bacterial fermentation can be stopped by vigorous shaking[139] and this effect has been attributed to the displacement of bacteria from the cellulosic surface, but it will be recalled that shaking has an inactivating effect on some cellulases from fungi[140]; bacterial cellulases have not been so tested. Knowledge of the decay of wood brought about by bacteria is still scanty, although such attack has been noticed in waterlogged pine sapwood[141], on the surface of redwood slats in a water cooling tower[142], and probably in some cases of heartwood decay in standing aspen and poplar[143]. Cellulolytic extracts have been prepared from some twelve species of bacteria (see Chapter III), but few of these are thermophilic. Of course, it must be borne in mind that, once fungal attack has been initiated, the bacteria may play a dominant rôle in the further decomposition of the hydrolysates from cellulose and hemicelluloses, and of lignin oxidation products. In bacterial attack on wood components the main products are acids such as acetic, butyric and lactic acids[138,144].

DECAY OF WOOD BY ANIMALS

The ability to metabolize wood is possessed only by insects, molluscs, some crustaceans and the Protozoa among the animals. Claims that cellulose is digested by the higher animals and man can usually be ascribed to the presence of micro-organisms in the animal[145,146]. In particular, the breakdown of carbohydrates by the enzymes of rumen flora will be described later. Much of the classic work of Karrer on the hepatopancreatic juice of the snail and its cellulases has been mentioned in Chapters IV and VI. However, the enzymes of the wood-boring insects have not received the attention they deserve from the enzymologist, although it is likely that these insects rely upon the production of cellulases by symbiotic micro-organisms for their apparent ability to digest wood; the exact relationship between cellulases and their producing organisms will not be determined until further experiments along the lines of the work of Lasker and Giese[147], who succeeded in breeding silver fish free of micro-organisms, have been completed.

The importance of cellulases to builders of water-submerged structures must have been realized in biblical times, but more recently an extract of the livers of shipworms (*Teredo norvega*) was shown to degrade wood to glucose[148]. Marine wood borers cause a large decomposition of cellulose in wood, and these insects do secrete cellulases[149], but the lignin appears to be indigestible. *Teredo* is able to utilize plankton as a foodstuff, but some marine Crustacea appear to feed only on wood, as only this material has been detected in the gut of certain *Limnoria*; cellulases have been found in *Limnoria lignorum*[150].

In land insects, the termites attack wood in all forms, and are frequently found in symbiosis with fungi in forests. The guts of *Termitidae* are swarming with protozoa and spirochaetes, and these were suggested as the prime agents in bringing about the decomposition of cellulose[151]. Other cellulolytic bacteria have also been found in the gut of termites[152]. However, a further complication has been mentioned by Hendee[153], who envisaged that cellulolytic bacteria may adhere to intestinal protozoa; however, he was only able to culture one cellulolytic species from the 120 bacterial species isolated from the intestinal tracts of 30 specimens of *Reticulitermes flavipes*, although a type of symbiosis of bacteria and protozoa may make separate culture difficult. Mansour and Mansour Bek[154] have proposed that wood is the food substance of the gut micro-organisms, but the termites themselves live on these microbial hordes, and this view was supported by Parkin[155]. However, other work contradicts this hypothesis, and the symbiotic association of wood borers and micro-organisms was regarded as essential for the survival of both species[156]. The destruction of wood by beetles has been discussed by Campbell in the Wise and Jahn monograph on *Wood Chemistry*[65], and will not be dealt with here, except that it is interesting to note that Ripper[157] demonstrated the presence of cellulase in filtered gut juices of a number of beetles, including the death watch beetle larva (*Xestobium rufovillosum*); it appeared that the cellulolytic action was not due to bacterial enzymes. The centrifuged gastric juice of some Cerambycidae also contained cellulases, but no decision was made concerning their origin[158].

The diseases of standing trees have not been considered, but good reviews already exist[159,160]. The whole field of the biological decay of wood has been discussed by Campbell[65] and reference is made therein to the effects of biological action, such as in coal formation and metal corrosion.

CELLULASES IN THE PAPER INDUSTRY

Wood constitutes about 90 per cent of the fibrous raw material used in the manufacture of paper-making pulp, and it is appropriate, therefore, to devote some space here to the occurrence of cellulases in paper making. In general, softwoods are more desirable for pulping than hardwoods. although the latter are being used on an increasing scale. Whilst it is preferable to exclude all decayed woods from stockpiles at pulp mills, it is almost impossible to attain this goal. Microbial infection of wood pulp leads to a decrease in fibre length, and a reduction in tensile strength, thereby reducing beating qualities, apart from serious loss of small wood particles during chipping and screening operations. Decayed pulp is brash, free and brittle, and subsequent treatment may require some modification; for example, pulp prepared from infected wood is more difficult to bleach than sound pulp[161]. The bacteria present in ground wood produce enzymes, including catalase, which make peroxide bleaching less easy[162]. Although many micro-organisms and spores are killed by heat during grinding, the use of already decayed pulp may lead to a loss of 75 per cent of the original strength of the pulp, with consequent effects upon the strength and colour of the finished sheet.

The principal sources of infection in wet wood pulp at a mill are:

(i) the wood, (ii) the fresh water, (iii) the mill air, and (iv) the white water.

The occurrence of cellulose decomposition in wood has already been discussed, and if sound wood is used the major contribution to infection is from the white water. The mill air plays a very minor part, although the contribution from the fresh water may not be negligible. The action of micro-organisms on cellulose during paper manufacture has not been widely studied from the standpoint of the mechanism of breakdown, the major concern of the industry being the protection of pulp from microbial decay. Many other materials used in paper production are readily attacked by micro-organisms, . notably the starches, soya flour, adhesives, size and other proteins, as well as the wool of felts[163]. The whole subject of the microbiology of pulp and paper has been excellently reviewed up to 1955[164].

In the fresh water supply, bacteria are the most numerous contaminants, and include the filamentous iron bacteria and sulphate reducing bacteria, as well as capsulated and spore-forming types. In open-water systems, fresh water may account for as much as 10 per cent of the fungal infection, while in closed systems this infection falls to around one per cent[165]. Rennerfelt[166] has also discussed the contribution of airborne spores to fresh water contamination. The two major results of excessive biological activity in mill waters are slime production and corrosion; other difficulties are the production of bad odours, spotting of the paper and its weakening brought about by the decomposition of cellulose. Although mill slime has an extensive literature of its own, little attention has been given to the cellulolytic activities of the micro-organisms producing slime. Bacteria convert food substances in the pulp system into slimes which may then be distributed throughout the system or may remain as a sheath or capsule surrounding the bacteria. Such slimes usually contain polysaccharides, often a levan, galactan, glucan or araban, which swell in water but do not dissolve. Slime is also produced by fungi, but it is often loose and stringy compared with the tough bacterial slimes; yeasts produce rubbery slimes. On the other hand, not all slimes can be attributed to microbial sources, and it has been suggested that aluminium hydroxide is a factor in such cases.

BACTERIAL SLIMES

While not all the micro-organisms present in slimes are responsible for its production, their presence may be the source of losses of cellulose. *Table 3* draws attention to some of the bacteria detected

Table 3. Bacteria in Slimes

Bacterial genera in slimes	Cellulolytic activity claimed for certain species		Species from which cellulases have been isolated
Achromobacter[167,168]	A. picrum[175]	c.	
Aerobacter[167,168,169]	A. aerogenes[176]	c.	
Alcaligenes[170]			
Bacillus[167,168,169,171]	B. hydrolyticus[177]	c.	B. hydrolyticus[178]
	B. apporrhoeus[175]	c.	
	B. subtilis, B. megaterium[1]	n.c.	
Cellulomonas[167]	Cellulomonas sp.[1]	s.	Cellulomonas sp.[179]
	C. flavigena[1]	w.	
	C. fimi[1]	m.	C. fimi[180]
Chromobacter[167]			
Cladothrix[172]			
Clonothrix[169]			
Crenothrix[167,169,172]			
Escherichia[168]			
Flavobacterium[170]			
Gallionella[169]			
Leptothrix[169,172]			
Micrococcus[173]	Micrococcus sp.[1]	n.c.	
	M. pustulatus[1]	c.	
Pseudomonas[322]	P. ephemerocyanea, P. lasia and P. erythra[175]	c.	P. fluorescens var. cellulosa[181]
Serratia[173]			
Vibrio[174]	Cellvibrio fulvus and C. vulgaris[1]	s.	

Key: c.—activity present, but not measured.
n.c.—not cellulolytic.
s, m, w.—strong, medium, weak activity, respectively.

in mill slimes, to their cellulose decomposing ability, and in some cases to the isolation of cellulases from such bacteria. It appears that the most important slime-forming bacteria are the capsulated rod-shaped forms, and in this connection the finding of a cellulase in *Aerobacter aerogenes*[176] is particularly significant. Indeed, Martin and Dobson[169] reported that the principal genus in 50 per cent of the slimes they examined was *Aerobacter*, while *A. aerogenes* was the most common species; a similar observation was recorded by Holmes[168].

FUNGAL SLIMES

Although capsulated bacteria are so common in slimes, fungi are by no means absent; in one Swedish newsprint mill more fungi were found in slimes than bacteria[182]. As has been emphasized throughout this book, the fungi contain many cellulolytic species, and although this aspect of contamination has been stressed in the pulp industry, the importance of the occurrence of these fungi in the water systems of paper mills seems somewhat overlooked. It is probable that fungi contribute more to the volume of slime than do bacteria[174]. Some of the fungi, yeasts and actinomycetes found in mill slimes, together with their cellulolytic properties are listed in *Table 4*. The cellulolytic activities of many of the micro-organisms listed have been examined by Reese and Levinson[70], who recorded two types of activity: (a) the loss in tensile strength of cotton duck as a measure of C_1 activity, and (b) the amount of reducing sugar produced by enzymic hydrolysis of the sodium salt of carboxymethylcellulose, as a measure of C_x activity (see Chapter VI). Protozoa probably play no part in slime formation, although they are frequently present in white waters of strawboard manufacture.

MICROBIAL SYMBIOSIS

Symbiosis is the mutual benefit, as denoted by rapid multiplication and enhanced growth, derived by organisms during growth in cultures containing more than one species. The symbiosis of the bacterium *Rhizobium* with the roots of legumes is well known; the bacteria are able to fix atmospheric nitrogen into compounds which the plant roots can utilize. Some organisms and enzyme systems can only bring about a chemical reaction to a small extent unless a second organism or enzyme system (often of similarly weak activity) is present in the medium; this effect is known as *synergism*. Both synergism and symbiosis are known in the case of cellulolytic micro-organisms[9,186]. The production of antibiotics by certain fungi may lead to the destruction of other fungi and bacteria growing in close proximity; this antibiosis has been suggested as a method of control-

Table 4. Micro-organisms (other than Bacteria) in Slimes

Genera Found in Slimes	Cellulolytic Activity of Certain Species[1]	Cellulases isolated from species in Column 2	
		C_1	C_x
Actinomyces[168]	Actinomyces sp. c.	p	p
Aleurisma[171]			
Ascochyta[173]			
Cephalothecium[173]	Cephalothecium sp. m-w.		
Cladosporium[182,185]	Cladosporium sp. d.		
	C. herbarum d.	p	p
Fusarium[173]	Fusarium sp. s.	p	p
	F. moniliforme m.		
Geotrichum[174]	Geotrichum sp. w.		
Monascus[173]	Monascus sp. n.c.		
Monilia[173]	Monilia sp. d.		
	M. sitophila d.	p	p
Mucor[174,185]	Mucor hiemalis c.	very low	low
	M. mucedo n.c.		
	M. racemosus n.c.		
Oidium[168]	Oidium sp. n.c.		
Penicillium[168,174,185]	P. frequentans d.		
	P. luteum m.	p	p
	P. pinophilum d.	a	a
	P. puberulum n.c.		
	P. spinulosum n.c.	very low	p
Pullularia[174]	Pullularia pullulans n.c.	a	a
Pyrenochaeta[174]	Pyrenochaeta sp. s.		
	P. humicola c.		
Rhodotorula[173]	Rhodotorula sp. n.c.		
Torula[168]	Torula sp. s-m.	p	p
	T. convoluta s.		
Trichoderma[168]	Trichoderma albus c.		
	T. viride s.	p	p
Verticillium[174]	Verticillium sp. s.		

Key: c.—activity present, but not measured.
     n.c.—not cellulolytic.
     s, m, w.—strong, medium, weak activity, respectively.
     d.—definite activity, as recorded by Siu[1].
     p—present, a—absent.

ling the population of blue stain fungi in pulp[187,188]. The thermophilic fermentation of cellulose was studied by Sniesko and Kimball[189], who tried to compensate for the exclusion of symbionts when working with pure cultures; the importance of symbiosis has been stressed[190], and Enebo[191] has considerably enlarged the scope of these studies by employing pure and mixed cultures of three bacterial species. Thus, *Clostridium thermocellulaseum* produced a cellulase, but it was able to decompose only a small amount of cellulose (1 to 1·5 per cent of the medium) and this decomposition was retarded by the accumulated hydrolysis products; however, a mixed culture of this bacterium with *Clostridium thermobutyricum* and *Bacillus thermolacticus* speeded up the attack considerably, due to the consumption of the hydrolysis products by the symbionts[9]. A synergistic effect on cellulolytic action has been noted by Gilligan and Reese[64] in enzyme extracts from both *Trichoderma viride* and *Myrothecium verrucaria*. Each extract was separated into several components by chromatography on a calcium phosphate column, and recombinations of such components had greater swelling factor activity and greater hydrolytic activity on Walseth cellulose than had the individual components.

ATTACK ON FINISHED PAPER

In common with both wood and textiles, finished paper is liable to attack by a wide range of micro-organisms, molluscs and insects. From stored papers some 55 fungi have been isolated[192], while a review of other findings has been given by Wessel[193]. As with textiles, the presence of sizes and fillers may profoundly affect the flora. However, it should be realized that although the loss of cellulose by biological attack is of great economic concern, such attack is also very important especially in the breakdown of paper, vegetable and plant remains in sewage disposal plants and garden compost heaps. Fungi are able to penetrate many of the finishes applied to paper; for example, *Chaetomium globosum* was able to degrade the cellulose in blotting paper, vegetable parchment paper, waxed glassine paper, asphalt-impregnated paper and a laminated greaseproof board[194]. In previous chapters the use of filter paper as a substrate for cellulase has been noted frequently, and any further discussion of the action of cellulolytic enzymes on paper would only involve discussion of the effects of modification of the paper; as the modification of the cellulose molecule has been dealt with in Chapter VI and the effect of physical barriers will be mentioned later, no further consideration will be given to the microbial decay of paper.

The destruction of hemicelluloses has not been mentioned, but as many fungi produce hemicellulases (see Chapter VII) it is obvious that such decay must occur, and indeed, the formation of slimes infers the swelling and breakdown of hemicelluloses. Attack on paper cellulose by the cellulases of algae has not been mentioned, as it is presumed that these plants would be removed from the fresh water by chemical treatment or at the intake strainers; however, their existence in water cooling towers may lead to degradative action on wooden equipment, as well as impairing the efficiency of heat exchange. It appears that, if algae do enter the mill systems, they can thrive, but their influence on slime formation is negligible compared with that of the fungi and bacteria[195].

PREVENTION OF ENZYME ACTION

Great economic losses are incurred every year due to the biological decay of cellulose, and this decay may occur during plant growth, during processing, during storage or during actual use of timber, paper or textile products. While theoretically it is possible to prevent damage by control of moisture, temperature and availability of food supplies, and indeed a careful control of these factors combined with efficient ventilation during storage does cut down damage to an absolute minimum, in practice it is often impossible to achieve such control and some form of chemical protecting agent is imperative. Such protection can be achieved in several ways, the principal treatments being:

  (i) by modification of the cellulose molecule to render it resistant to the action of organisms and their enzymes,
 (ii) by imposing a continuous, inert physical barrier between the cellulose surface and the deteriorative agent,
(iii) by treatment of the cellulose with an agent which is toxic to the attacking organisms,
 (iv) by treatment of the cellulose with a specific enzyme inhibitor.

MODIFICATION OF THE CELLULOSE MOLECULE

The resistance of substituted celluloses to enzymic action has been discussed earlier. Since the demonstration by Dorée[196] of the resistance of cellulose acetate the problem of imparting such qualities to fabrics by this means has been studied widely. Other treatments claimed to improve or impart rot resistance to fabrics include esterification with other organic acids, cyanoethylation[267], phosphorylation[1], methylenation[25,202] and phosphonomethylation[199]. Earlier workers[197] believed that one substituent per anhydroglucose unit was necessary to render cellulose resistant to attack; however, more recently it has been shown that periodate-oxidized cellulose reacted with such molecules as hydrazine, hydroxylamine and particularly phenylhydrazine supported very little mould growth at very low degrees of substitution (e.g. one substituent per 270 anyhdroglucose units)[198]. It is possible that such substituents still retain some of the toxicity of the original compound, and this toxicity may play some part in the efficacy of the treatment as a proof. While no enzymic hydrolysis of cotton so treated was observed with cellulase preparations from *Stachybotrys atra*, inhibition of cellulase activity was not observed using oxidized phenylhydrazine-treated filter paper as a substrate even at a degree of substitution of 0·019. Thus, the hypothesis that the degree of substitution must be at least 1·0 for adequate protection does not necessarily apply to fabrics proofed for rot resistance. A dependent factor in such proofing is probably the processes involved in the treatment of the cloth; for example, if swelling occurs during treatment, a greater degree of substitution may be necessary for protection[200]. This effect is further illustrated by the work of Reeves et al.[201] who found that cotton methylated to a degree of substitution (DS) of 0·7 by diazomethane was rot resistant, but if the same DS was achieved by dimethyl sulphate and alkali treatment the cotton was not resistant. Reese[200] suggested that the minimal degree of substitution for a particular treatment of a given fibre be defined as 'the least alteration which gives the desired result'; such minimal values for cotton are given in *Table 5*.

Table 5. Minimum D.S. for Protection of Cotton
(by courtesy, *Industrial and Engineering Chemistry*, 1957, **49**, p. 93)

Fabric Treatment	Minimum D.S.
Methylation	0·7
Acetylation	0·5 to 0·7
Cyanoethylation	0·5–
Formaldehyde	0·2 to 0·3
Phosphate + urea	0·25
Phenylhydrazine on oxidized cotton	0·004

Other modifications of the anhydroglucose unit apart from substitution may occur during such treatments, and may affect susceptibility to hydrolysis; another contributory factor may be the suppression of after-swelling found in substituted celluloses preventing enzymic access[202]. As a general method for rot proofing substitution has much to commend it, provided that the treatments, which may often serve a dual purpose, do not affect the desirable fibre or fabric properties adversely.

THE INERT BARRIER

Theoretically it should be possible to prevent biological damage to cellulose by imposing a continuous, inert physical barrier between the attacking agent and the substrate, and the success of this method depends on the continuity of the inert barrier. Early workers[203-206] found that the application of a continuous surface layer of waxes, oils and rubber to textiles retarded breakdown. The wide use of synthetic resins in textile finishing has led to the investigation of these materials as proofing agents; it is possible that excess of any raw materials used in the reaction remaining in the finished resin (e.g. formaldehyde) acts as a toxic agent, and that cross linking of cellulose molecules by resins occurs, and these may account for any proofing properties possessed by the resin finishes. Summaries of earlier reports in this field present conflicting evidence for the efficacy of resins as proofs[25,207]. Later work still provides no conclusive data; thus, Cooke[208] reported that melamine- and urea-formaldehyde resin-treated cotton fabrics were very resistant to microbial deterioration, while Bell, Ramsey and Whewell[209] found that, of the urea-, melamine- and phenol-formaldehyde resins tested, only the halogenated phenolic resins provided effective treatments at practical resin weights. However, more recently it has been reported that halogenated phenolic resins had no advantages over un-substituted phenolic resins, both types imparting improved rot resistance to cotton fabric[210]. These workers obtained the best proof using an o-(hydroxymethyl) phenol-formaldehyde resin treatment.

The wide application of amine-formaldehyde resins in crease-resist finishes is providing much information on the difficult problems of ensuring uniform impregnation of the fibre with resin, and of the possible bonding of such resins to cellulose molecules. These difficulties and uncertainties are just those which are preventing the utility of these resins as rot proofing agents being realized in practice. The modified amine-formaldehyde resins (e.g. halogeno-triazine- or cyclic ethylene urea-aldehyde) require examination as proofing agents.

Treatment of paper with waxes affords some protection against fungal attack provided that the coating is continuous[194], and roofing papers treated with waxes, oils and tars also show improved resistance. Although wide use is made of asphalt-treated paper, this treatment does not necessarily render the paper immune from decay, and the incorporation of a toxic agent in addition is recommended. An effective, but expensive, method of ensuring resistance is the application of a plastic film to the paper; thus polyethylene, vinyl polymers and copolymers may be used to form the inert barrier. Use has also been made of phenol- and amine-formaldehyde resins, and it has been reported that paper containing 20 per cent of a phenolic resin withstands prolonged soil burial without ill effects[211]. However, smaller amounts of phenolic resins have also been found effective[212]. In all types of resins and plastic films, the incorporation of plasticisers which provide microbial foodstuffs (e.g. castor oil and fatty acid esters) must be guarded against.

Paint, varnish and some pitch films on wooden surfaces afford no certain protection against wood rots, unless a toxic agent is included in the formulation. In the case of water paints the casein, glue or other protein acts as a foodstuff for micro-organisms and a preservative must be included to prevent microbial growth both in the can and on cellulosic surfaces to which the paint is applied[213-215].

The advantages of the application of inert barriers are that the finishes are water-repellent and often non-leachable; however, the surface characteristics (e.g. the handle of textiles) of the finished material are profoundly altered. In particular, the changes in flexibility and air permeability may make such barriers unsuitable for many purposes.

TOXIC AGENTS

The most widespread method of preserving wood, textiles and paper (both as pulp and finished sheet) from microbial attack has been and still is the treatment of the material with a chemical which is inhibitory or toxic in some way to the growth of the attacking organism. The chemicals used may be antiseptics, merely inhibiting development of the organisms, or may be disinfectants which are actively microbiocidal. It is probable that, all other factors (e.g. resistance to leaching) being equal, disinfectants will have a longer lasting action than antiseptics. The efficiency of any inhibitor is limited by external factors, such as the availability of extraneous nutrient material, amount of moisture present, time, temperature and humidity of exposure, and the number and type of organisms present. The type of inhibitor chosen depends largely on the location of the proofed material; thus, textiles in storage for a few months will require a much milder preservative (if any) than will the fabric used for sand-bags to be piled on the ground. Some toxic agents act by causing irreversible changes in the cell structure of the attacking organism, while others interfere with vital reactions within the cell. The mode of action of some toxic agents has been studied in great detail, but it is not possible yet to predict new classes of microbiocides or preservatives solely through a knowledge of their chemical functional groups.

In assessing a toxic agent for a particular purpose various criteria must be applied, apart from its toxicity to attacking organisms; thus such factors as cost, availability, harmless character to man,

Table 6. Proofing Agents and Cellulase Inhibition

General Class of Compound	Wood	Textiles	Paper		Known Cellulase Inhibitors
			Pulp	Finished Sheet	
INORGANIC Copper salts	$CuSO_4$, Cu and As salts in ammoniacal solution, acid cupric chromate.	Cuprammonium hydroxide process, other Cu salts.	$CuSO_4$	Cu_2O, copper salts, cuprammonium process.	$CuSO_4$ and other Cu salts.
Chromium salts	Na chromate ($+NaF$ $+ Na_2HAsO_4$ + dinitrophenol).	Mineral khaki (Cr and Fe oxides).			Cr^{2+}.
Zinc salts	$ZnCl_2$, alone or mixed with Na_2CrO_4 and $CuCl_2$, $ZnSO_4$, Zn meta-arsenite.	$ZnCl_2$.	$ZnSO_4$.	$ZnCl_2$, $ZnSO_4$.	Zn^{2+}.
Others	$HgCl_2$, NaF, $Na_2B_4O_7$, H_3BO_3.	$HgCl_2$.	NaF, Cl_2, hypo-chlorites, Cl_2 + NH_3.	$HgCl_2$, colloidal Ag, borates, H_3BO_3.	Hg^{2+}, NaF, Ag^+, borates, Cl_2, $Ca(OCl)_2$, $FeCl_3$.
ORGANIC Phenols	Creosote alone, and mixed with coal tar and petroleum, tetrachlorophenol, pentachlorophenol and its Na salt, other phenols, wood tannins.	Chlorinated phenols, particularly 2:2'—methylene bis (4-chlorophenol), pentachlorophenol, salicylanilide, tannins.	Chlorinated phenols.	Chlorinated phenols especially penta-chlorophenol, sali-cylanilide, diphenyl.	Chlorinated phenols, other substituted phenols, salicylani-lide, octyl gallate.

General Class of Compound	Wood	Textiles	Paper — Pulp	Paper — Finished Sheet	Known Cellulase Inhibitors
Surfactants			[Alkyl Me$_2$Bz] N$^+$Cl$^-$, pyridinium compounds.	Quaternary ammonium compounds.	[AlkylMe$_2$Bz] N$^+$Cl$^-$ and other quaternary ammonium compounds.
Metallo-organic	Cu and Zn naphthenates, ethylmercuric phosphate, organo-tin compounds.	Cu naphthenate and Cu deriv. of 8-hydroxyquinoline, phenol and pyridyl Hg compounds, Zn naphthenate, Zn dimethyldithio-carbamate, trialkyl tin compounds.	Aryl, alkyl and heterocyclyl-mercury compounds.	Cu naphthenate, phenyl and pyridyl Hg compounds, organo-tin compounds, metal complexes (esp. Cu) of 8-hydroxyquinoline, Metal-alkyl-bis-(dithiocarbamates).	Some phenyl and ethyl Hg compounds, Na naphthenate, metallic-alkyl-bis-(dithiocarbamates).
Other classes		2–mercaptobenz-thiazole, quinones, azo-dyes, acridine and anthraquinone dyes.	Chloramines, naphthalene sulphonic acids and derivatives.	2–mercaptobenz-thiazole salts.	Some azo-dyes, quinones, chloramine, dichloramine, N-halo-succinimides, monochlorohydantoin, chloromelamine, trichloroiso-cyanuric acid.

animals and crops, method of application, permanency to give adequate service life, and chemical stability must be considered. Other desirable properties may be lack of odour and colour, inability to promote or accelerate tendering of the material, and lack of interference (physical and chemical) with other finishes or with the properties of the cellulosic material. Many hundreds of toxic agents have been used for proofing, and comprehensive reviews of industrially available fungicides for wood, textiles, rope, cordage and paper have been published[1,216-219].

The choice of toxic agents has been purely empirical, and often the decision to apply a certain compound to cellulosic materials has arisen solely from the knowledge that the compound is a disinfectant and that it is not very water soluble or highly coloured. Few fundamental approaches to this problem have been made, and it is urged that a systematic study be made to discover if degradation can be prevented by the application of substances which completely inhibit the activity of cellulolytic enzymes. The inhibition of cellulases has been discussed at length in Chapter V, and many of the toxic agents in use for cellulose preservation have not been tested for their inhibitory properties. However, it must be borne in mind that not only must cellulase action be prevented, but also the action of hemicellulases, other carbohydrases and lignin-decomposing enzymes, including S factor and enzymes catalysing the decomposition of applied finishes, such as starches, gelatin and oils. A summary of the most effective proofing agents is given in *Table 6*, with some idea of the efficacy of these or similar compounds as cellulase inhibitors. It should again be emphasized that compounds inhibiting the cellulase synthesized by one fungus do not necessarily inhibit cellulases from different organisms; the relationship between inhibition of cellulase and inhibition of microbial growth has been studied[220], and it was shown that a greater quantity of a toxic compound was required to inhibit the enzymes than to inhibit the growth of the organisms.

ATTACK BY OTHER BIOLOGICAL AGENCIES

Cellulose is also attacked by insects (e.g. roaches, beetles, crickets, grasshoppers, silverfish, termites) and marine organisms (e.g. shipworms, clams), although cellulolytic action in the gut often arises from the enzymes of symbiotic micro-organisms. Such organisms cause the decay of all cellulosic materials, and the treatment given to one class may well be applied to another type of material. Prevention of attack most frequently relies on the use of toxic agents, and fumigants such as methyl bromide and hydrogen cyanide are used to check any attack of land-based or airborne insects. Insecticides also serve to check invasion of cellulosic materials, but their volatility and toxicity to animals may, in some cases, limit their use. The presence of nutrients profoundly affect the fauma, and insects like silverfish do not attack dried plant stems unless it is to obtain starchy material, so that farinaceous finishes on paper and textiles render them susceptible to attack[221]; however, cellulases have been isolated from silverfish (see Chapter III). Protection by the inert barrier method can only be applied where a thick surface coating does not detract from the utility of the article, so that wooden structures are principally protected in this way; even in this latter case it is essential to include toxic agents in the composition, especially in water-submerged or partially submerged structures. In such cases, copper naphthenate, phenols, mercury salts and arsenicals all find use. Paper coated with nitrocellulose, cellulose esters and ethers, shellac or vinyl resins has proved resistant to roaches, and toxic treatments for paper include the use of hexachlorocyclohexane, halogenated phenols, dinitrophenols, coal tar and creosote, mercuric chloride and thiocyanates; however, more work is necessary to find satisfactory protectants for paper against insect damage. Certain fungicides applied to cotton textiles prevent termite attack, although the use of common insecticides (e.g. D.D.T., pyrethrum, sodium fluoride) is widespread in preventing infestation by cellulose-destroying insects. Full accounts of the prevention of insect and marine organism attack will be found in various reviews[65,193,219].

EVALUATION OF CELLULOSE PRESERVATIVES

A detailed discussion of test methods for the evaluation of preservatives is outside the scope of this book; reviews of recommended methods can be found elsewhere[1,160,211,222], and many workers have evolved their own procedures[25,223,224]. Apart from standardized methods suggested by various institutions (e.g. the American Associations of Textile Chemists), no universally acknowledged test methods exist; indeed, the test methods of the British Standards Institution appearing in 1946 are no longer recommended, and the whole subject of textile testing for rotproof qualities is under consideration. Other workers[225,226] have attempted to standardize test procedures. Nearly all such tests are based on the measurement of some physical property of the proofed cellulosic material after incubation with pure cultures of a single cellulose-decomposing organism, with mixed cultures of up to six or seven organisms usually some cellulolytic and some non-cellulolytic, or with soil, horse dung, or other material rich in micro-organisms, and a comparison of the values thus obtained with those of untreated material incubated in a similar manner. The soil incubation procedures are usually considered to be the most severe. A manometric procedure has been developed by Mandels and Siu[227]. Ultimately preservatives can only be assessed satisfactorily by field trials, but these accelerated methods at least serve to eliminate many ineffective materials and treatments.

A few workers only have applied cellulolytic enzyme solutions to the evaluation of preservatives, and it has been shown that such methods are less effective than culture procedures[198,228]. Indeed, it is doubtful if any enzyme solutions so far produced would provide an attack severe enough to be considered satisfactory in the evaluation of preservatives for the highly crystalline native cellulose fibres.

CELLULASES IN ANIMAL DIGESTION

It has been pointed out previously that no vertebrates can utilize cellulose directly as an energy source, but rely upon symbiotic organisms (bacteria and protozoa) in their alimentary canals to break down cellulose with the aid of cellulases. This account of digestion will be confined to discussing the initial stages of cellulose decomposition, particularly in the ruminant; this subject has been rather neglected until recently, although many reviews exist upon various aspects of the whole subject of ruminant digestion[229,230,294]. Several workers[231–4] have succeeded in obtaining cell-free cellulolytic extracts from rumen micro-organisms. The supernatant liquid from centrifuged rumen fluid contained no extracellular cellulases[233,234], and preparative methods for cellulases involved cell disruption. However, indirect evidence has been obtained for the production of extracellular bacterial cellulases[235,236], and such enzymes have been isolated from the culture medium of *Clostridium thermocellulaseum*, an anaerobic thermophilic bacterium found in compost[9], but many bacterial cellulases have been obtained only by autolysis or disruption of cells. Bacterial cellulases appear to be surface enzymes causing disintegration of cellulose only in the immediate vicinity of the bacterium concerned. During growth micro-organisms adhere closely to the substrate, and if agitation occurs cellulolysis ceases, and is resumed when the disturbance ceases[234]. Denaturation of cellulase by shaking has been noted[140], and it is possible that anomalous results obtained by different workers can be explained by partial denaturation, in line with Whitaker's conception of the modification of the active centres of the enzyme and its effect on enzyme specificity[15].

Dissolution of cellulose by rumen micro-organisms is a much more efficient process in mixed culture than in pure cultures of single bacterial species, but no comparative data are available on the cellulases derived from such cultures, although the enzymes have been prepared from both pure and mixed cultures[233]. Such preparations have very little ability to hydrolyse native cellulose (cotton), but substrates decomposed include carboxymethylcellulose, finely ground filter paper, cellophane and cellodextrins. Since the cellulose digested by animals is closely associated with other substances (e.g. hemicelluloses) in animal feed, consideration must also be given to the presence of enzymes which bring about the decomposition of these components in the rumen. Pentosans are known to be largely decomposed during passage through the rumen[237,238]; pentosan-degrading bacteria[239,240] and xylanases[241,242] have been isolated from rumen contents (see also Chapter VII). Studies have been made of the *in vitro* fermentation of water soluble pentosans by toluene-treated suspensions of bacteria derived from rumen fluid[243]; complete hydrolysis occurred and during the course of the reaction several oligosaccharides were identified, in addition to xylobiose, xylose and arabinose. Enzymes derived from pure cultures of xylan-fermenting bacteria could be separated by electrophoresis on a starch support into two components; one was a xylanase giving rise to xylobiose from xylan, while the other was a xylobiase acting upon xylo-oligosaccharides by the removal of single xylose units and also upon phenyl–β–xyloside[244]. The enzyme β–glucosidase has been found in rumen contents[245,246]; thus the enzymes necessary for the primary degradation of cellulosic plant materials to simple sugars occur in the rumen. Bacteria with the enzymes required for the conversion of these sugars to fatty acids have been obtained from the rumen[247,248].

The influence of lignin on cellulolysis has been discussed earlier in this chapter. The older and more lignified the plant becomes, the less easily digested it is, and lignin itself appears practically indigestible[249,250]. The addition of starch to the fodder depresses digestion of cellulose[251,252], and the addition of sugars above certain concentrations has a similar effect[253]; the effect of sugars on cellulase action has been discussed in Chapter V. Other substances reported to depress cellulose digestibility include the antibiotics aureomycin[254] and chlorotetracycline[255], although the addition of dietary antibiotics often have a favourable effect on the growth of animals[256]. Antibiotics have little effect on cellulase activity[257] (also see Chapter V), and their effects have been attributed to their influence on the growth of gut micro-organisms or on the associated production of carbo-hydrases.

Substances stimulating cellulose digestibility include members of the vitamin B group[258], the amino-acids leucine, *iso*leucine and valine[259], and certain fatty acids[260,261]; the influence of fatty acids was attributed to their effect on the growth of micro-organisms rather than to their effect on cellulases[234]. Conversely, it has been noticed that vegetable diets stimulated riboflavin synthesis[262], and this effect may be due to the cellulose in the vegetable, as later work[263] showed that the addition of vegetable cellulose to a meat diet resulted in increased faecal excretion of riboflavin by man. Diets with added cellulose increased the metabolic faecal nitrogen of growing rats, although there was no influence on the urinary endogenous nitrogen[264]. However the complexity of such experiments does not permit any conclusions of the fate of the cellulose itself. The stimulatory effect of proteins on enzyme activity is well-known (see Chapter V), but some protein supplements are known to depress the digestibility of cellulose[253]. Complex mixtures of salts are found in alfalfa extract ash[265], and the addition of such materials (plant or extracts) which are known to improve digestion of crude fibre[271], would increase the concentrations of calcium, magnesium and phosphorus in the rumen[229]. The influence of such minerals on cellulase activity should be borne in mind, as has been demonstrated earlier. However, the rumen is such a delicately balanced and complex system that at the present time it is difficult to attribute the influence of any of these stimulators and inhibitors solely to their direct action on cellulases.

As mentioned above, the breakdown of cellulose in non-ruminants has not been fully investigated. After feeding ^{14}C–cellulose to rats and analysing faeces, the expired breath and carcass indicated that a large proportion of cellulose was altered in the alimentary canal to a form which the rat could utilize readily; only half of the labelled material was excreted in the faeces[266]. Organisms from gastro-intestinal tracts are known to degrade cellulose[145,146,269,270], converting it ultimately to fatty acids and other products. There is evidence that chickens can utilize wood waste in their feed[272], and are able to digest crude fibre to a small extent[273]. At present, it appears that non-ruminants can utilize cellulose to some extent largely, if not solely, due to the enzymes of the gut micro-organisms and protozoa.

The inclusion of cellulolytic enzymes in diets for poultry and mice gave larger increases in weight and better utilizations of cellulose than in control animals[274-6]. Such enzyme supplements have also been tried for human diets. However, until enzymes capable of bringing about extensive degradation of native celluloses to sugars have been obtained, the enzymic pre-treatment of woody and plant materials is not a commercial proposition, although their inclusion with green plant material for ensilage has been suggested[277]. The breakdown of cellulose in silage has not been demonstrated, except in the case of silage made with metabisulphite[278]. The loss of fibre in poor silage has been mentioned frequently, but little work has appeared on the enzymic hydrolysis of hemicelluloses in silage, although this action is of importance. The use of enzyme supplements to animal feeding stuffs is becoming widespread, and although amylases and pectinases may enhance the nutritive value of foods, the inclusion of other enzymes such as hemicellulases and cellulases (with action on native celluloses) is worthy of further research.

SACCHARIFICATION OF WASTES

The fermentation of natural materials to give useful sugars, solvents, antibiotics, fertilizers and even gases is operated on a large industrial scale. However, wood waste produced annually in Great Britain amounts to approximately 60,000 tons, while another 114,000 tons of branches, stumps, roots and tops are destroyed by burning[279]. Although straw and husks are often composted for return to the land and are not utilized for fermentation, it is considered that over one million tons of such material could be spared for saccharification[280]. Other carbohydrate-containing materials, not at present fermented, include bracken peat, sphagnum moss and sugar beet pulp; some 291,000 tons of the last-named material was produced in the year 1948–9[279]. Textile and paper mill processes may also lead to useful substrates; kier boiling and sulphite waste liquors are two examples of such products, while other sources of fermentable wastes occur in the natural rubber plantations. It is not implied that all such materials are wasted at present, but until collection difficulties are overcome, such valuable substrates must continue to be ignored. The use of molasses and paper industry waste liquors has led to convenient and readily available sugars for the production of dextran, antibiotics, and citric acid. However, the breakdown of cellulosic wastes is our primary consideration here, and this has been accomplished by acid hydrolysis of wood wastes by the Scholler or Bergius processes[281], and the Madison process which employs a continuous acid feed into the waste and continuous sugar removal[282]. The final hydrolysate from such processes can be fermented to the extent of 65 to 85 per cent by the yeast *Saccharomyces cerevisiae*, while some 41 per cent of the sugars can be converted to ethanol by the yeast *Torula utilis*[283]. The pre-treatment of wastes requires considerable care, particularly in the removal of substances toxic to the micro-organisms used for fermentation. The whole subject of the utilization of waste carbohydrates for fermentation process has been reviewed recently by Steel[284].

The production of fermentable sugars by hydrolysis of wood wastes in the presence of cellulases runs into a major difficulty; as the reaction proceeds the build-up of glucose concentration and the removal of amorphous areas in cellulose to leave the resistant crystalline regions soon bring about a great decrease in the rate of hydrolysis. For this reason, it has been suggested[285] that such processes can never compete with acid hydrolysis, although Reese[50] pointed out that enzymatic hydrolysis is more efficient than acid hydrolysis. A comparison of the two methods has been given in Chapter VI, but the major difference between them probably lies in the relative molecular sizes of the catalysts and their ability to penetrate the fibre structure[285]. However, such enzymes have been tried for saccharification processes; for example, Toyama[286] reported 75 per cent decomposition of an unboiled sweet potato pulp by the amylases in a culture filtrate from *Trichoderma koningi*, but hard wastes such as sawdust and rice hulls were not hydrolysed by the cellulases in the filtrate. While it would be difficult to recommend the pursuit of processes based on isolated cellulases, the utilization of carbohydrate wastes by micro-organisms has attracted much attention. As long ago as 1932, the Langwell process produced ethanol and acetic acid from the growth of thermophilic bacteria on corn-cob liquor[268]. The fermentation of wood wastes depends on their lignin content, and the removal of lignin could lead to their wider utilization; for ready fermentation it was suggested that the lignin content should be below one per cent[287]. Other factors influencing the digestion of wastes were discussed by Rudolfs and Heukelekian[288]. Pre-treatment of wood by radiation with high-velocity electrons[289] or by chlorine dioxide[290] has been suggested. The animal rumen provides a source of bacteria to carry out both the initial breakdown of cellulose and the further fermentation of the sugars produced. In general, only low concentrations of cellulosic materials can be fermented, but removal of the fermentation products, by dialysis or ion-exchange resins, resulted in 84 per cent of a cellulose suspension (containing 4·12 per cent cellulose) being fermented at 40° in 72 hours in a model experiment[291].

At least sixteen products are listed by Siu[1] as arising from the decomposition of cellulose by micro-organisms; if the fermentation products of glucose and cellobiose are considered separately the list could run into hundreds of compounds. The fermentation of cellulose has been discussed by Anderson[292], and it is interesting to note in his account that many cellulolytic bacteria (e.g. *Cellulomonas* sp., *Cytophaga* sp.) occur in the processes for obtaining methane, hydrogen, fatty acids, solvents and fertilizers from wastes. Cellulose is one of the principal components of sewage solids and cellulolytic bacteria are present in very large numbers, although the rate of cellulose breakdown may be the limiting factor in sewage sludge fermentation[293]. It is also possible that cellulolytic activity of micro-organisms could be utilized in the breakdown of paper in city refuse.

Other uses for cellulolytic enzymes have been recorded as the improvement of coffee quality and rubber yields. The addition of a mixture of pectic enzymes, cellulases and hemicellulases to green or partially ripe coffee beans, followed by overnight steeping, washing and sun-drying was claimed to enhance the flavour of the beverage[296]. Unsterilized ground scrap rubber was fermented in a medium containing cellulolytic mesophilic and thermophilic fungi of sulphur-resistant types; the rubber became cellulose-free and could be sheeted without adding other softeners[297]. A similar process for freeing *Cryptostegia* leaves from crude celluloses resulted in an increase in the yield of rubber[298]; cellulases have also been applied to the guayule plant[299].

CEREAL ENZYMES

In the field of cereal chemistry, systematic studies of the non-starchy polysaccharides and of the enzymes responsible for their degradation have made it possible to describe the changes occurring during malting of grains, principally due to the work of Preece and his co-workers at the Heriot-Watt College in Edinburgh. Since these changes are very important in the brewing industry it is proposed to discuss the β–glucanase and hemicellulase systems of cereals here, although some of these enzymes have received mention earlier.

POLYSACCHARIDES OF CEREALS

Polysaccharides present in cereals, apart from starch, include pure cellulose[300] and various types of hemicellulose. Both water soluble and water insoluble but alkali soluble hemicelluloses have been found; the latter class can be obtained from the husks and endosperms of the grain. These husk hemicelluloses are characterized by a high xylan content, the presence of uronic acid residues, and by having a low viscosity in alkaline solution[295,301–304]; they have some similarities to the hemicelluloses of straws[305]. Alkali soluble endospermic hemicelluloses have also been studied, and are characterized by having a lower pentosan content, fewer uronic acid residues and a higher viscosity in solution than the husk compounds[295]. Also found in the endosperm are the water soluble hemicelluloses or cereal gums, first extracted in 1882 and termed 'amylan'[306]. A lichenin-type polysaccharide has been isolated from oats[307], while the amylan of germinating barley has been studied further[308]. More recently a pure β–linked glucose polymer has been obtained from both oats and barley[309,310]. This water soluble β–glucan from barley consists of unbranched chains of β–linked glucopyranose units having approximately equal numbers of $(1\rightarrow3)$ β– and $(1\rightarrow4)$ β–linkages, although these two types of linkage are not arranged alternately, but each type is concentrated in a certain region of the chain[311,312]. Other water soluble hemicelluloses obtained from cereals include pentosans, such as the araboxylan from wheat flour[313], which had a chain of $(1\rightarrow4)$ β–linked xylose units with side chains of single arabofuranosyl units joined by $(1\rightarrow3)$ and $(1\rightarrow2)$ bonds to the xylose chain. Rye araboxylan[310,314] had a similar highly branched structure with a xylan backbone, and to every second D–xylose unit a terminal L–arabofuranose residue was linked through position 3. The removal of these side chains renders the hemicellulose progressively more insoluble in water[313]. Other water soluble hemicelluloses present include mannans[309] and galactans[310].

OCCURRENCE OF CELLULOLYTIC ENZYMES

The enzymes of barley have been studied most widely, and a variety of substrates have been used in the measurement of their 'cellulolytic' activity. Early workers noted the presence of enzymes catalysing the hydrolysis of lichenin and reprecipitated cellulose in barley malt[315,316], while other substrates studied include carboxymethyl-cellulose[317], hydroxyethylcellulose[318] and ethylhydroxyethylcellu-lose[319]; thus apart from the lichenase present, the term 'cellulase' has been applied to enzymes acting in the hydrolysis of these cellulose derivatives. However, after the isolation of water-soluble barley β–glucan, detailed systematic studies of its hydrolysis have been made, and the term 'β–glucanase' coined for the active catalysts; whether the lichenase, cellulase and β–glucanase systems are entirely different from each other is yet to be decided, but it should be recalled that differences in the proportions of different enzyme components, all belonging to one system, can account for quite wide variations in enzyme action patterns. The presence of hemicellulases has been demonstrated in a large number of cereal grains; thus, an enzyme from barley catalysed the hydrolysis of the mannogalactan of carob seeds[317], and two types of xylanase, an arabinosidase, and a xylobiase

244

have been found in barley and are active in the hydrolysis of rye araboxylan[320]. A β–glucosidase (cellobiase) is also present in barley[316,321]. The relative amounts of pentosanases and β–glucanases in various grains is shown in *Table 7*[320,321].

Table 7. *Cellulolytic Enzymes in Cereals*

Cereal	β–glucanases			Pentosanases			
	Exo-enzyme	*Endo-enzyme*	*Cello-biase*	*Exo-xylanase*	*Endo-xylanase*	*Arabino-sidase*	*Xylo-biase*
Barley	R	M	VR	R	M	R	M
Maize	T	M	T	M	M	M	T
Oats	M	R	T	R	R	R	R
Rye	R	M	T	R	M	R	M
Wheat	M	M	VR	T	T	M	M

VR—very rich in activity, R—rich,
M—moderate, T—trace of activity.

PROPERTIES OF CELLULOLYTIC ENZYMES

Cellulase: Purification and properties of green malt cellulase have been described in Chapters IV and V[319]. It was postulated that the degradation of ethylhydroxyethylcellulose involved the action of at least two enzymes, one probably being a hydrolytic poly–β–glucosidase and the other a non-hydrolytic transglycosylase. Barley malt cellulase appeared to attack all linkages between the glucose units of a hydroxyethylcellulose substrate with equal ease[318], while the enzymic hydrolysis of lichenin and reprecipitated cellulose probably involves three stages; an initial disintegration of the complex polysaccharides to anhydroglucose chains, followed by hydrolysis to cellobiose and finally to glucose[315].

β–Glucanase: Studies on the degradation of a mixture of barley gums led to the postulation that two enzyme systems were required: (i) rapidly acting cytoclastic enzymes, whose action resulted in a decrease of the average molecular weight with little increase in reducing power and (ii) cytolytic enzymes, which produced a large number of reducing groups by forming free sugars and oligosaccharides[323]. Further studies on these enzyme systems[321,324] became possible after the isolation of a pure β–glucan[309]. It was shown that two β–glucanases (obtained by ammonium sulphate precipitation) are present in barley. Endo–β–glucanase corresponded to the cytoclastic enzymes, its activity being measured by the fall in viscosity of the β–glucan solution, and in the early stages of the reaction the reducing power of the solution was directly proportional to changes in specific fluidity. Evidence for exo-β-glucanase activity, corresponding to the cytolytic enzymes, was obtained from the increase in reducing power in the early stages of the reaction over and above that which could be assigned to endo-β-glucanase action. Exo-β-glucanase can be inactivated by treatment with phenylacetic acid or phenylmercuric nitrate, so that endo-β-glucanase action can then be studied alone.

Laminaribiose, cellobiose and higher oligosaccharides were identified as products of hydrolysis in the presence of endo-β-glucanase, in addition to glucose being produced by cellobiase action. These results are consistent with the production of higher oligosaccharides, which are then progressively hydrolysed to smaller molecules with the ultimate production of the two disaccharides. The higher oligosaccharides have mixed linkages, and remaining after prolonged hydrolysis was a resistant fraction containing twenty to thirty anhydroglucose residues also having mixed linkages. The presence of exo-β-glucanase in the enzyme preparation was proved by the early production of cellobiose and glucose, these compounds only being produced on prolonged incubation with the endo-β-glucanase.

Pentosanases: In studies of the pentosanase activity of barley, a water soluble rye araboxylan has been used as a substrate[310,314], and this substrate was further purified by treatment with a-amylase[320]. Enzyme systems were prepared by extraction of the ground cereal with sodium chloride solution, followed by autolysis, dialysis and finally acetone precipitation[320]. The enzymic reaction was followed by measuring changes in viscosity of the substrate solution, determination of liberated pentoses (arabinose and xylose), and chromatographic analysis of the hydrolysate at different stages of the reaction. Arabinose was produced from the start of the reaction, while xylose and xylobiose appeared only after some hours, and prolonged action resulted in the production of oligosaccharides higher than xylobiose and containing up to six anhydroxylose units carrying varying proportions of arabofuranose units as side chains. From this evidence it was suggested that four enzymes took part in the hydrolysis of araboxylan:

(i) an arabinosidase which brings about the hydrolysis of arabinose side chains to free arabinose,

(ii) an endoxylanase degrading xylan chains to a series of oligosaccharides regardless of the presence of side chains (cf. endoglucanase),

246

   (iii) an exoxylanase, whose action is dependent on the prior
         action of the arabinosidase, and which produces xylobiose
         from araboxylan and from the higher oligosaccharides,
   (iv) a xylobiase catalysing the hydrolysis of xylobiose and
         possible xylotriose.

It was not considered that transpentosylation occurred as the
enzymic attack on xylobiose and xylotriose gave no evidence of
products other than those expected from direct breakdown, and the
incubation of mixtures of arabinose and xylose (in the concentrations
obtained during hydrolysis of araboxylan) with the enzyme system
also yielded no new products[320].

CHANGES OCCURRING DURING THE MALTING OF BARLEY

Malting is the process which raw cereals undergo in preparation for
brewing and consists of three principal stages:

   (i) steeping, where the raw cereal is soaked in water at about
         13° for 48 hours or more,
   (ii) flooring, taking 9 to 13 days during which germination
         occurs,
   (iii) kilning, a heat treatment to give the malt the desired colour
         and flavour, and by removal of water to make it stable and
         friable.

Low dried malt is produced by carefully controlled heating, and still
has high activity in the enzymes (amylases and proteases) required
in the mashing process. During malting, changes takes place both in
the enzyme activities and in the components of the grain, but this
account will only consider changes in cellulolytic enzymes and their
substrates.

No changes in cellulase activity occurred during steeping, but a
marked increase took place during flooring[319]. Cellobiase activity
increased towards the end of the steeping process, then declined in
the early stages and increased again in the later stages of flooring,
to be followed by a second fall in the finished malt[321]. Endo-β-
glucanase activity increased only towards the end of flooring, reaching a maximum value in the early stages of kilning, and falling again
in the finished malt; on the other hand, exo-β-glucanase activity
was highest towards the end of flooring, none being detectable after
kilning[321]. Both cellobiase and endo-β-glucanase activities were
considerably higher in finished malt than in raw barley. A summary
of the changes in hemicellulase activities during malting is given
in *Table 8*.

247

Table 8. Relative Enzyme Activities During Malting[320]
(by courtesy, Institute of Brewing, **64**, p. 499)

Product	Stage of Malting	Endoxylanase	Arabinosidase	Xylobiase
Barley	raw grain	1·0	1·0	1·0
Green malt	after flooring	3·1	1·8	2·3
Low dried malt	after special kilning	2·0	2·1	1·2
Finished malt	after ordinary kilning	1·8	1·1	0·5

Activity of enzyme preparation from raw barley taken as 1·0.

Little change in cellulose and husk-type hemicelluloses (having high pentosan content) due to enzymic action occurred during malting[325,326] but considerable changes took place in the soluble hemicelluloses. There was a marked increase in water soluble β–glucan content during flooring, reaching a maximum value towards the end of the flooring period, after which a decline occurred which continued during kilning to give a finished malt with a very low β–glucan content. The residual alkali-soluble hemicellulose of the β–glucan type was degraded steadily throughout malting. Water soluble pentosans increased from the middle of the flooring period onwards, while alkali-soluble pentosan content maintained a maximum value to halfway through flooring, then slowly decreased up to the start of kilning when it decreased sharply. Finished malt contained more soluble pentosan than raw barley, but it was thought to have a lower molecular weight from viscometric studies[309]. Mechanical factors may also influence changes in hemicelluloses during malting.

This picture of enzymes occurring in barley finds a parallel in the work of numerous investigators on cellulases and other carbo-hydrases. Recently, Reese, Smakula and Perlin classified poly-saccharases as [327]:

(i) endo-, or random-splitting enzymes,
(ii) exo-, or endwise-splitting enzymes with (a) removal of one monosaccharide unit at a time, or (b) removal of one disaccharide unit at a time.

Most cellulases appear to be random-splitting types, and the production of relatively large amounts of cellotriose during the hydrolysis of Walseth cellulose indicated that the cellulase of a *Streptomyces* sp. was also of this type[327]. On the other hand, the cellobiase of *Stachybotrys atra* splits off glucose units from the end of a cellodextrin[329], and its activity is independent of the molecular size of the dextrin up to a degree of polymerization of eleven. In this case the combining site for the enzyme probably involves only one cellobiose unit at the end of the dextrin chain, so that the length of the chain would have no effect on the activity until the substrate molecule was long enough to create difficulties in the orientation of the chain end with respect to the active centre[328]. The turnover number of Whitaker's cellulase reached a maximum at a molecular size corresponding to cellotetraose, and below this size the value declined sharply[330]; it appears probable that this upper limit of four anhydroglucose units is the combining site for the enzyme. This molecular size for the enzyme-substrate combining site has also been found in the *iso*maltodextrins in combination with antibodies against dextran[331].

REFERENCES

1. SIU, *Microbial Decomposition of Cellulose*, 1951, Reinhold Publishing Corporation, N.Y., U.S.A.
2. ELSDEN AND PEEL, *Ann. Rev. of Microbiol.* 1958, **12**, p. 145.
3. DARBY AND GODDARD, *Amer. J. Botan.* 1950, **37**, p. 379.
4. HIGUCHI, *J. Japan Forest. Soc.* 1955, **37**, p. 147.
5. PERLIN, MICHAELIS AND McFARLANE, *Canad. J. Res.* 1947, **25C**, p. 246.
6. MANDELS, *Plant Physiol.* 1954, **29**, p. 18.
7. LOPEZ-RAMOS AND SCHUBERT, *Arch. Biochem. Biophys.*, 1955, **55**, p. 566.
8. WHITAKER, *Canad. J. Bot.* 1951, **29**, p. 159.
9. ENEBO, *Studies in Cellulose Decomposition*, 1954, Stockholm.
10. CROOK AND STONE, *Biochem. J.* 1957, **65**, p. 1.
11. MICHIE, SHARPLES AND WALTER, to be published.
12. MARK, *J. phys. Chem.* 1940, **44**, p. 764.
13. STONE, *Ph.D. Thesis*, University of London, 1954.
14. JERMYN, *Aust. J. Sci. Res.* 1952, **B5**, p. 409.
15. WHITAKER, *Canad. J. Biochem. Physiol.* 1956, **34**, p. 102.
16. MELLER, *J. Polym. Sci.* 1949, **4**, p. 619.
17. MELLER, *Holzforschung*, 1955, **9**, p. 149.
18. BULLER quoted by HAWKER, *Physiology of Fungi*, 1950, University of London Press Ltd., London.
19. MANDELS, G. R. and NORTON, *Microbiology Series Report No. 11*, U.S. Army Quartermaster Gen., Laboratories, Philadelphia, 1948.
20. DARBY AND MANDELS, G. R., *Plant Physiol.* 1955, **30**, p. 360.
21. BORLAUG, *Rayon Text. Monthly*, 1943, **24**, p. 416, 475.
22. BURKHOLDER AND SIU, *Topical Report No. 23*, May 1947, Biological Laboratories, U.S. Quartermaster Depot, Philadelphia, U.S.A.
23. TWEEDIE AND BAYLEY, *Amer. Dysestuff Rep.* 1944, **33**, pp. 373, 378.
24. BOSE, *Science and Culture*, 1952, **17**, p. 435.
25. RAMSEY, M.Sc. Thesis, University of Leeds, 1954.
26. HEYN, *Textile Inds.* 1956, **120**, No. 5, p. 137.

27. HEYN, *Text. Res. J.* 1957, **27**, p. 591.
28. HEYN, *Text. Res. J.* 1958, **28**, p. 444.
29. BASU, *J. Text. Inst.* 1948, **39**, T232.
30. CALLAO AND MONTOYA, *Microbiol. españ.* (*Madrid*), 1955, **8**, p. 419.
31. JENSEN, *Aust. J. Sci.* 1941, **4**, p. 59.
32. ISHIMARU AND TOYAMA, *J. Ferment. Technol. Japan,* 1950, **28**, p. 215.
33. MENON, *J. Text. Inst.* 1936, **27**, p. T229.
34. ELKIN AND WHITE, *J. Text. Inst.* 1939, **30**, p. P340.
35. SARKAR, *J. Indian Chem. Soc.* 1935, **12**, p. 23.
36. REGE, *Ann. Appl. Biol.* 1927, **14**, p. 1.
37. FULLER AND NORMAN, *J. Bact.* 1943, **46**, p. 291.
38. BASU AND GHOSE, *J. Text. Inst.* 1952, **43**, p. T278.
39. BASU AND BOSE, *J. Text. Inst.* 1956, **47**, p. T329.
40. TURNER, *J. Text. Inst.* 1949, **40**, p. P857.
41. FARGHER, *Biological Transformations of Starch and Cellulose,* ed. Williams, Biochem. Soc. Symposia No. 11, 1953. Cambridge University Press.
42. FARGHER, *The Incidence and Control of Mould and Bacterial Attack on Textiles.* British Cotton Industry Research Assn., 1945.
43. BASU, *J. Text. Inst.* 1948, **39**, p. T237.
44. BUSTON AND BASU, *J. gen. Microbiol.* 1948, **2**, p. 162.
45. BASU, *J. gen. Microbiol.* 1952, **6**, p. 199.
46. BASU AND BOSE, *J. Text. Inst.* 1956, **47**, p. T343.
47. BASU AND GHOSE, *J. Text. Inst.* 1952, **43**, p. T355.
48. WAGNER, WEBBER AND SIU, *Arch. Biochem.* 1947, **12**, p. 35.
49. ABRAMS, *Text. Res. J.* 1951, **21**, p. 714.
50. REESE, *Appd. Microbiol.* 1956, **4**, p. 39.
51. SAEMAN, MILLETT AND LAWTON, *Industr. Engng Chem.* 1952, **44**, p. 2848.
52. GOODALL, GORTON AND SUMMERSGILL, *J. Soc. Dyers Col.* 1946, **62**, p. 189.
53. MARSH, BOLLENBACHER, SAN ANTONIO AND MEROLA, *Text. Res. J.* 1955, **25**, p. 1007.
54. ROSE, MITTON, GARDNER, LAIRD AND BAYLEY, *Text. Res. J.* 1957, **27**, p. 99.
55. STANIER, *Bacteriol. Rev.* 1942, **6**, p. 143.
56. SIU, *Text. Res. J.* 1950, **20**, p. 281.
57. GREATHOUSE, *Text. Res. J.* 1950, **20**, p. 227.
58. BLUM AND STAHL, *Text. Res. J.* 1952, **22**, p. 178.
59. MARSH, *Text. Res. J.* 1957, **27**, p. 413.
60. WAKEHAM, STICKLEY AND SPICER, *Text. Res. J.* 1954, **24**, p. 1037.
61. MARSH, GUTHRIE AND BUTLER, *Text. Res. J.* 1951, **21**, p. 565.
62. ARNDT, *Text. Res. J.* 1953, **23**, p. 533.
63. MARSH, BOLLENBACHER, BUTLER AND MEROLA, *Text. Res. J.* 1954, **24**, p. 31.
64. GILLIGAN AND REESE, *Canad. J. Microbiol.* 1954, **1**, p. 90.
65. WISE AND JAHN (editors), *Wood Chemistry,* 1952. Reinhold Publishing Corporation, New York, U.S.A.
66. SCHELLENBERG, *Vierteljahrsschr. Naturforsch. Ges.* (*Zurich*), 1920, **65**, p. 31.

67. HUBERT, *J. Agric. Res.* 1924, **29**, p. 523.
68. DE BARY, *Botan. Zeit.* 1886, **44**, pp. 377, 420.
69. GARREN, *Phytopathol.* 1938, **28**, p. 839.
70. REESE AND LEVINSON, *Physiol. Plant.* 1952, **5**, p. 345.
71. BOSE AND SARKER, *Proc. Roy. Soc., London,* 1937, **123B**, p. 193.
72. KILROE-SMITH, *J. South African Chem. Inst.* 1957, **10**, p. 29.
73. HIGA, O'NEILL AND JENNISON, *J. Bact.* 1956, **71**, p. 382.
74. BOSE, *Ergeb. Enzymforsch.* 1939, **8**, p. 267.
75. NARAYANAMURTI AND VERMA, *Holz, Roh und Werkstoff,* 1953, **11**, p. 7.
76. BAYLISS, *J. Econ. Biol.* 1908, **3**, p. 1.
77. SISON, SCHUBERT AND NORD, *Arch. Biochem. Biophys.* 1958, **75**, p. 260.
78. MAYO, *New Phytol.* 1925, **24**, p. 162.
79. SCHMITZ AND ZELLER, *Ann. Mo. Botan. Garden,* 1919, **6**, p. 193.
80. PLOETZ, *Hoppe-Seyl. Z.* 1939, **261**, p. 183.
81. FINDLAY, *Ann. Appl. Biol.* 1932, **19**, p. 331.
82. MAHOOD AND CABLE, *Paper,* 1929, **25**, p. 1149.
83. SCHACHT, *Jb. wiss. Botan.* 1863, **3**, p. 442.
84. BAILEY AND VESTAL, *J. Arnold Arbor,* 1937, **18**, p. 196.
85. BARGHOORN AND LINDER, *Farlowia,* 1944, **1**, p. 395.
86. SAVORY, *Ann. Appl. Biol.* 1954, **41**, p. 336.
87. CAMPBELL AND BOOTH, *Biochem. J.* 1929, **23**, p. 566.
88. WEHMER, *Ber. dtsch. Chem. Ges.* 1927, **45**, p. 536.
89. BOSWELL, *Biochem. J.* 1938, **32**, p. 218.
90. SMITH, V. M., *Arch. Biochem. Biophys.* 1949, **23**, p. 446.
91. APENITIS, ERDTMAN AND LEOPOLD, *Svensk. Kemisk. Tisdkrift.* 1951, **63**, p. 195.
92. ENKVIST, SOLIN AND MAUNULA, *Pap. ja Puu,* 1954, **36**, pp. 65, 86.
93. PEW, *Tech. Ass. Pulp Pap. Ind.* 1957, **40**, p. 553.
94. FALCK AND HAAG, *Ber. dtsch. Chem. Ges.* 1927, **60**, p. 225.
95. CAMPBELL, *Biochem. J.* 1932, **26**, pp. 1829, 1838.
96. SCHEFFER, *U.S. Dept. Agric. Tech. Bull. No. 527,* 1936.
97. CAMPBELL, *Biochem. J.* 1931, **25**, p. 2023.
98. CAMPBELL, *Biochem. J.* 1930, **24**, p. 1235.
99. BRAUNS AND YIRAK, *Paper Trade J.* 1947, **125**, p. 55.
100. PLOETZ, *Ber. dtsch. Chem. Ges.* 1939, **72B**, p. 1885; 1940, **73B**, pp. 57, 61, 74.
101. MARCH, *Tech. Assoc. Papers,* 1948, **31**, p. 240.
102. ANDERSON, KASTER AND SEELY, *J. biol. Chem.* 1942, **144**, p. 767.
103. BOYCE, *Forest Pathology,* 1938, McGraw-Hill Book Co., New York.
104. DAVIDSON, CAMPBELL AND BLAISDELL, *J. Agric. Res.* 1938, **57**, p. 683.
105. FÅHRAEUS, NILSSON AND NILSSON, *Svensk. Botan. Tidskr.* 1949, **43**, p. 343.
106. LAW, *Ann. Botan. (n.s.),* 1950, **14**, p. 69.
107. LAW, *Ann. Botan. (n.s.),* 1955, **19**, p. 562.
108. FÅHRAEUS, *Physiol. Plant.* 1952, **5**, p. 284.
109. FÅHRAEUS, *Physiol. Plant.* 1954, **7**, p. 704.
110. LINDEBERG AND FÅHRAEUS, *Physiol. Plant.* 1952, **5**, p. 277.
111. YOSHIDA, *J. chem. Soc.* 1883, **43**, p. 472.

112. GREGG AND MILLER, *J. Amer. chem. Soc.* 1940, **62**, p. 1374.
113. KEILIN AND MANN, *Nature Lond.* 1939, **143**, p. 23.
114. BERTRAND, *Bull. soc. chim. biol.* 1944, **26**, p. 45.
115. TISSIÈRES, *Nature Lond.* 1940, **162**, p. 340.
116. KUBOWITZ, *Biochem. Z.* 1938, **299**, p. 32.
117. MALMSTRÖM, FÅHRAEUS AND MOSBACH, *Biochim. Biophys. Acta*, 1958, **28**, p. 652.
118. MALMSTRÖM, MOSBACH AND VÄNNGÅRD, *Nature Lond.* 1959, **183**, p. 321.
119. KERTESZ, *Nature Lond.* 1957, **180**, p. 506.
120. DAY, PELCZAR AND GOTTLIEB, *Arch. Biochem.* 1949, **23**, p. 360; 1950, **25**, p. 449.
121. VAN VLIET, *Biochim. Biophys. Acta*, 1954, **15**, p. 211.
122. HIGUCHI, KAWAMURA, I., AND KAWAMURA, H. *J. Japan Forest Soc.*, 1955, **37**, p. 298.
123. HENDERSON, *Nature Lond.* 1955, **175**, p. 634.
124. BIRKINSHAW et. al., *Biochem. J.* 1944, **38**, p. 131.
125. BIRKINSHAW AND FINDLAY, *Biochem. J.* 1940, **34**, p. 82.
126. HIGUCHI, KAWAMURA AND HAYASHI, *J. Japan. Wood Res. Soc.* 1956, **2**, p. 31.
127. WHITAKER AND GEORGE, *Canad. J. Botan.* 1951, **29**, p. 176.
128. SAVORY AND PINION, *Holzforsch.* 1958, **12**, p. 99.
129. KLEINERT AND JOYCE, *Svensk. Papperstidn.* 1959, **62**, p. 37.
130. ADAMS AND LEDINGHAM, *Canad. J. Res.* 1942, **C.20**, p. 13.
131. FINDLAY AND SAVORY, *Roh- u. Werkstoff*, 1954, **12**, p. 293.
132. SAVORY, *Rec. Conv. Brit. Wood Preserv. Assoc.* 1955, p. 3.
133. AOSHIMA AND KOBAYASHI, *J. Jap. Forest. Soc.* 1952, **34**, p. 289.
134. PETTIFOR AND FINDLAY, *Forestry*, 1946, **20**, p. 57.
135. BLAIR, *Pulp and Paper Mag. Canada*, 1920, **18**, p. 451.
136. SCHMITZ, *Ann. Mo. Botan. Garden*, 1919, **6**, p. 93.
137. JACOBS AND MARSDEN, *Ann. Appl. Biol.* 1947, **34**, p. 276.
138. VIRTANEN AND HUKKI, *Suomen Kemistelehti*, 1946, **19**, p. 4.
139. LANGWELL, *J. Soc. Chem. Ind.* 1923, **42**, p. T.287.
140. BASU AND PAL, *Nature Lond.* 1956, **178**, p. 312.
141. LIESE, *Handbuch der Holzkonservierung* ed. Mahlke-Troschel, 1950, Springer Verlag, Berlin.
142. SAVORY, *J. Appl. Bacteriol.* 1954, **17**, p. 213.
143. CLAUSEN AND KAUFERT, *J. Forest. Prod. Res. Soc.* 1952, **2**, p. 62.
144. HAJNY, GARDNER AND RITTER, *Industr. Engng Chem.* 1951, **43**, p. 1384.
145. KHOUVINE, *Ann. Inst. Pasteur*, 1923, **37**, p. 711.
146. HIRSCHBERG, *J. Bact.* 1941, **41**, p. 78.
147. LASKER AND GIESE, *J. Exp. Biol.* 1956, **33**, p. 542.
148. HARRINGTON, *Biochem. J.* 1921, **15**, p. 736.
149. MILLER AND BOYNTON, *Science*, 1926, **63**, p. 524.
150. RAY AND JULIAN, *Nature Lond.* 1952, **169**, p. 32.
151. CLEVELAND, *Biol. Bull.* 1931, **61**, p. 85.
152. HUNGATE, *Ecology*, 1939, **20**, p. 230.
153. HENDEE, *J. Bact.* 1941, **41**, p. 268.

154. MANSOUR AND MANSOUR-BEK, *Biol. Rev.* 1934, **9**, p. 363.
155. PARKIN, *Ann. Appl. Biol.* 1936, **23**, p. 369.
156. BUCHNER, *Tier und Pflanze in Symbiose*, 1930. Borntraeger, Berlin.
157. RIPPER, *Zeit. vergl. Physiol.* 1930, **13**, p. 314.
158. MANSOUR AND MANSOUR-BEK, *Enzymologia*, 1937, **4**, p. 1.
159. WAGENER AND DAVIDSON, *Botan. Rev.* 1954, **20**, p. 61.
160. FINDLAY, *Forestry Abstracts*, 1956, **17**, No. 3, 4.
161. WEGELIUS, *Finnish Paper and Timber J.* 1938, **15A**, p. 125.
162. REICHERT AND PETE, *Tech. Ass. Pulp Pap. Ind.* 1949, **32**, p. 97.
163. APPLING, *Paper Trade J.* 1941, **113**, p. 173.
164. TECH. ASSOC. PULP AND PAPER IND. *Microbiology of Pulp and Paper*, 1955, Monograph No. 15, New York.
165. RENNERFELT, *World Paper Trade Rev.* 1939, **112**, p. TS.169; 1940, **113**, p. TS.1.
166. RENNERFELT, *Svensk. Botan. Tidskr.* 1947, **41**, p. 283.
167. NASON, SHUMARD AND FLEMING, *Paper Trade J.* 1940, **110**, p. 30.
168. HOLMES, *Tech. Ass. Pulp Pap. Ind.* 1942, **25**, p. 616.
169. MARTIN AND DOBSON, *Paper Trade J.* 1945, **121**, p. 39.
170. APPLING, RIDENOUR AND BUCKMAN, *Tech. Ass. Pulp Pap. Ind.* 1951, **34** p. 347.
171. SMITH O. A. *Paper Trade J.* 1941, **113**, p. 29.
172. STRACHAN, *Paper Maker*, 1947, **114**, p. TS.41.
173. SANBORN, *Tech. Ass. Pulp Pap. Ind.* 1951, **34**, p. 490.
174. PRENDERGAST, *Paper Maker*, 1948, **116**, p. TS.21.
175. FULLER AND NORMAN, *J. Bact.* 1943, **46**, p. 273.
176. TRACEY, in *Biological Transformations of Starch and Cellulose*, ed. Williams, Biochem. Soc., Symposia No. 11, 1953.
177. TERUI AND FUJIWARA, *J. Ferment. Technol. Japan*, 1948, **26**, p. 147.
178. TERUI AND FUJIWARA, *J. Ferment. Technol. Japan*, 1948, **27**, p. 203.
179. HAMMERSTROM *et al.*, *Arch. Biochem. Biophys.* 1955, **56**, p. 123.
180. MATTHIJSEN, *Diss. Abstracts*, 1957, **17**, p. 2141.
181. OKAMOTO AND ASAI, *J. Agric. chem. Soc. Japan*, 1952, **16**, p. 137.
182. PEHRSON, *Svensk. Papperstidn.* 1947, **50**, p. 497.
183. NUTMAN, *Ann. Appl. Biol.* 1929, **16**, p. 40.
184. LAWSON AND STILL, *Tech. Ass. Pulp Pap. Ind.* 1957, **40**, No. 9, p. 56A.
185. BROWN AND HARRISON, *Paper Maker*, 1947, **114**, p. TS.2.
186. FÅHRAEUS, *Högskol. Ann.* 1949, **16**, p. 159.
187. PEHRSON, *Svensk. Botan. Tidskr.* 1947, **41**, p. 354.
188. MELIN, *Svensk. Papperstidn.* 1936, **39**, p. 89.
189. ŚNIESKO AND KIMBALL, *Zentr. Bakt. Parasitenk. II*, 1933, p. 393.
190. IMSHENETZKII AND BORJARSKAJA, *Mikrobiol.* 1939, **8**, p. 657.
191. ENEBO, *Nature Lond.* 1949, **163**, p. 805.
192. BECKWITH, SWANSON AND ILAMS, University of California (Los Angeles) *Pub. Biol. Sci.* 1940, **1**, No. 13, p. 299.
193. GREATHOUSE AND WESSEL (editors), *Deterioration of Materials*, 1954. Reinhold Publishing Corp. New York.
194. SHEMA, *Paper Trade J.* 1948, **127**, p. 41.

195. WEST, *Slime Control and Prevention*, The Institute of Paper Chemistry, Bibliographic Series No. 170, 1949.
196. DORÉE, *Biochem. J.* 1920, **14**, p. 709.
197. SIU, DARBY, BURKHOLDER AND BARGHOORN, *Text. Res. J.* 1949, **19**, p. 484.
198. THOMAS, *Text. Res. J.* 1955, **25**, p. 559.
199. HOBART, DRAKE AND GUTHRIE, *Text. Res. J.* 1959, **29**, p. 885.
200. REESE, *Industr. Engng. Chem.* 1957, **49**, p. 89.
201. REEVES, ARMSTRONG, BLOUIN AND MAZZENO, *Text. Res. J.* 1955, **25**, p. 257.
202. GOLDTHWAIT, BURAS AND COOPER, *Text. Res. J.* 1951, **21**, p. 831.
203. HOLMAN AND JARRELL, *Industr. Engng Chem.* 1923, **15**, p. 236.
204. THAYSEN, BUNKER, BUTLIN AND WILLIAMS, *Ann. Appl. Biol.* 1939, **26**, p. 750.
205. BARKER, *Rev. Appl. Mycol.* 1940, **19**, p. 538.
206. RACE, ROWE AND SPEAKMAN, *J. Soc. Dyers and Col.* 1945, **61**, p. 310.
207. HAMLIN, *J. Text. Inst.* 1953, **44**, p. P.745.
208. COOKE, *Resistance to Microbiological Deterioration of Resin-treated Fibres*, Bulletin No. 136 , 1954. American Cyanamid Co. Inc.
209. BELL, RAMSEY AND WHEWELL, *J. Soc. Dyers and Col.* 1955, **71**, p. 660.
210. CHANCE, PERKERSON AND McMILLEN, *Text. Res. J.* 1959, **29**, p. 558.
211. HERSCHLER, as ref. 164, p. 169.
212. SEIDL, KUENZI, FAHEY AND MOSES, *U.S. Forest Products Lab.*, *Report No. R.1796* June 1951, Madison, Wisconsin.
213. GASCOIGNE, J. A., *British Ind. Finishing*, 1949, **1**, p. 709.
214. GALLOWAY, *J. Appl. Bact.* 1954, **17**, p. 207.
215. MORRIS AND DARLOW, *J. Appl. Bact.* 1959, **22**, p. 64.
216. WESSEL AND BEJUKI, *Industr. Engng Chem.* 1959, **51**, No. 4, p. 52A.
217. BRITISH PAPER AND BOARD MAKERS' ASSOC. 'A review of the problems arising from the presence of micro-organisms in paper and board making,' *Proc. Tech. Section*, 1957, **38**, Part 2.
218. CARLSON, *Chem. Specialities Mfs. Assoc. Proc.* May, 1957, p. 110.
219. CARTWRIGHT AND FINDLAY, *Decay of Timber and its Prevention*, 1958, H.M. Stationery Office, London.
220. REESE AND MANDELS, M., *Research Report, Microbiology Series No. 17*, Pioneering Research Division, Q.M. Research and Development Centre, Natick, Mass., U.S.A. February, 1957.
221. GOODALL, GORTON AND SUMMERSGILL, *J. Soc. Dyers and Col.* 1946, **62**, p. 189.
222. BURGESS, *J. Appl. Bact.* 1954, **17**, p. 230.
223. SHERRILL, *Text. Res. J.* 1956, **26**, p. 343.
224. HOWARD, *J. Appl. Bact.* 1954, **17**, p. 219.
225. SHAPIRO, *Text. Res. J.* 1957, **27**, p. 753.
226. ASHCROFT, *Text. Res. J.* 1958, **28**, p. 422.
227. MANDELS, G. R. and SIU, *J. Bact.* 1950, **60**, p. 249.
228. HAUSAM AND RUPP, *Melliand Textilber.* 1958, **39**, p. 429; 1959, **40**, p. 658.

229. PHILLIPSON, in *Biological Transformations of Starch and Cellulose*, ed. Williams, Biochem. Soc. Symposia No. 11, 1953.
230. PHILLIPSON AND CUTHBERTSON, *7th Intern. Congress Animal Husbandry*, Madrid, 1956. Subject 6, p. 1.
231. FESTENSTEIN, *Biochem. J.* 1958, **69**, p. 562.
232. STANLEY AND KESLER, *J. Dairy Sci.* 1959, **42**, p. 127.
233. KITTS AND UNDERKOFLER, *J. Agric. Food Chem.* 1954, **2**, p. 639.
234. HALLIWELL, *J. gen. Microbiol.* 1957, **17**, pp. 153, 166.
235. HUNGATE, *J. Bact.* 1947, **53**, p. 631.
236. SIJPESTEIJN, *J. gen. Microbiol.* 1951, **5**, p. 869.
237. MARSHALL, *British J. Nutrition*, 1949, **3**, p. 1.
238. HEALD, *British J. Nutrition*, 1953, **7**, p. 124.
239. BRYANT AND SMALL, *J. Bact.* 1956, **72**, p. 16.
240. DOETSCH, HOWARD, MANN AND OXFORD, *J. gen. Microbiol.* 1957, **16**, p. 156.
241. INAOKA AND SODA, *Mem. Ehime Univ.* Sect. VI., 1955, **1**, p. 1.
242. SØRENSEN, *Nature Lond.* 1955, **176**, p. 74.
243. HOWARD, *Biochem. J.* 1957, **67**, p. 643.
244. HOWARD, JONES AND PURDOM, *Biochem. J.* 1960, **74**, p. 173.
245. CONCHIE, *Biochem. J.* 1954, **58**, p. 552.
246. FESTENSTEIN, *Biochem. J.* 1958, **70**, p. 49.
247. HEALD, *Biochem. J.* 1952, **50**, p. 503.
248. BRYANT, *J. Animal Sci.* 1951, **10**, p. 1042.
249. NAUMAN, *Z. Tierenahr. Futtermittelk.* 1940, **3**, p. 193.
250. MILES, *J. Dairy Sci.* 1951, **34**, p. 492.
251. BURROUGHS, GALL, GERLAUGH AND BETHKE, *J. Animal Sci.* 1950, **9**, p. 214.
252. SUMMERS, BAKER AND GRAINGER, *J. Animal Sci.* 1957, **16**, p. 781.
253. HOFLUND, QUIN AND CLARK, *Onderstepoort J. Vet. Sci. Animal Ind.* 1948, **23**, p. 395.
254. HARROLD, BARTLEY AND ATHESON, *J. Dairy Sci.* 1957, **40**, p. 369.
255. LODGE, MILES, JACOBSON AND QUINN, *J. Dairy Sci.* 1956, **39**, p. 303.
256. VONK, McELROY AND BERG, *Canad. J. Biochem. Physiol.* 1957, **35**, p. 195.
257. VONK, McELROY AND BERG, *Canad. J. Biochem. Physiol.* 1957, **35**, p. 181.
258. HALL, CHENG AND BURROUGHS, *Proc. Iowa Acad. Sci.* 1955, **62**, p. 273.
259. MURRAY AND McLEOD, *J. Nutrition*, 1956, **60**, p. 245.
260. STIFFLER, *Diss. Abstracts*, 1957, **17**, p. 2124.
261. BENTLEY, LEHMKUL, JOHNSON, HERSCHBERGER AND MOXON, *J. Amer. chem. Soc.* 1954, **76**, p. 5000.
262. IINUMA, *J. Vitaminol. (Osaka)*, 1955, **1**, p. 90.
263. NAGASE AND FUJITA, *J. Vitaminol. (Osaka)*, 1956, **2**, p. 102.
264. MEYER, *J. Nutrition*, 1956, **58**, p. 407.
265. BURROUGHS, FRANK, GERLAUGH AND BETHKE, *J. Nutrition*, 1950, **40**, p. 9.
266. CONRAD, WATTS, IACONO, KRAYBILL AND FRIEDEMANN, *Science*, 1958, **127**, p. 1293.
267. COMPTON, *Text. Res. J.* 1957, **27**, p. 222.
268. LANGWELL, *J. Soc. Chem. Ind.* 1932, **51**, p. 988.

269. OLMSTEAD, *Proc. Amer. Diabetes Assoc.* 1949, **9**, p. 387.
270. TAMURA, *Japan. J. Nutrition*, 1949, **7**, p. 151.
271. BURROUGHS, GERLAUGH AND BETHKE, *J. Animal Sci.* 1950, **9**, p. 207.
272. McGINNIS, MacGREGOR AND CARVER, *Poultry Sci.* 1948, **27**, p. 459.
273. BOLTON, *J. Agric. Sci.* 1955, **46**, p. 420.
274. MESSERLE, *Biochem. Zeit.* 1926, **172**, p. 31.
275. HASTINGS, *Poultry Sci.* 1946, **25**, p. 584.
276. MASOERO, UBERTALLE AND MALETTO, *Atti soc. ital. Sci. Vet.* 1957, **11**, p. 466.
277. BOHNE, German Patent, 1940, D.P. 701, 217.
278. MACPHERSON, WYLAM AND RAMSTAD, *J. Sci. Food. Agric.* 1957, **8**, p. 732.
279. MARSTON, REID, K. C., STEWART AND WOODWARD, *A Survey of Agriculture, Forestry and Fishery Products in the U.K., and their Utilization*, 1953. H.M. Stationery Office, London.
280. REID, K. C., *Chem. and Ind.* 1953, p. 144.
281. SAEMAN AND ANDREASEN in *Industrial Fermentations*, Vol. I, ed. Underkofler and Hickey, 1954. Chemical Publishing, New York.
282. HARRIS AND BEGLINGER, *Industr. Engng Chem.* 1946, **38**, p. 890.
283. HARRIS, HANNAH, MARQUARDT AND BUBL, *Industr. Engng Chem.* 1948, **40**, p. 1216.
284. STEEL, *Biochemical Engineering*, 1958. Heywood and Co. Ltd., London.
285. WALSETH, *Tech. Ass. Pulp Pap. Ind.* 1952, **35**, p. 233.
286. TOYAMA, *Miyazaki Daigaku Nôgakubu Kenkyû Jihô*, 1958, **4**, p. 40.
287. OLSON, PETERSON AND SHERRARD, *Industr. Engng Chem.* 1937, **29**, p. 1026.
288. RUDOLFS AND HEUKELEKIAN, *Chem. Engng Prog.* 1952, **48**, p. 449.
289. LAWTON, BELLAMY, HUNGATE, BRYANT AND HALL, *Science*, 1951, **113**, p. 380.
290. STRANKS, *Pulp and Paper Mag. Canada*, 1956, **53**, p. 220.
291. STRANKS, *Canad. J. Microbiol.* 1956, **2**, p. 56.
292. ANDERSON, *An Introduction to Bacteriological Chemistry*, 2nd Ed., p. 323 (1946), E. & S. Livingstone, Ltd., Edinburgh.
293. MAKI, *Antoni van Leeuwenhoek J. Microbiol. Serol.* 1954, **20**, p. 185.
294. HUNGATE, *Bacteriol. Rev.* 1950, **14**, p. 1.
295. PREECE AND HOBKIRK, *J. Inst. Brewing*, 1954, **60**, p. 490.
296. JOHNSTON AND FOOTE, U.S. Patent 2 607 690, 1952.
297. STEWART, CRAWFORD AND MILLER, *India Rubber World*, 1953, **127**, pp. 794, 801.
298. NAGSHKI, WHITE, HOOVER AND WILLAMAN, *J. Bact.* 1945, **49**, p. 563.
299. ALLEN AND EMERSON, *Industr. Engng Chem.* 1949, **41**, 346.
300. PREECE, *Biochemistry of Brewing*, Ch. III, 1954. Oliver and Boyd, Edinburgh.
301. NORRIS AND PREECE, *Biochem. J.* 1930, **24**, p. 59.
302. SCHMORAK, BISHOP AND ADAMS, *Canad. J. Chem.* 1957, **35**, p. 108.
303. ASPINALL, FERRIER AND HIRST, *J. Inst. Brewing*, 1957, **63**, p. 101.
304. MONTGOMERY AND SMITH, *J. Amer. chem. Soc.* 1957, **79**, p. 695.

305. PREECE, *Cereal Carbohydrates*, Royal Institute of Chemistry Lectures, Monographs and Reports No. 2, 1957.
306. O'SULLIVAN, *J. chem. Soc.* 1882, **41**, p. 24.
307. MORRIS, *J. biol. Chem.* 1942, **142**, p. 881.
308. PIRATZKY AND WIECHA, *Wschr. Brau.* 1938, **55**, p. 97.
309. PREECE AND MACKENZIE, *J. Inst. Brewing*, 1952, **58**, p. 353.
310. PREECE AND HOBKIRK, *J. Inst. Brewing*, 1953, **59**, p. 385.
311. ASPINALL AND TELFER, *J. chem. Soc.* 1954, p. 3519.
312. AITKEN, EDDY, INGRAM AND WEURMAN, *Biochem. J.* 1956, **64**, p. 63.
313. PERLIN, *Cereal Chem.*, 1951, **28**, pp. 370, 382.
314. ASPINALL AND STURGEON, *J. chem. Soc.* 1957, p. 4469.
315. PRINGSHEIM AND BAUR, *Hoppe-Sel. Z.* 1928, **173**, p. 188.
316. GOERDELER, *Hoppe-Seyl. Z.* 1948, **283**, p. 262.
317. VAN SUMÈRE, *Naturwiss.* 1953, **40**, p. 582.
318. KRISTIANSSON, *Svensk. Kem. Tid.* 1950, **62**, p. 133.
319. ENEBO, SANDEGREN AND LJUNGDAHL, *J. Inst. Brewing*, 1953, **59**, p. 205.
320. PREECE AND MACDOUGALL, *J. Inst. Brewing*, 1958, **64**, p. 489.
321. PREECE AND HOGGAN, *J. Inst. Brewing*, 1956, **62**, p. 486.
322. MARTIN AND DOBSON, *Tech. Assoc. Papers*, 1945, **28**, p. 235.
323. PREECE AND ASHWORTH, *J. Inst. Brewing*, 1950, **56**, p. 40.
324. PREECE, AITKEN AND DICK, *J. Inst. Brewing*, 1954, **60**, p. 497.
325. PREECE, *Wallerstein Labs. Commun.* 1957, **20**, p. 147.
326. PREECE AND HOGGAN, *Proc. Europ. Brew. Conv.*, 1957, p. 72.
327. REESE, SMAKULA AND PERLIN, *Arch. Biochem. Biophys.* 1959, **85**, p. 171.
328. STONE, *Nature Lond.* 1958, **182**, p. 687.
329. JERMYN, *Science*, 1957, **125**, p. 12.
330. WHITAKER, *Arch. Biochem. Biophys.* 1954, **53**, p. 439.
331. KABAT in *Chemistry and Biology of Mucopolysaccharides*, Ciba Foundation Symposium, 1958. J. and A. Churchill, London.

INDEX

Cellulase—*contd.*
from Fungi Imperfecti, 60
from Lichens, 57
from Molluscs, 53
from Nematodes, 55
from Phycomycetes, 59
from plants, 56
from Protozoa, 55
from wood rotting fungi, 216, 217
fungal, 58
in cereals, 244
in diet, 240
inhibition, 135, 234, 235
in industry, 204
mode of action, 167
molecular size, 159, 176, 179
pH value effects, 124
preparation of crude extracts, 72
products of hydrolysis by, 182,
185, 205
properties, 53, 124, 234, 245,
248
purification, 72, 130
by adsorption, 88
by chromatography, 89
by electrophoresis, 97
by precipitation, 80
sources, *Chapter.* 3
separation from *S*-factor, 172
substrates, 53, 104, 168, 174
synthesis, 159
temperature effects, 130
uses, 238, 242, 243
Cellulose, α, β, γ, 9
acetate, 11
acid hydrolysis, 9, 179, 241
adsorption of cellulase, 189
amorphous content, 6
anomalies in structure, 4, 205
breakdown in non-ruminants, 240
breakdown in ruminants, 238, 242
changes from enzymic action, 171
chemical structure, 2
crystalline structure, 5, 206
crystallinity, 6, 168
degree of polymerization, 3, 95,
164, 170, 175, 184

derivatives, 11
degree of substitution, 11, 13,
109, 112, 184, 231
enzymic hydrolysis, 183
effect on D.P., 170, 175
nature of residue, 175
endwise cleavage, 170, 189, 248
enzymic hydrolysis products, 182
esters, 11
ethers, 12
hydrolytic attack, 4, 46
influence of alkalis, 8, 177
influence of electrolytes, 9
influence of moisture, 7
mechanical properties, 6, 116,
173, 210, 212, 214, 225
modification, 183, 230
molecular structure, effect on
hydrolysis, 168
molecular weight, 3
nitrate, 11, 78
oxidation, 10, 44
preservatives, evaluation, 237
prevention of degradation, 230
prevention of insect attack, 236
random cleavage, 177, 190, 248
reactivity, 7
sources, 1
theories of enzymic decomposition, 43
xanthate, 12
Cell wall, plant, 2
Cereal enzymes, 39, 243, 244
Cereal polysaccharides, 243
Chelating compounds, effect on
activity, 156
Chitin, 15, 42
Chitinase, 42
Chromatography,
on alumina, 89, 91, 94, 196
on calcium phosphate, 89, 92, 93,
151
on Celite, 89
on cellulose, 89, 92, 95
on ion exchange resins, 96, 196
on paper, 93
on starch, 96

262